Bob
BROWNELL'S

GUNSMITH KINKS

GUNSMITH KINKS

A Fascinating and Widely Varied Accumulation of Shop Kinks, Short Cuts, Techniques and Comments sent by Practicing Gunsmiths from all over the World to

F. R. "BOB" BROWNELL

Edited and Compiled by his son
FRANK BROWNELL

F. BROWNELL & SON, Publishers
Montezuma, Iowa, 50171, U. S. A.
1969

Library of Congress Catalog Card Number: 77-90353

TYPOGRAPHY AND PRINTING IN THE U. S. A.

TABLE OF CONTENTS

This book of Shop Kinks is especially - and particularly - dedicated to all the people whose names appear on the following pages...the Professional Gunsmiths, Gunnuts, Writers, Magazine Editors, Artists, Manufacturers and other folks who sent in, or let us reprint, the material which makes up this book.

It is a long list - a finer group of friends you could not ask for - and it is a list to be mighty proud of, for it includes most of the finest craftsmen and most knowledgeable gun men in America today.

Special thanks must go also to my wife, Nancy, who somehow managed to type so much manuscript and do all the proofreading while going through the pregnancy and delivery of Number 2 Son, at the same time keeping up with the wet diapers of Number 1 Son. To June Fleming (Mrs. Wayne) who toiled so many hours on layouts. And, of course, to "Bob B." - my Dad, the Boss - for collecting all these kinks...and for letting me do the whole thing in the first place.

Therefore, it is to these fine people that we gratefully dedicate this book.

Frank Brownell

Montezuma, Iowa
May, 1969

FOREWORD

The ingenuity of the independent American Gunsmith knows no bounds when he is compared to his counterparts in the other countries of the world. This ingenuity, this coming-up with new and better ways of doing the same old job, is downright inspiring. No "tried and true", the "way grandfather did it" with the American craftsman. No shocked horror over a new innovation - no throwing up of the hands in dismay over an impossible job...quite to the contrary, as the following pages of this book will clearly prove. No matter how obtuse or stubborn the problem, the general philosophy is, "Somebody will find a way to whip it". Sure enough, somebody always does.

And this is what this book is all about: How somebody did it!

This telling of the "how" is intended to be of value to the old pro, a great time-saver and fountain of information for the average, a revelation of boundless proportions for the novices and a mighty damned interesting bit of reading for the armchair gunsmith. It covers the gamut of operational techniques (kinks) from the production shop all the way down to the woodshed or attic "nut" who tinkers with guns because of a pure and unadulterated love of the things - often to his wife's great consternation. And all of it is presented with one great hope: To further the development (or pastime) of that strictly distinctive American priviledge of "working on guns".

In the way of background, it has always been my categorical belief that if you will "show me a community without someone to work on guns, I will show you a community without shooting activity." There must be some individual around who will fix the shooting pieces, or else the whole shooting game ends, but quickly. Without the radio man, no TV...without the mechanic, no cars. Simple as that.

Devoted souls are constantly finding themselves embroiled in the task of repairing their friends' and neighbors' guns. The word spreads, and the devoted souls find that they have backed into the gunsmithing profession through the backdoor without exactly knowing how it all happened - but they love it. There they are with the multiple problems of a mushrooming variety of gun models smacking them squarely between the eyes, and not much of anywhere to turn for solutions other than to depend upon their own cleverness. Furthermore, each gunsmith is so remotely located from the other that the free exchange of ideas and suggestions by word of mouth is an impossibility. Nor do many of the firearms manufacturers go to any kind of lengths to supply service manuals as is done in most other industries. Makes for a case of "fight it out for yourself, sink or swim, do a good job or botch it up". Even the graduates from the excellent gunsmithing schools have found that a need for communication within the profession is a Must.

In 1948, this inability to communicate (blow off with a loud noise) had me busting a gunion here in Montezuma - a fur spit and holler from very many other gunsmiths. To relieve a real head of steam, I mailed a little newsletter to my customers. It was chock-full of brilliant wit, clever shop practices (I thought at the time) and a bit of selling on some of our products. The exchange of gunsmithing ideas took hold immediately with many of the customers writing back saying how they'd done it better and quicker. So, another baby was born - Brownell's Newsletter.

This book is the result of that Newsletter. Several times a year (sometimes twice, sometimes four times, and sometimes even six) the letter goes out to an average of 6,000 full or part time gunsmiths, only. It is available to no one else. The material is all gunsmith originated - other than a few wisecracks by the editor, and even these result from cleaned-up stories sent in by the readers! The service, repair and building ideas sent in by the Newsletter readers are as wide and varied as there are models of guns and problems connected with them. Almost without fail, each gunsmith letter starts out with "here is an idea that maybe the brethren can use..." And almost without fail, it is something no one had thought of before as an easier and better way of handling a tough problem.

The material you are about to read is filled with the "hidden secrets" of a fine and respectable profession - that of Gunsmithing. Altho trade names are used throughout the book, for that is the way the material was submitted by each gunsmith, the basic information applies to all similar products. Use the secrets well, improve on them if you can, pass on whatever little gems you might discover so that others can benefit from your skills...and above all, enjoy the craft to the fullest.

Bob Brownell

Montezuma, Iowa
May, 1969

CHAPTER 1

THE GUNSTOCK

DESIGNING THE HUNTER'S RIFLE

My friend Bob has asked me if I would make a few random comments concerning practical rifle designs for the hunter. Yes, Bob, I will. I'm not going to deal much with caliber, or type of action--I'll probably precipitate enough argument over the weight, shape, etc. I've found that an awful lot of hunters have deep seated, precise, and very firm ideas about what a rifle should be. When they read an article like this, many of them aren't really looking for advice at all. They're searching for areas of disagreement.

A few years ago I revealed in a magazine article, two separate pictures of one of my favorite short barreled, lightweight big game rifles. The stock I made myself. That was before the short and light rifle had become popular. I believe it was truly a pleasingly contoured

Pete Brown holding his custom "Hunter's Rifle".

design, and it looked particularly handsome in the picture. At least that was the opinion expressed by a lot of shooters and they generally don't lie about such things.

In the first picture the rifle had a full but rather modest pistol grip. The second picture was exactly the same, except the rifle had a straight grip. I had whittled away the pistol grip completely.

I was merely presenting an idea, but I did inject the statement that I liked straight stocks on hunting rifles. Yes, even on bolt action rifles. I don't remember whether I went so far as to say that I think pistol grips on hunting rifles are a completely unnecessary and clumsy protrusion, and detract from the handling qualities of the rifle in the field. I couldn't see where the pistol grip removal destroyed the lines of the rifle at all. As a matter of fact, I thought it enhanced them. In large measure, this feeling was no doubt a result of my knowing that, to me at least, I had rendered the rifle a simpler and more practical game weapon.

I've seldom uncovered such feeling as was expressed in some of the letters I received from readers of my article. Some people just wanted to know "why did you do it?" I thought I had explained that in the article, but I suppose the horrible shock of just seeing this fine stock with the pistol grip removed and knowing that it could never be replaced was more than they could take at one time.

Some others were furious with me. You'd have thought that I had advocated repeal of the second amendment.

I don't know that anyone ever removed a pistol grip as a result of this article, or made a new stock without one. I have handed this straight grip rifle to hunters and they have been enthusiastic about the way it handles, but they would in some way, by looks--if not by word, express the idea that "this sort of thing just isn't being done." I suppose one runs into about the same sort of reactions when offering advice on most any subject.

I started toting a BB rifle at a very early age and real guns, including a 12 gauge shotgun, before I was twelve. I had a lot of safety and shooting judgment pounded into me--once or twice from the bottom end--before I was turned loose with a gun, however. The point is: I've spent a lot of time carrying a gun. Since I enjoy hunting on foot and sometimes covering a lot of ground that way, I've become very sensitive to the carrying qualities of a gun. The design of a gunstock in itself can make a tremendous difference in the pleasure derived from hunting afield.

Take a stock which is thick or generally bulky--too much wood-- around the receiver. That's the way most custom gunsmiths and most of the factories were making stocks a few years ago. Many of them haven't gotten entirely away from this club-like design yet. Clubbiness is all right for benchrest rifles or specialized varmint rifles which the shooter won't be hiking with, but for the field gun I think it is one of the biggest oversights in design. The balance point in a rifle comes very near the receiver and at this point it should be thin, small in circumference, and as comfortable to the hand as possible. In rough country or when chasing around over the hills on foot, I carry the rifle in one hand or the other at my side. Here it adds to my balance in rough places and it feels like a part of me. If the stock is too large to permit closing or nearly closing my fingers on it, the gun becomes a burden and fatiguing. This can readily be explained by means of simple mechanical principles but all you need do is hunt for a few days with a bulky stock and then switch to a slim and trim one. Care in designing a stock for ease in carrying is even more important than weight.

Generally speaking I think far too much wood is left in the buttstock of our hunting rifles. I like the slender buttstocks which have long been a characteristic in European design. However, I think the Europeans could be a trifle more generous with wood in the fore-end. I like a little suggestion of beavertail or flatness on the bottom of the fore-end. Maybe it's psychological, but I have the feeling that this is an aid to avoiding cant in the rifle, or at least helping one develop consistency in the direction and amount of canting.

The rifle you take afield should, in my opinion, be light in weight and short barreled. I prefer a 20 inch barrel, but have settled for 22 inches a number of times. If a cartridge won't perform within this barrel limitation, then I'll use a cartridge that will. The barrel doesn't need to be either long or heavy in order to get fine hunting accuracy. I mean accuracy in the order of one minute of angle or better.

If I've said it once, I've said it a dozen times, and I'll say it again. A gun designer should capture all of the carrying qualities he can from the Winchester Model 94 or the Marlin 336. I can carry one of these little rifles all day long and for miles without the rifle adding anything to my fatigue. I feel sure that this is the big reason why so many of these rifles--in spite of the lower powered cartridges--are still being sold today.

Safeties are another very important consideration in a hunting rifle. On lots of rifles the safeties appear to be an afterthought and protrude from the wood or metal as a sort of outcropping rather than for positive and quick use. I think the tang type sliding safety so familiar on break action shotguns is the safest, most convenient, and fastest safety. In addition to all its other advantages, it can be used by both left and right handed shooters.

I've often wondered if the gun designers who determine the position and shape of some of the safeties on rifles today, ever put on a pair of gloves and try to disengage the safety as the rifle is being brought up to shooting position? Once again, I feel compelled to mention the old lever actions with the hammer serving as the safety-- convenient, fast, and easy to use with the gun in any position. Another reason why no modern design has made these guns obsolete.

I've tried to mention some of the simple and practical fundamentals in rifle design which have been overlooked by most of our modern gun designers. You may not agree with all--perhaps none--of my very general analysis of the outward gun design problem. I certainly have no argument with the hunter who disagrees. If a man likes a certain style of gun I don't care if it has a fence post for a stock, I am a firm believer in his using that gun. If he takes pleasure in it, then that is the gun for him.

- *Pete Brown, Gun Editor of* Sports Afield, *Author, Hunter and Authority*

COLD CREAM "INLETTING BLACK"

I have found that the best inletting black for stock work that I've seen yet is plain old cold cream such as my wife tries to "get beautiful" with. By mixing some liquid lamp black in it, it does a neat job that isn't greasy and the consistency remains the same at either hot or cold temperatures. Also, never hardens in the jar or on the metal and brushes on with no effort.

Just remember to clearly label the jar of cold cream you swipe from the wife...she is not going to be too happy if she comes across

the jar you've mixed up and tries to use it on her face!
- *Bob Blackburn, Fort Worth, Texas*

INLETTING "BLUE"

I wonder whether any of the brethren have discovered Dykem "Hi-Spot Blue" by the Dykem Co., of St. Louis, Mo. (Ed. Note:-2301 E. North 11th St., St. Louis), for fitting actions to stocks. It is just as messy to use as any of the other spotting mediums, but does not dry so it is not necessary to clean off when work is laid aside even for a couple of weeks. (Note from Bob B.: A few days after getting the above, Harold was in and suggested that when the boys write to the Dykem Company for literature they also get literature on their dye for Aluminum as he has used it with success on the colored aluminum receivers for touching-up purposes.)
- *Harold Mishkin, Chicago, Illinois*

INLETTING ORANGE

I find that mixing vaseline and a little of your orange dye (orange 11 conc.) together gives you the perfect stuff for fitting stocks. Not messy, comes off easy, won't rust parts...
- *Skip Baker, Cowan, Tennessee*

PRUSSIAN BLUE

I mix Prussian Blue with some of the wife's cooking (Crisco) shortening. Works even better if it is left in an open container for 3 or 4 days before putting the lid on the container for storage.
- *Kester's Gun Shop, Paducah, Kentucky*

CHEEK PIECE FITTING

Aathar Anderson says about the gorilla beating a coyote to death: "A lot of Yi, Yi, Yi, Yi, and a little booming on the chest!" But before Booming and Yi-Yiing too much, just for the hell of it put some of your wife's face powder on your cheek and then cheek to cheekpiece. Chances are you'll discover you are only using about 1/10th of the cheekpiece, and the rest is just a bunch of excess to carry around. Sure looks purty but that's all!
- *Aathar Anderson, Richford, Vermont*

BOLT INLETTING

When cutting a bolt handle notch into a stock, I use a piece of carbon paper between the bolt and the wood when I'm ready to make the final fit. Works real nice, leaves a good mark and no mess!
- *John Sellers, San Manuel, Arizona*

STOCK ROUTING FIXTURE

Russ Carpenter was in the booth visiting about this and that. We got to talking about stock inletting. He not only showed me a picture of the outfit he uses - but was kind enough to let us have the picture for use here. What he uses is a regular hand routing outfit in a homemade fixture as per the picture. The right hand guide is adjustable and you'll notice holes in the bottom plank for lengthwise adjustment. Russ says that after you get on to it and learn to take your time, you can do a great deal of the routing (inletting) free-hand; and it is a terrific time saver.

- Russ Carpenter, Carpenter's Gun Shop, Plattekill, New York

STOCKING MANNLICHER'S WITHOUT A BARREL BAND

I like to build Mannlicher style rifles and I like to do it without a barrel band. Here's how.

I make a round stud that looks a lot like the female half of your Latigo Sling stud set. It has a 1/2" diameter head about .015 to .020 thick; a 1/4" shank that is about 5/16" diameter and is internally threaded to take a front swivel screw, usually 10-32.

Then I mill a flat on the bottom of the barrel where I want the front sling swivel to come, and silver solder this stud in the flat, holding it with a C-clamp until it cools. I have found that the silver soldered lug cannot be pulled from the barrel unless you let the screw bottom - and if that were to happen, even a weld would be strained to the break point. Also do not believe that the relatively low heat required for the silver solder applied uniformly ever made any difference in accuracy.

When I install the action to the wood, I just pull the front swivel screw down along with the guard screws till you get a perfect, full length fit over my Acraglas bed (of course) and no dependence on a barrel band or a muzzle cap.

- George Hout, Jr., Columbus, Ohio

CIRCUMSTANTIAL EVIDENCE?

A dangerous thing, for it can surely be so wrong. Take the case of one of our local gunsmith/farmers. Last winter this guy was out doing the milking of his one and only cow - a beast of dubious character and ornery disposition. He just got things going merrily and the "Poing-Pwang" of the milk hitting the bucket at the right pitch, when the cow let fly with a kick that sent the bucket sailing across the barn and the milk spraying over everything in sight. This had been happening too regularly before, and my ingenious friend had his plans all made. He took a spike and nailed the hoof of that cow firmly to the barn floor. Chuckling with evil glee, he went back to the business at hand, patting himself on the back in time with the squirts of the milk. He had not, however, figured on the brain power of his beast. With her other foot she dealt my friend a vicious cross-cutting kick. "Ho! Ho!" quoth he, after wiping off the milk and brown stuff from the floor, off his face and clothes, "I have one more nail and the same hammer." So he pried her feet as far apart as he could and nailed the other hoof to the floor. "This will be heaven," he mused, and went back to milking...messed up but triumphant.

Now, you who know nothing about cows in the winter do not realize that the fine plume on the end of a cow's tail becomes a brown frozen mass in the winter with the weight and heft of a 15 lb. sledge hammer. With unerring accuracy, the cow used this weapon to deal our friend a cold-cocking blow to the back of the head just as he had his face buried in the warm flank of her side. In high umbrage - which means he was just madder than seven kinds of hell - he went to the machine shed, got a short step-ladder and a spike. Back at the barn, he pulled that tail up with one hand and reached high overhead to nail the end of it to the overhead beam. Being stretched out like he was, his pants fell down. And just then his wife walked through the barn door.

- *Harold Lofgreen, Montezuma's Postmaster*

ACTION MODELS

Directions for making action models of "Acraglas" to simplify bedding a rifle into a stock without removing the barrel:

Two ways to do it. First way, make a small box. Coat action with release agent. Mix Acraglas and make a female mold of action. When cured, remove action. Now take piece of soft wood and carve so that it fits quite close. Mix Acraglas and force block into prepared box. (Don't forget to put release agent in female mold.) This makes a slightly undersize glass action. Easier than grinding down an old action.

Easiest way - works if you have old stock or military stock: - Put a heavy layer of release agent in old inletted stock. Proceed as before with soft wood plug. This method takes very little Acraglas as compared to the first method. The wood plug can be made of pieces - that is - a round peg, flattened at base slightly smaller than action diameter. To this, nail small pieces of wood to a rough but smaller shape of the action. This you cover with Acraglas and ram into the inlet in the old stock which has lots of release agent on it.

- Julius J. Nelson, Burke, South Dakota

RELIEVE THAT RECOIL LUG

When bedding Mauser type actions with lug and recoil shoulder on bottom of receiver, after Acraglas has cured, scrape bottom of lug recess to insure that the bottom of the receiver lug itself does not bottom. This often can prevent the flat portion of the receiver and that portion of the barrel that is bedded from making solid contact in the bedded area. (I bed about 2" of the barrel and float the rest. I really want full contact for those 2"!!) All that is needed is a few thousandths clearance to insure that the guard screws cinch the receiver flats and the barrel tight.

One match rifle I built shot about 2-1/2 minutes of angle until I scraped the bottom of the lug recess. Scraping and pulling down tight made 1/2 m.o.a. groups possible. This rifle was a 1909 Spandau 98 Mauser with heavy .30 cal. machine gun barrel and has grouped 4-1/2 m.o.a. in extreme elevation at 600 yards!

- M/Sgt. Richard A. Corbett, Nellis AFB, Nevada

RECOIL LUG RELIEF

Been working on some exceptionally nice match rifles and wanted to get a completely accurate and uniform relief on the recoil lug. So, cemented some .008 thick acetate to the bottom of the recoil lug and to the flat immediately behind the lug. Trimmed the sides off very accurately and applied the release agent liberally to it. This does away completely with the digging out of the glass, and it insures that you are able to attain a uniform space exactly where you want it to be. The balance of the glassing of the jobs is carried out as usual.

The groups have improved so markedly on the rifles I have done this to that I have decided they are just like the rest of the gals in our lives...a little trip to the "Beauty Shoppe" and a new uplifter one size smaller just seems to bring out all the best in them!

- William Ehlers, Fox Point, Wisconsin

RECOIL LUG RELIEF

When Acraglassing the Rem. 721 (and it should work on others) take black plastic electrician tape and put on the front and sides only, of the recoil lug. When cured and taken apart, strip off the plastic tape and the clearance is 100% perfect...and don't forget release agent!

- C. S. Maltby, Arlington, Virginia

RECOIL RELIEF, FREE FLOATING & WRIST PINS

Got to thinking one day as was getting ready to Acraglas a gun, that the only real contact needed on the recoil lug was on the back. . . (got to thinking this just after I had bedded the lug in tight and had to warm the action and beat the lug all the way out of the recess!) So, now I use plastic electrical tape on the bottom, sides and front of the lug when I am bedding. The rifle comes out of the wood much easier now, and I still get the contact I want.

When a customer wants the barrel free floating, I use the same electrical tape, only this time, I use two layers and get just the amount of free float desired. Even have found that I get along real well using it around the magazine and other places I want a little clearance and the strength is not needed so the action and wood will separate a little easier. The electrical tape works much better for me than the traditional "scotch" type as is stronger and thicker so will take more abuse and not need as many layers to get the thickness wanted.

When I am inletting and bedding any of the rifles that have a tang that is inletted into the wood, I drill a 1/4" or 5/16" hole at an angle down through the center of the pistol grip about 3 to 3-1/2 inches deep. Then I make a steel pin either 1/8" or 3/16" just long enough to clear the tang. When the Acraglas is all mixed, but before the glass floc is added, I pour the hole full and drop in the pin. The steel pin helps get the air bubbles out of the small hole, and I figure with a steel reinforced slug of Acraglas right down through the middle of the weakest part of the stock, the recoil is not going to hurt anything. With the pin in place, I add the floc to the rest of the Acraglas and proceed as usual. Have put some mighty big magnums on light stocks with this technique, and not had a one of them split out yet!

- Henry Mar, Brookings, South Dakota

SUPER STRENGTH BARREL-BEDDING TIPS

I have been bedding all sporters full length in glass, and have cut down any forearm wandering tendencies by the following method. The barrel channel is grooved from the recoil lug depression to the point where the foretip and wood meet with 1/8" wide by 3/16" deep channels. As many of these channels as there are room for are put in and vented into the recoil lug depression where possible.

This venting eliminates the possibility of having a 'lock' of glass under the recoil lug when the metal parts are set in, making it impossible to fully seat the barrel and action. Before grooving the forearm, I usually gouge out a good 1/16" or more clearance under the barrel in the forearm, so when the glass bedding is done, I end up with a generous 1/16" tube of glass under the barrel and in addition, have these full length 'spines' of glass. I have never seen a forearm done in this manner go wrong. . . .

Besides strengthening the forearm in the above manner, I also use the glass to attach tips rather than the old dowel method. The tip tenon is cut on the forearm to a loose fit into the plastic tip, the tip clamped in place, and three or more 1/4" holes are bored thru tip and forearm tenon from the inside of the tip (barrel channel side). The tip is filled with Acraglas, pressed onto the tenon, and clamped in place until hardening takes place. On dowel-type tips, opposing holes are bored in tip and fore-end, and vented up in the same manner as with tenons. These drilled areas are filled with glass and the job is done. I have fitted tips on purpose that had an equal bearing surface to the barrel, the same as the forearm, and have never had one shoot loose.

Besides using glass on rifles, I find it very handy to fit axe, hammer and sledge hammer handles to heads. . . . We travel by dogteam a lot up here, and this winter I'm going to apply glass to one set of sled runners. Some of the bush pilots have done this to aircraft skis, and it proved out more satisfactory than the usual wood or aluminum running surfaces when slush conditions are present on the lakes.

- *Irv Benson, Ontario, Canada*

BED WITH INLETTING GUIDE SCREWS

Next time you're bedding a rifle with Acraglas, instead of using the trigger guard screws to pull the action down, try this trick.

Fill the forward and rear holes in the trigger guard with plastic wood. Place the guard in the stock. Now put the stock inletting guide screw in the forward hole of the action. Fill the stock cavity with Acraglas and place the barrelled action in the stock. The forward inletting guide screw will force the plastic wood out of the bottom of the forward trigger guard hole. Clamp the stock, barrelled action and trigger guard together with C-clamps using small wooden shims to protect the metal. Will take 4 clamps - two on the barrel and two on the action. When the glass is set, just rap the stock with a rubber mallet, unscrew the inletting guide screws and disassemble.

- *Richard Turner, Wichita Falls, Texas*

ACRAGLAS BARREL RELEASE METHOD

Sorry I took so long in answering your letter. . . .caught me in the hospital. Nothing serious, just a little hernia! You know your Acraglas really does the job. . . No, the doc didn't use it on me (tho it probably would have worked--BB!), but in full length bedding a Mauser Mannlicher stock, I found the best way to effect a release was to clamp the stock to the ceiling of my shop and hold on the barrel and action and jump off my bench. Came away slick as a whistle! All kidding aside, that little completely Acraglassed gun gives me 3" and better groups

at 200 yards!
- *Terry Miles, Hermosa Beach, California*

REMOVING GLASSED-IN GUARD SCREWS

If you get a little sloppy when glassing an action and later discover you cannot get the guard screws loose, just heat up a soldering iron and hold the tip on the guard screws until they get warm - NOT hot - and they will back out with little more than normal pressure!
- *Bob Snyder, Easton, Pennsylvania*

SEPARATING AN ACRAGLASSED ACTION AND STOCK

When separating the stock and action the first time after the glass is set, on the mauser type actions, use the longer rear guard screw in the front hole - where it is nearest the recoil lug which usually does the sticking.

Just put the fore-end in the left hand, barrel down; heel of stock on the bench on a protective pad. Strike the screw head with a soft hammer and the action will drop out. Can use junker screws if you like, and then can rap with a machinist's hammer as marring won't matter.
- *John Sellens, San Manuel, Arizona*

ACRAGLAS REMOVAL

I find that I can successfully remove Acraglas from barrel channels with the flame spreader tip on my hand torch which distributes the heat evenly over the glass. Altho I cannot prove my theory as to why it works so well, I believe that what I am doing is applying heat to the epoxy which transfers it to the wood. Altho the epoxy does not shrink, I feel that the wood does change in dimension enough to pop the epoxy up. This permits the epoxy to be removed with a spatula or screwdriver. This is especially handy if the customer wants the barrel partially free-floated. With a knife I remove about 1/8" of Acraglas across the barrel channel where the free-floating is to start. Then heat the glass beyond that and remove. Personally, I've found no improvement in shooting qualities from doing this - but "beauty" is in the eye of the customer, so who am I to argue?
- *Lincoln Radio & Electronics, Brooklyn, New York*

FILLING VOIDS

Took a letter from Edgar Roupe to simply clear up an Acraglas problem that's been a puzzler. "When I applied the second batch (of Acraglas) to fill in some voids I did not get a bond between the two applications. This brings out, I believe, the necessity to clean thoroughly the first coat of Acraglas with a solvent that will remove the release agent that has adhered to the outer surface of the first application!!!"

(Note from Bob B.: When I first read Ed's comment my reaction was to get a ball bat and start beating myself over the head. Why in the ever-loving-blue-eyed-blazes hadn't I thought of that many years ago and gotten it into the instructions? Surely would have saved some problems for it is so right and so darned true. That release agent is meant to keep the Acraglas from sticking to ANYTHING and of course it will prevent one coat from sticking to the next unless it is removed first. Take off the green release agent with alcohol or warm water; the pink with Energine.)

- Edgar Roupe, Pine Bluff, Arkansas

BEDDING WITH A "SKIM-COAT"

Got a picture of 200-YD, 10-Shot group, shot by Gerry LeMay with a Mauser bench rest series 400 heavy Douglas barrel, 51 gr. 4831 in 284-6mm and Sierra HP Boat-tail. Bedded in a Fajen semi-inletted laminated Varminter stock. Says Gerry: "Bedded with your Acraglas with lots of floc in the first bedding. And here is the secret - the second bedding is just a lick in the right spots so there is absolute contact in the right places. Don't use any floc in the second bedding so that it really flows in the right spots. I've tried them all and yours can't be equalled - mainly because of the varied consistencies obtainable with the varying amounts of floc. No fabrication - I've got witnesses!" (Note: Naturally Gerry is proud of such a group - but I think we here are even prouder!!)

- Gerry LeMay, Sherbrooke, Quebec, Canada

THREE WISHES

"One sunny day in the pasture," says Fred Moulton, "three bulls were talking shop and the subject of wishes came up. 'I wish,' said the first, 'that I was in London. I could be a bull in a China shop.' 'I wish,' said the second, 'I was a bull on Wall Street.' 'I wish,' said the third with a sigh: 'I could just stay right here for heifer and heifer and heifer.'"

- Fred Moulton, The American Rifleman

SUPER-STRENGTH OF TWIN-WELD

For the acid test, I sanded a piece of Brazilian Rosewood smooth and Twin-Welded one of my S & W recoil shoulders to it. Next day used a cold chisel and hammer and just beat the C.R.S. steel recoil shoulder out of shape!! Nothing has dislodged the thing yet...for a quick job it is the most positive wood to metal bond I've seen yet...

- Verne Hunt, Custom Craft, Pasadena, California

THIN EDGE BONDS

If you want a real bond on a very thin edge, use wood alcohol as a whiskering agent. Use it about three times, but do NOT rub off the whiskers. This will permit bonding clear out to zero. Also, mixed with different color pigments, it makes wonderful inlay material. Mixed with Aluminum powder it is far superior to dental amalgam and will never loosen. . .

- *Orville B. Bell, St. Louis, Missouri*

TUNE UP YOUR RIFLE FOR LESS THAN $5

It's as inevitable as death and taxes - rifles will go sour, and almost invariably just before hunting season. Most shooters know enough about guns to suspect scope and scope mounts and will promptly and hopefully check those screws. Hopefully, because this seems to be the thing to do, and because it is also the simplest job. Everybody has heard about some fellow missing a target or a buck the size of a large cow because the scope had shot loose. But what if those scope screws and mount screws are tight, and that does not account for those misses?

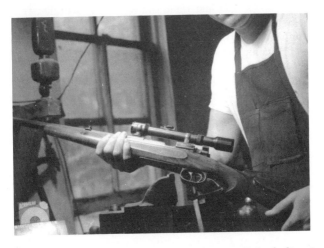

At this stage of the game, a lot of the boys pull the bolt out of the rifle, sagely peer down the barrel and declare that the tube has been shot out. After all, they reason, Old Betsey has been fired at least 500 to 1,000 times, and the barrel must be plumb wore out. Barrel steel just doesn't wear out that way, and modern barrels last a lot longer than that. The simple fact of the matter is that the stock and the barreled action have either parted company, or the wood has warped and this warpage affects barrel bedding. And don't think that an old stock can't warp. Given enough variations in humidity and temperature, any piece of wood will be affected, and stocks are no exception.

To restore the gun's inherent accuracy, and perhaps even improve it, the best and also the least expensive and easiest way to get the gun back on target is to glassbed it. A new custom stock could, of course be installed, but this costs considerably more than a box of glassbedding compound and it also takes a lot longer. Glassbedding you can do yourself. The cost will be under five bucks and the whole job won't take more than a couple of hours including touching up the finish once the bedding job has been completed.

Here's what you need to tackle the job yourself: A heavy bench vise that will hold your gun safely, the jaws should be padded either with felt or several layers of rags so that the vise jaws won't mar the wood; one or two properly ground screwdrivers that fit the guard screws of your gun; a small, well-sharpened wood chisel to remove wood where needed; masking tape; a couple of pieces of fine sandpaper; some fine steel wool; and some touch-up finish, in case you louse up the original finish of the stock here and there. If the stock was originally finished with some sort of oil finish, then an aerosol can of Casey's Tru-Oil stock finish for $1.75 is just what you want. Incidentally, this Casey stuff is real handy to have around, but it won't work on such finishes as DuPont's new RK-W finish. Last, but not least, you'll need a good glass-bedding compound. My choice is Acraglas, sold by Bob Brownell of Montezuma, Iowa.

Glassbedding a rifle is simple, but when you do tackle the job, don't try to rush it. Careful mixing of the ingredients and proper timing of the mixing is essential, and the best advice anybody can give you is to follow the mixing directions carefully. Directions are simple, and although the mixture begins to harden fairly fast, desperate last minute rushing before the Acraglas sets is not necessary.

Remove the stock from gun. To prevent damage to screwheads, professionals clamp the gun into the bench vise, stock up. This way, they can see the screws, and working under good light the job is a cinch. When the barrel is locked into the padded jaws of the vise, the rear weight of the gun should be supported. You can do this by means of a couple of blocks of 2x4's, something like sanding blocks. When the stock is free from the steel, look at the steel-to-wood contact points. You can, in most cases, locate the trouble spots. If you can't then you have two choices. If you have a good inletting blue on hand, such as Jerrow's Inletting Blue, put a small amount of it on the action and the part of the barrel that fits into the stock. The dye will be transferred onto the wood, indicating the pressure points where some wood should be removed. If you don't have any inletting blue on hand, then carefully remove a little bit of the wood from the action area of the stock -

it will be replaced by the Acraglas - and the bedding compound will, of course, conform to the steel contours.

If the barrel is now free floating, you can glassbed the entire length of the barrel channel. If the barrel has not been free floated previously and a free floating barrel is desirable, then enough wood must be removed from the barrel channel to accomplish free floating. If free floating is not desired, remove enough wood to, in effect, free float the barrel, then glassbed the full length of the barrel channel. Incidentally, here is a trick that will allow you to glassbed the entire barrel channel to the very end of the stock fore-end, and at the same time, free float the 3 or 4 inches of the barrel at the fore-end. After you bed the barreled action in the newly applied glass, carefully tighten all stock screws. Remove the gun from the vise and clamp it back into the vise upside down so that the stock is uppermost. A 3 or 4 pound weight can now be attached by means of string or tape to the barrel at the point where fore-end meets steel. Once the glassbedding compound has completely dried, you have a fully bedded, yet partially free floating, barrel.

Begin the actual bedding job by coating all of the steel parts of the action, the magazine, the barrel, and the bedding screws with the release agent that comes with the complete Acraglas kit. One handy trick that I picked up from a professional stockmaker is to coat the screws with some grease, something like Vaseline. This assures you that the screws will come out of their holes at a later stage. If you don't get enough release agent on the threads of the screws, you'll run headlong into trouble. Once a glassbedding compound sets, it sets, and there's little you can do to break the bond between it and the threads of a screw.

Fasten masking tape along outside of forearm to speed cleanup.

Once the extra wood has been removed, fasten some masking tape to the outside of the fore-end, forming a small trough with the tape. It is better to use a little more tape and cut off the surplus than to have not enough tape when you begin to spread the bedding compound. Now make up the Acraglas mix, and watch your timing. Acraglas comes with a small vial of stain, but go easy with adding stain. This is powerful stuff and a little goes a long ways. Now add the Floc. This is the glass, and again follow directions. With the mix having a creamy and smooth consistency, you are now ready to spread the bedding compound. Use the paddle that is supplied and spread the mix into the

Mix Acraglas with great care, following the instructions exactly.

barrel channel and the recoil shoulder where the recoil lug presses against it. Press down barrel and action, and tighten the stock screws. The excess bedding compound will ooze out, and the masking tape will prevent stock damage and unnecessary touching up of the stock finish.

When mix is ready, add glass floc. Add slowly & mix thoroughly.

After a couple of hours, the surplus Acraglas that oozed out of the barrel channel can be removed with a dull knife or a spatula. If the Acraglas has not set sufficiently, it is better to wait a little longer. Temperature and humidity control the setting of these bedding compounds, and a too-early removal can lead to an unsatisfactory job. It

With spatula spread mix evenly in barrel channel, recoil lug area.

Carefully seat action/barrel, avoiding slop-overs. Tighten screws.

is best to let the work rest, after the initial removal of the surplus, for 24 hours, and if you want a perfect job, 36 hours are even better. Since I was not able to take the pictures and do the glassbedding at the same time, I asked John Juda, a stockmaker at the Chicago Gun Center, to do the glassbedding. His advice was to let the work rest 36 hours, then clean up the surplus and do whatever stock touch-up is needed. Although the bedding compound is hard as a rock then, he suggests that the gun not be fired for another 24 hours. This extra day helps to set the glass still further and allows the touched-up stock finish to dry completely.

Surplus Acraglas oozes out, is caught by tape trough. Let Acraglas set somewhat, then carefully remove excess along stock with knife.

A pro trick: use shaped dowel to set, then lift action from glass.

Now remove the stock again, and clean off the release agent from all metal parts. If the stock fit is extremely tight, use a rubber mallet to pound - not a hammer. Now strip off the masking tape, clean the Acraglas off the stock. John likes to use very fine steel wool to remove any glass that might stick to the steel, and with careful handling, you won't even need to touch up the bluing. Energine Spot Remover or lacquer thinner can be used to remove the release compound from the steel parts. (Ed note: Use Energine for removing the Pink Release Agent. Use alcohol or warm water to remove the Green Release Agent.) With fine sandpaper remove the bits of Acraglas that might have over-flowed on the fore-end, and with the aerosol can of Tru-Oil stock finish, touch up the finish where needed. Put the barreled action back

Use steel wool, sandpaper to clean up. Green release agent removes with alcohol or warm water. Pink type with lacquer thinner.

Unlike free-floating, glassbedding can not be seen. Despite careful work, stock showed some marks which touched out with Tru-Oil.

into the stock after you have cleaned up the surplus glass from such areas as the magazine well, tighten the screws, and you'll have restored the accuracy of your rifle.

The use of a glassbedding compound is not restricted to restoring accuracy. On heavy recoil rifles that have not been inletted properly or where a light stock or soft wood was used, glassbedding should be used to prevent possible cracking of the stock due to recoil. Although I have never tried it, glassbedding of an O/U or S/S shotgun has proved beneficial, especially in some of the older shotguns where stock replacements are not obtainable.

Cracked and split stocks can be salvaged with Acraglas; inlays, grip caps, and contrasting fore-ends may be attached with it. The nice thing about it is that Acraglas does not shrink (less than 1/10th of one percent while setting) and thus it resists all atmospheric changes. If you have ever tackled the inletting of a stock blank, you know how tedious the job can be. Remove a bit more wood than you needed to remove, and the tight fit that you had been hoping for is spoiled. But "it ain't necessarily so," as the song says. One way to lick the problem of "chisel a bit of wood and try the fit" is to take out more wood than is needed right to begin with. Then simply fill the area with Acraglas and you'll have the tightest fit that you could possibly hope for. That's how I salvaged a nice but poorly inletted blank that I tried to finish not long ago. That bedding stuff saved a beautiful piece of wood from being consigned to the fireplace.

- *R. A. "Bob" Steindler, Reprinted by special permission from* SHOOTING TIMES, *July, 1967*

COTTON PACKING WHILE ACRAGLASSING

Thought that I should mention that when I am doing an Acraglas bedding job, I just pack cotton tightly into the trigger and magazine holes in my stock to keep the Acraglas out. Works real well, is easy to use, and keeps the Acraglas out of where you don't want it to go.

- *Donald Shaw, DCSLOG - USAREUR*

KEEPING GLASS OUT OF THE ACTION WHILE BEDDING

Some time ago I was Acraglassing a Model 70, and got to wondering how in the world I was going to keep the stuff out of the action by way of the front guard screws without using beeswax to be dug out later. I tried scotch tape, covered it liberally with release agent and let it dry. It worked perfectly - not one speck of glass in the action! Must be dumb for not trying it before, so hope the tip helps another of the fraternity.

- *John Turnbull, Toulon, Illinois*

TRIGGER CAVITY

I use the modeling clay you buy for kids in dime stores to put in the trigger cavity of stocks when Acraglassing.

- *Robert S. Sutton, Jacksonville, Florida*

BEESWAX THE STOCK DEPRESSIONS

Here is an old pattern maker's trick: use plain old bee's wax in all depressions when glass bedding with Acraglas.

- *Aaron Reichard, Goodyear, Arizona*

ACRAGLAS DYE

W. Beckstrom writes that the dye that comes with Acraglas also works well with Twin-Weld. The dye is the Resorcin Brown 5G Conc. 200%.

- *W. E. Beckstrom, Eureka, Montana*

SAWDUST DYE

Discovered that by using the sawdust from a stock job in Acraglas as I mixed in some of the dust a rich color immediately began to appear. As I added dust, the color deepened. You can easily get it too dark. A little experimenting will show about the right amount to use. I like it as well, if not better than the coloring agent, and it is about as easy and convenient to use.....

- *Mark Stirman, Killeen, Texas*

MEASURING SMALL QUANTITIES

I have little double-end mixing spoons I use when mixing up Acraglas for repair or touch-up jobs. You should tell your customers they'll have better lives if they measure with spoons - wipe dry afterwards with Kleenex - for those little jobs. Much more accurate than guessing.

- *Julius J. Nelson, Burke, South Dakota*

ACRAGLAS MIXING TIME

Be sure to stress the mixing time in the directions. I stir a full three minutes by the clock and get a beautiful set-up.

- *D. G. Russell, Kansas City, Missouri*

MIXING IN ACRAGLAS FLOC

Take a 6" piece of 3/8" copper tubing and make two 3/4" cuts in the end and bend the pieces back at right-angles to the tube...sort of like "peeling back" a dandelion stem. Gives you a small paint-mixer-type tool. Then, when I have several guns to do at one time, I estimate the amount of resin and floc and put these in my container. Put the mixer in the drill press and with the drill press at slow speed use it to thoroughly mix resin and floc. Takes about a minute. Later, when I am ready to use it I take the required amount, add the hardener, set it under the mixer for a minute, and am ready to go. I have found this eliminates lumps, air pockets and holes in the finished job, and it only takes a moment to mix a little more if you underestimate. I have glassed eight M1 rifles with only one mixing operation. (We would recommend this only for production work where you have several guns all set and ready to be bedded - and have had plenty of experience in glass bedding. BB)

- *Eugene M. Spencer, Fort Benning, Georgia*

STORING MIXED ACRAGLAS

After I mixed up a batch of Acraglas and had some left over - stored it in the freezer. The next day it took 15 minutes to thaw and worked well. Still have a sample in the freezer and after a week it still can be worked. Won't help sales for you but sure helps us in the shop!

- *Eldon L. Rodieck, Anaheim, California*

LIFE OF ACRAGLAS UNDER SEVERE CONDITIONS

Charles Dorr answered another question we've wondered about for several years regarding the life of Acraglas under adverse conditions. Writes Charles: "I got the first gun back this week I ever full bedded with Acraglas when you first brought it out years ago. The gun is a 30-06 Springfield and the owner says it has been wet for six months a year for the past 3 years and oil soaked the other six months a year. The bedding is still perfect and he says the gun has shot over 1000 rounds and still holds its groups. Some stock, huh?" (Note: We wrote Charles for more details and he advises us that the owner is a friend of his who works for the U.S. Justice Department in Alaska and the gun is outside 360 days of the year in all the various kinds of weather Alaska has to offer!!)

- *Charles R. Dorr, Bevier, Missouri*

MORE AMAZING TALES

Vernon Drake filled the holes behind a loose hinge on the house front door with Acraglas. Says, "Next morning was strong enough to swing on and much better than tearing down the house and putting in a whole new door frame..."

- *Vernon S. Drake, Staples, Minnesota*

ACRAGLAS CLEANER UPPER

When using Acraglas or Twin-Weld you generally mix the Twin-Weld in a saucer and pour the Acraglas with a shotglass. If you'll use common vinegar in the vessel when through and leave it 20 to 30 minutes, the residue wipes right out.

- *Joe M. Waring, Comanche, Texas*

ACRAGLAS FROM THE HANDS

To remove Acraglas from the hands use ordinary vinegar. It will remove either the individual fluids or the mixture. I also use vinegar with a tooth-brush to take away the surplus bedding compound from checkering when repairing a cracked or broken stock. (Note from Bob B.: Works great to take off Twin-Weld too!)

- *Paul Morton, Wichita Falls, Texas*

STAINING WALNUT STOCKS FOR FINISHING

First off, the stock has got to have the grain raised and cut off with No. 8/0 Durite Paper at least three times before starting with the staining. It is very important to get the pores of the wood as open as possible.

To begin staining, swab on a good warm mixture of equal parts of Tru-Oil and Turpentine. Leave this warm mixture on the stock, keeping the wood wet, for about 2 minutes. Then wipe dry with a lint-free rag and let dry thoroughly for two or three days.

For the second coat, make a pad by folding an old T-shirt in on the corners and tying them so as to make a round-ball pad - like an egg that is flat on one end. Make a teaspoon-full of Ebony dust from the hardest, blackest piece of Ebony you can get your hands on, with No.

610 Durite Paper. Mix this black dust with about 3 teaspoonfuls of regular-mix Acraglas without the floc or stain. This will make the blackest stuff you have ever seen! Now with the pad, rub this into the stock vigorously, really getting after it. It might be better the first time you try it, to mix up only half a batch at a time and do only half of the stock until you get the knack of working it into the pores before the Acraglas hardens. When this is well rubbed in, set aside and let dry (or cure). Sand smooth with No. 8/0 Durite.

Third coat is applied just like the second. Sand smooth when hard with No. 8/0 Durite and proceed with regular finish.

This process is the one I use on Walnut to really make the grain jump out. Take a cheapie stock and try it - will turn out like a real masterpiece. Be sure to sand smooth after each coat, and especially critical to get it very smooth after the third coat, regardless of what type of finish you decide to put on after the staining treatment.

- *Wayne Brickner, Chadron, Nebraska*

BEAUTIFYING CURLY MAPLE

While experimenting I discovered that your Resorcin Brown Stain does almost as good a job as the "Suigi" method (burning the grain with a torch) on curly maple. It brings out the curl much faster, easier and safer than any method used so far. For a GOOD job, whisker the stock with a fairly strong water solution of Resorcin Brown instead of plain water at least five times, dry the stock well with an electric heater after each application and before sandpapering. Apply a coat of Lin-Speed (or Tru Oil) and gloat over the beautiful finish.

- *Wilfrid Edward Feldman, Philadelphia, Pennsylvania*

STAINING STOCKS BY FUMING

Maple, sycamore, and some other blond woods are ideal for rifle stocks so far as strength, texture, etc., are concerned. But not many people like light-colored stocks; and staining the wood is never too satisfactory. So, to get the rich, mellow tone that normally only comes when the thing is 8 to 10 years old - fume it.

This is a process used an eon or two ago, before you were on the scene, when "mission" furniture was mostly made of oak. The cheaper grades were stained with spirit or oil stains; any color or shade from jet black "Flemish" to light yellow "golden oak". But the best quality was fumed with strong ammonia - 28% - 30%. This was done by simply sanding the surfaces smooth; then shutting it up in a box or tight cupboard with a dish of the ammonia and leaving it to its thoughts for a few days. It came out a really beautiful, soft shade of dull brown that went deep into the wood without obscuring the grain in the least. BUT, Oak contains tanic acid - and it was on this that the ammonia operated.

Maple and other blond woods contain little, if any, tanic acid. But tea does. So to fume blond woods, simply use a black tea as strong as you can make to raise the grain instead of using water. Then, put it in a box that is as near airtight as you can make it with masking tape or the like, insert the saucer of ammonia, wander off to commune with your pipe, shoot the breeze with the other gunnuts around - or, as a last resort, use the interval to get some work done.

At the end of three or four days your stock will be nicely "aged" to a beautiful golden brown, much as it would in ten years normal exposure to the atmosphere. Finish and checker as usual. That is all. It works perfectly; involves no extra work...and you can probably sneak the tea out when your wife isn't looking. Selah!

- *"Jack" Frost, Placerville, California*

DUPONT STAINS

If DuPont says their stains are light-fast, they are! And, I like them because you get gallons of stain at relatively low cost. They are simply measured with a powder scale, and easily applied and intermixed with each other for just the right color. I have found cutting Newell's formulas in half lets you make all the stains - plus having almost two quarts of each when finished. So that a gunsmith can use his powder scale, 480 grains equal an ounce.

Newell's No. 1 maple stain will make light walnut a rich red brown - much like the color of the best grade of Winchester stocks such as the Model 21 shotgun. Water stains will stay in the wood, not bleed into the finish like oil stains, which, you know, often lost their color by being sanded off during the finishing operations. Water stains won't offend this way.

- *Henry L. Woltman, St. Paul, Minnesota*

RAISING THE GRAIN

E. L. Knowles wrote saying the best thing he had ever used for raising the grain on a gun stock was "Solox" and that you could buy it in any grocery, paint or hardware store. I wrote right back and asked him what the heck it was - had never heard of it and if we mentioned it in the newsletter, guys would be wanting to know and I wouldn't be able to tell...

Answered he, "Solox is nothing but denatured alcohol, the general purpose solvent. It is very good to have around the shop for lots of uses, including fuel for alcohol torches or lamps. It is produced by the U. S. Industrial Chemical Co., of New York, and can be purchased practically anywhere...I suppose that the 'drinkin' kind of alcohol would RAISE the whiskers on a stock - in fact, I've seen some that would raise the hair on my head - and I am as bald as a billiard ball. But I don't think that even a gunsmith is that crazy - to waste good (??) drinking spirits to whisker a gunstock."

- *E. L. Knowles, Marietta, Georgia*

RAISING THE GRAIN

As a convenient way to raise the grain on a rifle stock for finishing, I use an electric gadget that is shaped like a trowel and has heating coils in it. It is called a "Chicken Singer". Works like a charm and easier to use than over the stove or blow torch...

- *Tom M. Blakemore, Chicago, Illinois*

RAISING THE GRAIN

I read your article about using the "Chicken Singer" for raising the grain when refinishing a stock. I use an electric paint remover for the same job. This gadget is about 4" X 6" and weighs less than two pounds. It is very handy, develops about 1000 watts. I picked it up some time back in a paint store, made by General Electric and retails for $12.00...

- *Lloyd E. Cary, LeGrand, Iowa*

TONIGHT, TONIGHT

The Kinsey interviewer was questioning a group of gun dealers. "How many more than once a week?" Five men raised their hands. "How many once a week?" Ten hands went up. "How many once a month?" Eight hands went up. "And how many once a year?" A little fellow in the back waved his hand violently. "Only once a year?" said the interviewer. "I don't see what you're so overjoyed about." Excitedly the dealer answered, "Maybe not, but tonight's the night!"

KNO-KLOG'S MANY USES

You-all who haven't tried Kno-Klog for cleaning up old stocks, semi-smoothing new stocks, taking the paint off the baby's hi-chair, the old lady's hi-backed rocker or cousin Susie's sofa are missing a real fast way of doing things...'Tis a bit messy and smells like the spit wad you use to clean a muzzle loader on a right hot day - but surely does the business.

- *Bob B.*

REFINISHING STOCKS WITH KNO-KLOG BLOCKS

On your Kno-Klog blocks, please be advised we cleaned up a stock that had smoke damage from a fire in about a third the time it would have taken otherwise. VERY useful item.

- *Morley's Gun Shop, East Wenatchee, Washington*

DURITE SANDING PAPER

Now for a little praise for that No-Fill Durite Carbide Sanding Paper you sell. In my 14 years of experience this is the finest thing that could happen to anyone doing stock work. Any stockmaker, or anyone doing repair and refinishing, should lay in a supply of this paper by all means.

- *Kirby Gun Shop, Susanville, California*

REMOVING OLD FINISH

I do a lot of refinishing and recheckering on good stuff. I run into the old heavy oil soaked wood so much - linseed and so called rosin finish, etc. Honestly, I admire them for the classic look, but #$%¢&*! they are hard to get out! I've been using a couple of methods with fair luck.

Soak in a cream can in pure methanol (as pure as I can get). Really bad cases, bundle them up in kleenex and cover with aluminum foil and bake at around 180° F. Also have had some luck with heating to about 120° and brushing with Oxalic acid, depending on things. Anything different than this that's better that you know of? (John also asked if we knew of a text we thought was tops on wood refinishing... Around here we depend upon that one by Newell - *Gunstock Finishing & Care* - as the final word. Not recent enough to have the epoxy finishes, but a fountain of finishing information otherwise.)

- *John H. C. Reid, Hopkins, Minnesota*

TAKE OFF THE SILICONE

These days a lot of the rust preventatives for metals - and many of the gunstock waxes - contain silicone as a basic component...and it spells trouble when you are going to just touch-up a stock instead of completely sanding down and refinishing it. Happened to me the other night when I was working over my wife's pet .22. Was sprucing it up for her, and the touch-up finish job would not set up properly. Finally remembered that I had really waxed it up the last time with a good silicone wax, and the wiping rag I used was one of those silicone ones which got rubbed over the wood every once in a while too.

So, scrubbed the stock down good with a naphtha solution I had on the bench, put on some more finish and set up right on schedule! (Note from Bob B. - Dow Corning Corporation who makes a lot of the commercial silicone says in their chemist's spec sheets that silicone is soluble in the following solvents - amyl acetate, benzene, chloroform, gasoline, kerosene, methyl ethyl ketone, naphtha, perchlorethylene, trichlorethylene and some others that are pretty hard to find or spell!)

- *Wayne Fleming, sometimes the left-handed man around here, too!*

TRU-OIL STOCK FINISH

For the fellow wanting a doggone fast stock finish it surely is the answer. Gives an oil finish in less than a day and if done right it both fills and finishes. Apply one coat quite heavy and in two hours rub it down to the wood with 400 Wet-or-Dry paper and water - let dry. Apply a second coat, but not so heavily, and repeat the rub. If the wood is not too brash, the third coat, hand rubbed, should do it. The next day (or that evening) apply a good silicone wax and, Brother! is it purty. A 2 oz. bottle is enough for several guns. A good retail item to go along with G-B Linspeed Finish.

- *Bob B.*

SCUM-FREE TRU-OIL

In reading your Newsletter I noticed some of the fellows are bothered with scum on their bottles of Tru-Oil stock finish after using. Here is our method - we set 'er away upside down and let her scum be damned. You always have fresh stuff when you unscrew the cap.

- *Bob Wilson, Wichita, Kansas*

KEEPING THE BOTTLE SEALED

I have found that it is almost impossible to put the lid on a bottle of Tru-Oil without it forming a heavy film as paint does in a can not tightly sealed - and consequently losing a lot of it. I wrap a piece of half-inch masking tape around the lid, which seals it well enough that there seems to be very little loss.

- *Glen Malin, Santa Fe, New Mexico*

ACRYLIC STOCK FINISH

Acrylic MUST be sprayed on CLEAN wood. You can put a finish OVER Acrylic but you cannot put Acrylic over a different finish.

- *Struthers-Turner, Wichita Falls, Texas*

STOCK FINISH FOR MUZZLE-STUFFERS

Nearly fill a 4-oz. bottle with 3/4ths linseed, boiled, and 1/4th turpentine...shake up and add a few drops of vinegar until the mix turns cloudy...apply sparingly and rub in...

- *Harold J. Vollink, Holly, Michigan*

STOCK FINISHING

When finishing a gunstock with Lin-Speed, Tru-Oil, and some of the resin finishes, apply the first coat fairly liberally and immediately take a piece of 180 grit wet-or-dry paper, wet it with the finish and sand the stock lightly. Let dry. Take finish back to the wood and proceed in the normal manner to finish. This fills the pores of the wood and cuts down on the time and coats required to get a nice finish. (Note by Bob B.: This is the way I always finished, but I made it the second coat that I sanded on, rather than the first. The first one I like to use to get as much to soak into the wood as possible and then let it dry until fully oxidized...Then apply the second coat as above.)

- *Max J. Lindauer, Washington, Missouri*

CURING LINSEED OIL STOCK FINISH THAT WON'T SET UP

"If you give a stock a linseed oil finish and the finish won't set up, go to a machine shop and buy a small can of yellow, old-fashioned, pure axle grease...the kind farmers put on wagon axles. Smear a small amount of this over the stock, rub smooth with your hand and set the stock away. Usually will set up by the next morning to a glass-hard finish."

- *Benny Newman, Gunsmith, Agency, Iowa*

LACQUER STOCK FINISH

Sold a can of your stock finish lacquer to an amateur stockfinisher the other day, and he had a little trouble with it because he didn't know what he was doing. It peeled away near some of the edges, and on questioning him, I found out that he did not clean away any of his run-overs on the inside edges of the inletting. When he installed the metal and shot it a few times, the finish sort of "fused" to the metal, and on removal, some of the finish came off with it. Judging from the length of time it took him to do the stock, he probably did not give it nearly enough time to harden either. I like to give it about a month to cure before installing the iron.

- *Ernest Paulsen, Chinnok, Montana*

GETTIN' MARRIED

The guys in the trade are a tough bunch of characters and perfectly capable of withstanding all sorts of adverse vicissitudes (a two bit word meaning repeated changes from feast to famine) and still come thru in fine shape, as witnesses this report from Fred Moulton. Fred was interviewing (so he says!) the winner of a 4-position match who was 52 years old. "I'm not the man my father is," the shooter said, "he just toted his elk out of the Rockies single-handed at 74."

"I'd like to meet your father," said Fred. The shooter replied, "You can't. He's in Phoenix attending grandpa's wedding. Grandpa was 103 last week."

Fred was naturally somewhat taken aback. "Why in the world does a man that age want to get married?" Said the shooter: "He didn't want to...He had to..."

- *Fred Moulton*, The American Rifleman

STOCK FINISHING WITH BRUSH-ON LACQUER

Early in my stockmaking career I became interested in the use of many fine tropical hardwoods. Today our shop specializes in building stocks of these beautiful and exciting woods.

One of my favorite woods is the Brazil Rosewood with its colorful swirls, blotches and color variations. Another is the African Zebrawood with its varied stripes. The lavender colored Purpleheart from British Guiana, the crimson Vermillion from Africa and the exotic orange and black Coco Bolo from Central America as well as many others make fine stock woods.

For some years I floundered about trying to find a suitable finish for these woods. About every stock finish and finish used in the furniture trade was tried. Oil finishes, while doing an excellent job on some woods, are useless in the finishing of such woods as Rosewood and Coco Bolo.

These woods contain a natural oil that when mixed with oil-type finishes, creates a sticky non-drying substance. When such woods are used for fancy foretips and grip caps on the walnuts, many times a finishing problem is created. To solve this problem we turned to the various lacquers and synthetic plastic finishes on the market. We needed a finish that was durable, weather resistant, would dry on these exotic woods and leave their natural color. Also the finish had to serve as a filler since most fillers are intended for the oil type finishes, and the lacquers tend to act as a solvent on them. In addition, most fillers contain abrasives that will ruin the checkering tools.

In light of the foregoing, we got a can of Brownell's Brush-on Lacquer. After all our previous disappointments, I fully expected it not to work. Much to my surprise, it seemed to fill the bill in every way. Since that time we have come to use it almost exclusively in our shop. It can be used as a quick finish on cheap guns where the usual time required for a hand rubbed finish would be prohibitive, as well as for a professional finish on the finest of custom stocks.

Quick Finish Method

For a quick finish on new wood, sand and prepare stock in the usual way. Space does not permit going into the details of stockmaking, but after final shaping, I use No. 1/0 or 80 grit aluminum oxide paper for the first sanding. A solid block should be used on as much of the stock as possible for the first sanding to remove any ripples or low spots. This is very important since these will become much exaggerated when the stock is finally finished. Next, sand again with the same paper, using two or three fingers for a backing to round off minute square spots that may have been created by use of the block. The second sanding is done the same way, this time using 4/0 or 150 grit, followed by a final sanding with No. 320 wet or dry garnet paper used dry. Leave as much of the fine sandings as possible on the stock to act as a filler on porous woods. If staining is to be done, it should be done at this time. When refinishing old stocks, all traces of the old finish must be removed. The stock is now ready for Brownell's Lacquer.

Mix one part lacquer to one part thinner for a seal coat. While I believe any lacquer thinner will do, I prefer the type put out by the automotive paint companies. This thinned preparation should be liberally applied with a brush to both inside and outside of the stock. Spend about twenty minutes at this, paying particular attention to the points where end grain shows. After about twenty minutes the

Ernie Paulson shown in his shop lacquering a stock

wood has absorbed about all it will take. This will permanently seal the wood as good as wood can be sealed. It is not necessary to make any further applications on the inside of the stock. Further applications can cause bedding problems, especially where close inletting has been done. If desired, more lacquer can be applied to areas where wood does not contact metal. When dry, sand off grain rise with 320 garnet paper.

At this point I might add that I do not use spar varnish as a filler. The lacquer acts as a solvent on any varnish and can cause trouble. It is not necessary and should not be used. The above preparation may also be used for sealing and firming up new checkering by rubbing in with a tooth brush.

The second and subsequent coats should be used as it comes from the can. Generally the consistency is about right but if it appears sticky and tends to sag, thin slightly to where it will work freely. Flow the lacquer on freely and work rapidly as it dries very fast. Apply brush so as to work into the areas already covered to avoid lapping. Particular attention should be paid to getting liberal application to all sharp corners and edges. Apply where you have good sunlight so that you can readily spot runs and sags. The number of coats will depend on the wood used. Too heavy a buildup is not desirable and from five to seven coats, including seal coat is usually sufficient. Due to its rapid drying qualities, the entire finish can readily be put on in one day. It is, however, desirable to let it cure for at least 48 hours before rubbing down. Cut down any runs or sags with 400 or 500 garnet paper, rub down with real fine steel wool and you have a finish you can be proud of.

Some lapping along the edges of the inletted areas will occur during finishing. This should be scraped clean with a dull pen knife as soon as all finish is applied. It is still soft at this time and will cut away cleanly along the edges. This is very important. If this is not done these laps may interfere with bedding and when metal parts are removed at some future date, chipping may occur as this buildup may fuse to the metal.

Professional Finish

For a professional finish on fine custom stocks, I whisker the stock before applying any finish. Then proceed as with the quick finish, seal and apply two or three coats of lacquer. Let dry for about 48 hours and sand off with 320 garnet paper nearly down to the wood. While this finish can be rubbed within several hours, it is more desirable to let cure for about 48 hours. When rubbed too soon it tends to "roll off" rather than cut and gums up your paper. Take great care so as not to sand into the wood, especially around sharp points and edges. Such spots will frequently show a slightly different shade of color than the rest of the stock after final finishing.

Some woods will be leveled off by this time but if pores are not quite filled, apply several more coats as necessary and sand off again until all pores are leveled. At this stage something with a good firm backing should be used to rub with. A large typewriter eraser can be used, but better still, make a sanding block by cementing about one quarter inch thickness of hard rubber to a wooden block. This eliminates any low spots which will reflect light differently on the final finish. Take your time and let the garnet do the cutting. Apply only very light pressure, avoiding gumming up of your paper. Keep the garnet paper clean at all times.

Next apply two more coats of lacquer slightly thinned down. Since all pores should be filled by this time, a more even and exacting application can be applied with thinner lacquer. Now hang the stock in a warm, dry place and go on a vacation for from 30 to 45 days. This will give the finish time to harden and cure and a much neater job of final rubbing can be done.

After this curing time has passed, examine stock carefully for any runs or buildup that may have occurred. Cut these off with 320 garnet. Now take one quarter of a sheet of 400 wet or dry paper, folded in half and with your fingers as a backing, cut the sheen down. Shiny areas indicate low spots and these should be rubbed down until these spots disappear. Be sure to use two or three fingers so as not to concentrate your rubbing in a small area, creating further low spots.

If a dull finish is desired, rub the entire stock again with 600 wet or dry paper, this time using mineral oil. Pumice and mineral oil will also do about the same job at this stage but if stock is to be checkered, the pumice is undesirable in that some of the abrasive may work into the finish. This raises havoc with checkering tools. If mineral oil is not available, water will do.

Many will consider the job finished here but if a higher sheen is wanted, the next step is to polish with a fine polishing compound. With this, you can polish to a mirror finish if you are willing to put forth the effort. This professional finish takes about eight hours of labor after all application and filling has been done.

Small scratches can very easily be repaired by applying a bit of lacquer as necessary to fill. Let dry and rub down as in finishing. This is one of the few finishes that can be patched-in to perfectly match the original.

A tip on finishing where fittings are perhaps more porous than the stockwood itself: Apply finish to these areas first. Since it dries so rapidly, these areas will be dry by the time you get to them again. In this way, these areas will get two coats every time you apply one coat to the stock.

Brush-on Lacquer creates a beautiful finish. It is durable, fast drying, easy to handle and gives an everlasting finish on any wood. To date I have successfully used it on some twenty-three different exotic woods from all parts of the world.

- Ernest Paulsen, Chinook, Montana

VARNISHING A GUNSTOCK

Have always had trouble with varnishing gunstocks because of the excessive dirt and runs that appear in the job no matter how careful I am. Now, I know, many of you are going to kid me for trying to varnish a gunstock to begin with. But after trying everything else available, I have decided to go along with Mr. Linden who says that the best stock finish is a good grade of Spar Varnish - providing you can get it to go on right and can keep the dirt out.

I finally hit on the idea of building an oblong box large enough to hold a stock mounted between centers. On one end is the barbecue motor from my grill which had a square hold in the driving shaft, and I used a piece of square stock in the socket and drilled a couple of holes near the other end to screw it into the barrel channel of the stock. On the other end, I have a piece of round stock pointed on the end that has a slip collar with a set screw in it and a bushing mounted on the end of of the box for it to slip through. Thus, can lock up the one end tight against the slip collar and let the motor turn the whole works from the other end.

When I am ready to varnish, I put a couple of coats of Val-oil on the stock, sanding between coats for filler. Then when dry, rub down carefully with tac rag to get all the grit and dust. Next, wash out the box with water, mount the stock between the centers and put on a fairly liberal coat of varnish. Start the motor and shut the lid of the box.

The beauty of this is that not only is the varnish kept clean, but because the stock is turning and the varnish cannot run, you can put on a fairly heavy coat of varnish each time. When all done, I rub it down with rottenstone and water which cuts the gloss - but it does not damage the varnish.

- *R. A. Jerrue, Abingdon, Virginia*

FINISHING ROSEWOOD

Noted that some of the fellows had a little trouble finishing Rosewood. Buddy, you're asleep at the helm - sell them Brownell's Stock Lacquer. I have finished up a number of rosewood stocks as well as stocks with rosewood fittings and have not had a stick of it yet that I couldn't finish with your lacquer!

If the wood seems extremely oily, it is a good idea to thoroughly wash and scrub the wood with lacquer thinner. Had to soak a whole stock in a tank full of thinner one time to get out the oil. Even if you already have a couple of coats of the lacquer on the wood and the oil starts to pop through, you can still scrub it off with the thinner.

In my experience, none of the oil finishes will work on woods such as rosewood or coco bolo. The natural oils in these woods seems to blend with the oil in the finish to make a sticky, non-drying goop and never

will come out right.
- *Ernest Paulsen, Chinook, Montana*

FINISH ON ROSEWOOD

To get a finish to stick to Rosewood fore-end tips, prepare the fore-end tip at the same time and in the same manner that you do the rest of the stock. Saturate a pad with Acetone and go over the tip with this. Acetone removes the natural oils from the Rosewood - or any other exotic wood you might be using. This leaves the wood so it will accept the regular finish. (Works especially well, too, on ebony.)

Some use carbon-tet and alcohol prior to the Acetone treatment - but we do not recommend carbon-tet because of its very poisonous characteristics. After the surface of the wood has been treated with the Acetone and wiped dry, some apply a couple of coats of model airplane dope (Nitrate Dope) to seal the wood and prevent the oils and waxes from eventually working out. Others use Acraglas or other epoxy finishes for the same purpose...and then go ahead and apply the same finish (oil or whatever) to the tip as they apply to the wood stock.
- *Bob B.*

WORKING ON TROPICAL WOODS

When working on tropical woods - as rosewood, African Cherry, Zebra Wood, ebony - you name it - it is absolutely - and I mean absolutely - necessary to always wax it when not being worked on. In other words, when fitting a grip cap, fore-end tip, etc., to a stock with one of the exotic woods, rub on some stock finish, stock wax, floor wax or the like whenever you lay the piece down and until it is finally finished along with the rest of the stock. You see, it is practically impossible to kiln dry tropical wood and if you don't wax between operations it is apt to check with you. Once finished, however, with the usual finish, it will remain stable along with the rest of the stock.
- *Bob B.*

ACRAGLAS SEALER

We've a bunch of customers who never cease to T-totally amaze me - along with a flock of scientists, too! Every so often someone will write in giving us the answer to a problem we here, or some laboratory, have been trying to solve for years. Ever since about the year one we have been trying to find a good way to apply Acraglas to a rifle stock so's it would give good penetration and not be quite such a mess.

A couple of weeks ago T. M. Blackmon sent us the following: "Dear Bob: - You may be interested in another use for your Acraglas. It makes what is probably the world's best stock sealer. Mix as usual (less glass floc, of course) and spread out on the bottom of a flat pan or can lid so it doesn't heat and set up so fast. Apply with a woolen cloth pad which has been moistened with three or four drops of Toluene - a solvent that is available from most drug or paint stores. If necessary the mix can be thinned with a small amount of Toluene. Apply all over as evenly as can be done conveniently. Heat the stock with a paint drying lamp and the resin will soak into the wood, displacing the air which will make it foam slightly.

If dry spots appear, wet them again with the Acraglas and in about ten minutes wipe off ALL excess, again moistening the rag with Toluene if necessary. Rubber gloves should be worn. After 24 hours sand down to the wood and the wood is hardened and proofed against grease, oil, water, alcohol and almost anything except falling on granite rocks with it.

For a really deluxe job it can be used for the entire finish including filler. For the latter, stir in white silica flour to the desired consistency and, as before, wipe off the excess while it can still be done. Additional - clear coats finish the job. Sand - or better yet, buff each coat almost off. Try to avoid a heavy build-up. It is tedious, but with care, it is probably the finest finish that can be had."

(The following is from a follow-up letter from Mr. Blackmon). "One more thing about the application. It helps to have the stock warm and there really is no need to panic because if the third application, say, should begin to ball up or get too much lint in it, one can always wipe it all or nearly all off with the solvent and start over. Since the previous coat has already hardened it is not affected. I am sure you have had this happen, as I have, with ordinary varnish, only we washed that off with turpentine."

- *T. M. Blackmon, Albuquerque, New Mexico*

SILICA IN ACRAGLAS STOCK FINISH

That item on using white silica in Acraglas (minus the glass) for a wood filler. Just in case, don't you reckon you should mention that if checkering is on the program to leave out the sand (silica)? That stuff is sure rough on checkerin' tools, as I found out to my sorrow when I was wettin' my feet in this racket...

- *Monte Kennedy, Kalispell, Montana*

ACRAGLAS STOCK FINISH

Acraglas Stock Finish is even more outstanding than we say in our catalog and, we think, superior in every respect to anything else on the market, no matter what name it might be called. Bruce Meek did an outstanding job developing the method of application. In the catalog we recommend spray application - somehow I have a hunch that many of our customers, being what they are, will develop brush-on applications and get as good-as-or-better-than finishes!

And, by all means, try out that stock rubbing compound on old, oil-finished stocks. Utterly fantastic, believe me! See the complete instructions following.

Acraglas Stock Finishing

The use of Brownell's Acraglas for a stock finish is not new. The method of application used here was developed in the finishing of a number of gunstocks. This will be an explanation of that process. Being an inventive breed of craftsmen, many of you will see improvements that you will incorporate into your situation. So here goes......

With your stock prepared for its final finish, here are the materials used;

Brownell's Acraglas shows a minimum of color. It goes well over ivory and light colored stocks. The thinner used is regular Acraglas thinner, which I have found superior as it was developed especially for this sort of operation.

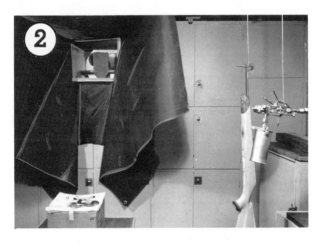

This procedure requires the use of a spray gun. This in turn demands some type of exhaust to carry away the fumes and spray. A simple box was made to slip into the basement window. Into this box was mounted a 1/3 h.p. electric motor. A baffle was mounted in front of the motor to protect it. A 16 inch three blade fan was mounted on the motor shaft. It really moves the air. In fact it requires a couple of open windows or door. They were forgotten once. It sucked the ashes right out of the incinerator and extinguished the pilot lights on the furnace and dryer. So a couple of hours were spent in cleaning the basement. A tarpaulin is used to funnel the fumes and keep them from spreading into the room. Photo number 2 will give you an idea of the crude but effective arrangement.

You can save some headaches by anticipating some of your activities and needs. Fix your stock so that you can hang onto it and handle it. A piece of aluminum 1/2"x1/8"x10" is used to mount in the barrel channel. A wood dowel could also be used. See photo number 1. This is blocked up from the bottom of the barrel channel. Block it up about 1/2" back from the tip of the stock. Block it up with folded paper or anything to space it away from the channel at the tip at least 3/16 of an inch. This will permit the spray to reach all of the tip unrestricted. A hole was drilled in the outer end of the aluminum strip by which the stock can hang while it is drying. Arrange a place to hang the spray gun close by. Also provide a place to hang the stock.

In photo number 9 you will see that the inside of the stock has been completely blocked off with tape. Leave about 1/16" of wood bare along the top edge and at the ends of the barrel and receiver channel. Tape off the trigger guard and magazine opening and the butt plate. In this case it was a rifle pad. On the stock shown even the holes for the swivel screws were covered. In case you are wondering why the covering of the inside of the stock, here is the reason. After completing the spraying, sanding and polishing of the stock the tape is removed. This leaves the inside perfectly clean except for the edges. Taping up close to the edges leaves only a small area to re-fit to the metal. More about the inside of the stock later.

Get three small clean glass jars. One in which to mix the Acraglas. One to contain the thinner and a third to hold a mixture of the two. They should have covers, or be covered to keep them clean and prevent evaporation.

Mix the Acraglas in the same proportions as for stock work. Into one of the containers pour 3 ounces of the resin. Pour 3/4 of an ounce of hardener into the resin. After stirring the two together for 3 or 4 minutes add 3 ounces of Acraglas thinner. Add a little at a time. For example, pour in a small amount 6 or 7 times instead of adding it all at one time. This amount has always given our sporter stocks 8 coats. This mixture will warm up but it will not harden before you have used it. This mixture will be referred to as your Stock Solution.

Let this mixture set while you direct your attention to the forend tip and grip cap (assuming them to be rosewood or cocobolo). Using the acetone, give these parts a thorough soaking and wiping with a well saturated cloth. See photo number 4. If you are doing a light colored stock such as maple, be careful because something comes out of cocobolo and rosewood that can stain. With this scrub-up completed the stock is ready for spraying.

The spray gun used is a Bink's model 15 touch up gun with an

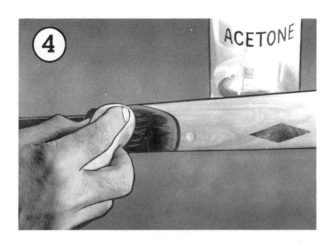

8 ounce container. It is equipped with a D765 nozzle. The number 76 needle size is .040 of an inch in diameter. This model has three fluid nozzle orifice sizes, 76, 77 and 78. The number 77 is .052 and number 78 is .070 inches in diameter. The number 76 has ample capacity and permits better control. It has a spray pattern that is adjustable from round fan shape and anything in between. The fluid flow is adjustable.

For those who are totally unfamiliar with air guns a few generalities are included here. Production guns are usually used at 50 to 65 pounds pressure, the type material used and viscosity being the governing factors. Too heavy a fluid will tend to "orange peel". Orange peel is a pebbly appearing surface. It is a result of the material being too heavy to flow and level out. Thinning the material to the point where it will flow is called for in this case.

The fan shaped spray is used where broader areas are to be covered. On gunstocks a round spray will give better control.

Air nozzles are made in two general categories: "External" mix and "Internal" mix. Either type can be had with siphon feed or pressure feed. As the name implies, external mix accomplishes atomization outside the nozzle by means of air jets. This type nozzle can be used on all types of fluid. The spray pattern is adjustable from round to fan with all intermediate patterns. As the spray nozzle is not affected by wear or build up of dry materials it is used for the fine finishes and most production work.

The internal mix nozzle achieves atomization by mixing the air and the fluid within the air nozzle. The spray pattern of an internal mix gun cannot be changed as it is determined by the shape of the nozzle. It is primarily used for maintenance spraying and for heavy materials where a fine finish is not required.

The pressure type nozzle requires pressure to feed the materials to the nozzle. This type nozzle is used for production work where the quality of fluid to be handled is large.

The siphon type with external mix is generally used for refinishing, touch up or spraying on small areas. It is especially good where a high quality finish is desired on areas not requiring a large quantity of material. The Bink's Model 15 is this type of spray gun and is highly recommended.

This spray gun calls for a compressor of 4.6 cubic feet per minute capacity. This would supply air for spraying a maximum quantity of material continuously.

Several factors would influence your selection of a compressor. The distance your compressor will be from the immediate spraying area. Will any other air-using equipment be used while you are spraying? The length of hose from the compressor to the spray gun. Long air lines will cut down the effective C.F.M. In the set up used on this job the air went from the tank through the gauges directly to the spray gun. The hose from the tank to the gun is 12 feet long. The compressor should be the tank type.

Actually the compressor used for this job is rated at 2.7 C.F.M. It has always had an ample supply of air for the shop needs. When the pressure in the tank falls below 60 p.s.i. the compressor motor cuts in and runs until the pressure reaches 80 p.s.i. At this point the motor shuts off. A safety valve that blows at 100 p.s.i. is incorporated into the tank. An air valve and gauge for regulating the amount of pressure through the spray gun is a necessity.

Now to spray the stock. Here again are a few pointers for those who have never handled a spray gun. Fill the container about 1/2 full of Acraglas thinner. With the regulator set at 40 pounds first adjust the spray pattern. With the adjusting screw at the forward end on the left side of the gun, adjust the pattern. By turning this screw in or out the pattern can be changed from fan shaped to round. Adjust it until you have a round pattern. The amount of material that you spray is adjusted by the fluid flow screw at the back of the gun. Turning the screw in will decrease the amount of flow. Turn this screw in all the way until the flow is shut off. Opening this screw 1/2 turn will give you a nice fine spray of the thinner. One full turn out will give you a fair deposit of thinner. This is the setting to try first.

This gun has a finger control and is very accurate. The first rule in using the spray gun is to keep it moving. Also keep it moving at as nearly the same speed as possible. As you can see if the gun is slowed down you are going to deposit more material. The reverse is true in that speeding up will deposit a thinner coat. The material will be applied with a number of passes with the gun. In photo number 5 a pass is being made from the top of the stock in a downward direction. In making the pass, start out beyond the stock with no pressure on the trigger. When you get to the stock you should be moving at the speed with which you intend to spray. Just before you are over the stock press the trigger and start the spray. The instant you have completed the pass release the trigger and stop the spray. After a few passes you will get the feel of the gun and automatically press the trigger and release it to control the flow. Even on short passes over the grip cap you will do this fingering without conscious effort.

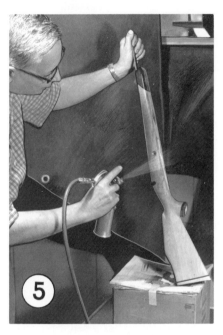

You will no doubt develop your own method. This is the method used here for the benefit of those who have to start some place. Turn the stock with the bottom facing the gun. Make a pass from the toe to up underneath the grip. While at the grip make a couple short passes across the cap from side to side. Turn the stock so that you can make a pass around the back and the underneath side of the cheek rest. Now turn the stock with the cheek rest facing the gun. Spray the side including the cheek rest and the grip. Turn the stock so that the top faces the gun and spray from butt to comb. Turn the side opposite the cheek rest to the gun and spray from butt to grip until covered. Turning the top of the stock to the spray gun again and starting at the comb make a pass over the grip and right up the barrel channel. Do this on each side. Turn one side to the gun and spray, blending off the grip. Usually two passes on a side will cover it. Go right on around the stock doing the bottom next; then the opposite side. Tilt the stock toward you and make two diagonal passes across the end lightly. There are an infinite number of ways of accomplishing the same results so do it the way that seems to suit you best.

Now to the actual spraying. Take the spray gun container and pour it about 1/2 full of the stock mixture. Dilute this stock mixture still further with 1 1/4 ounces of thinner. Stir well and it is ready to apply. This works very well through my equipment using 40 pounds of pressure. Turn on your exhaust fan. With the spray gun (using air only) blow off your stock and immediate spraying area. Spray the first coat on the stock.

After spraying the first coat on the stock, empty the spray gun container into one of the clean jars and cover. Take your clean jar of thinner and pour the container about 1/2 full of thinner and attach to the spray gun. Now clean out the nozzle with a good blast of thinner. Leave the thinner in the gun. Turn off the exhaust fan until you are ready for the next coat.

The main idea of this method is the spraying of each successive coat into a base that has not set completely. When the last coat has become good and tacky, that is the time to spray the next coat. Usually 45 minutes is about right. This time is not super-critical. This batch was all mixed at the same time and the chemical action is progressing approximately the same. As you spray you can see it melt into the former coats. There is absolutely no question of a good bond. They all flow together and form one homogeneous coat. As the coats build up there is no drying problem. Being epoxy, it will cure all the way through.

After you have sprayed the second and perhaps the third coat you will notice that the epoxy may have crawled in spots. This will likely occur on the forend tip and grip cap especially. Using the forefinger, wipe the epoxy until it smooths out. See photo number 6. If it has become too dry dip your finger in the thinner as a lubricant. Do not use any more thinner than is necessary. This will also help fill the pores of the stocks with more open grain. You will find that you may need to do this for several sprayings. Do not worry too much about finger marks. The main goal is to eliminate any tendency to crawl. Usually by the third or fourth coat it will flow on and stay in place.

From here on it is a case of spraying and cleaning the gun. Each time you add some of the stock mixture, thin it with some of the thinner that you keep in the gun between sprayings. For any given quantity that you add put in about 1/3 to 1/4 the same quantity of the thinner. As stated before, this quantity has always given us eight coats

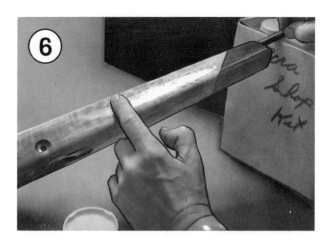

on a sporter stock. This is a good heavy coating that can be leveled down by the sanding operation without cutting through the finish.

Perhaps a word of caution might be in order at this point. No ill effects from skin contact has been noticed with these materials. However this is not being done day after day so it might be well to be alert for any adverse symptoms. One of the things to be tried is a nylon squeegee or some other material for this job. Since no difficulty has been experienced it is one of those things to be done someday.

With the stock sprayed, dried and before removing the tape from the inside of the stock it is sanded and polished. Photo number 7. The first sanding is with wet-or-dry 320 grip Speed-wet Durite Paper. This is a silicon carbide 3M product. This is quite coarse and removes the

high spots rapidly. This is used wet to keep the paper cutting cleanly. Oleum is a good lubricant (or kerosene which has more of an odor.) Gasoline has been used but it evaporates rapidly and is more of a hazard to have around. A combination of the two was tried and has some of the advantages of both. On this job we used a mixture of 4 parts oleum and 1 part white gasoline. It works very good.

The use of a block and round dowels in sanding is a must for a top notch job. It will give you that flat level surface to pass the critical inspection of the real "gun buffs". This is assuming that your final sanding of the stock prior to applying the finish was done with similar care. So wrap the sandpaper around the block. Dunk it in the lubricant and get going.

Next is a repeat performance with number 400 grit paper. Go over the stock and remove all the scratches made with the 320 grit paper. Be SURE that all scratches are removed. It is twice as easy to get them out with this grit than the next finer grit.

For the final treatment with sandpaper use 500 grit. This is the treatment that prepares the stock for its final finish. A good thorough job here will be the difference between a good job and a really fine one. It will not only produce that super job, but will also considerably reduce the time required to polish the stock. Do not plan on taking out any scratches with the polish. To be repetitious and emphatic, do get all the scratches out with the 500 grit. When finished simply wipe the stock well with a dry cloth. The polishing will remove every bit of the lubricant. Photo number 8.

Before going into the polishing I want to confess an accident that happened to this stock. In one of the maneuvers around the bench the cheek rest struck one corner of the vise. It put a three cornered

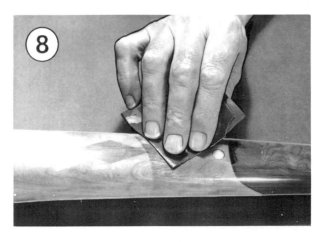

dent in the cheek rest that almost called for the old cold remedy. With visions of making a new stock spurring the imagination we came up with an old idea. Use Acraglas. The dent was a solid one. It proved that there was very good cohesion. There simply was no break in the surface between the wood and epoxy. The dent was filled with Acraglas. After filing, sanding and polishing the disaster completely disappeared. This event proved that scratches and mars can be removed quite easily.

Polishing the stock will be a breeze after all the preceding labor. For this Brownell's Stock Rubbing Compound was used. Some felt was purchased and cut into 4 inch squares. Some of the compound was put into a small container. A tongue depressor or any small stick was used for an applicator. See photo number 9. You can come up with any degree of polish that you desire from a satin finish to a high gloss.

With the polishing completed the tape is removed from the inside of the stock. The metal parts are refitted. See photo number 10. You will find that 8 coats of epoxy have built up quite a thick coat of epoxy on the inside of the barrel and receiver channel. Also in the trigger guard opening. This will be almost completely removed as you refit the metal. Take precautions to protect that finish you worked so hard to achieve. Here is used a part of a rubber blanket from an offset press. On the inside of this and contacting the stock is a piece of smooth plastic. In the past a nice piece of cloth has been used. The only thing wrong was that there was a perfect imprint of the weave of the material in our finished stock.

Apply epoxy to the inside of the stock. See photo number 11. Mix the epoxy again in the same proportions of 4 parts resin to 1 part hard-

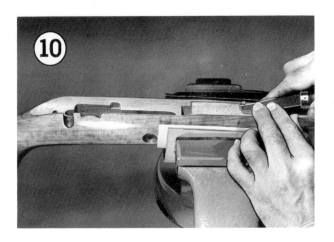

ener. A half ounce and an eighth ounce of hardener will provide more than enough. Thin this mixture still further using 3 parts of thinner to one part of the Acraglas mixture. With some clean rags handy, coat the inside of the stock. If you accidentally run over onto the polished stock wipe it off immediately with a rag. Keep the inside wet for a half hour with continuous applications. The end grains will naturally keep you more than busy. At the end of the half hour wipe out all the

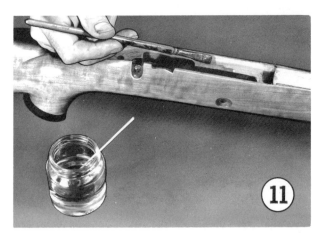

excess. For modern bolt action sporters this completes the process. If you have Acraglassed portions of the stock in fitting you are that much ahead. Simply apply your mixture to the wood portions exposed.

On shot gun stocks that butt up against the receiver (and rifle stocks in the same class) this process is repeated on all end grain portions. This will make a barrier that will prevent the wood from becoming oil soaked. It will also strengthen these portions. Do not allow the coating to build up.

After you have coated the inside of the stock and it has dried thoroughly examine the edges of the barrel and receiver channel and around the trigger guard. If they show any dulling from the epoxy run-over, simply polish it off.

This completes the project and we are sure that you will end up with a beautiful stock. In fact it will arouse a first class case of covetousness in most of those who view it. Good Luck.

- James B. Meek, Newton, Iowa

NO-MESS SPRAYING OF SMALL QUANTITIES OF ACRAGLAS

When I am using the Binks #15 gun for spraying small quantities of Acraglas for touch-up jobs, small pieces or the like, I take one of the little plastic bottles you show in the catalog - I use size F, but any of them would work - put the Acraglas mix into it, and put it into the 8-oz. cup that comes with the gun.

When I am through, I don't have any mess to clean out of the cup for I just throw the little plastic bottle away!

- Bill's Gun Shop, Port Angeles, Washington

PAINS ONE & TWO

Clyde Hart tells about the fellow who went to the dentist to have a tooth pulled PDQ - no time for Novocain. Doc told him it would hurt like H--l but the guy said he'd suffered the greatest pain and the 2nd greatest pain without it so go ahead and pull.

The Doc did so and then got curious about the Greatest Pain and asked for an explanation.

"Well," he said, "I was on a fishing trip and well out on the lake when I suddenly had to go. I paddled for shore at full speed and behind the first bush I squatted right into a bear trap."

The doctor decided that would be the Greatest pain, okay, but, "What was the 2nd Greatest pain?"

Said the guy: "When I came to the end of the chain!"

- Vic Hill, East Rochester, New York

STOCK HOLDING FIXTURE

Take a 3/8" rod about 20" long and weld a 1" ball bearing on one end and thread about 15" of the other end. Cut a 2"x2"x1/4" plate and drill a 3/8" hole in the center. Clamp the ball bearing in your vise with the plate next to the one jaw of the vise. Now, slip the butt stock on the rod through the draw-bolt hole and tighten the nut with a lock-

washer on it. You can both checker and carve as well as sand the stocks.
Honestly, it works fine.

- *Marcellus, Deer Park, Texas*

POWER ARM STOCK HOLDING FIXTURE

The great advantages and benefits to your physical self in using
the Power Arm Stock Holding Fixture are beautifully shown in the
pictures. They are of Bob Wilson, who came up with the idea and fired
it to us, along with pictures. Maybe you haven't been tearing your
hair out as Bob did (see left) trying to hold a stock in all positions
needed and won't have to shock your neighbor's as the pix at right
would do when the problem's cured...But as Bob allows: "Would almost - not quite - let my wife go first..."

- *Bob Wilson, Wichita, Kansas*

CHECKERING CRADLE

Tried something that may be a little different in the line of checkering cradles a couple of years ago and works O.K. for me. Had an old
little-used wood lathe taking up space, so tried it as a cradle. Tailend
of stock is supported by tailstock of lathe. A foot long piece of 1/2"
wood dowel is held in the barrel channel by a couple of wood screws.
The only precaution is to counterbore the screw holes slightly so the
wood doesn't pull up around the holes and goof up the bedding. Use
the dowel for the live center. The amount of effort needed to turn the
stock in the cradle can be readily varied by adjusting the tail stock.
If you have a real fancy wood lathe where the headstock pully can be
indexed in various positions, this makes carving really convenient.

- *Joseph Michaluk, Hyde Park, New York*

MAKING YOUR OWN CHECKERING TEMPLATES

Vinylite in .030" and .040" thickness is IT for making up your own checkering pattern templates. Absolutely limp, it will form around and fit like bark on a tree to any shape of gunstock. It is used for windows in convertibles and you can get it from your local automotive supply company.

- *Red Ballou, Riverside, California*

PATTERN LAYOUT

E. Knowles uses a sign painter's "pounce wheel" to lay out checkering jobs. Says he ran across one of them years ago while watching a guy paint Coke signs. It punches a series of small holes in the wood which are much easier to lay out than with a "V" tool and just as easy to follow. A "pounce wheel" looks like a miniature spur rowel on a checkering tool handle... (Note from Bob B.: ...seems to me they should be the ideal thing to use on those decal checkering patterns which have proven so very popular... being a round wheel, they won't tear the pattern like a knife or "V" tool or chisel is apt to do if not exceptionally sharp.)

- *E. L. Knowles, Marietta, Georgia*

CHECKERING PATTERN TRANSFER

Use a pounce wheel to transfer patterns from a book to a gun stock - such as from Monte Kennedy's book. Holes (from the pounce wheel) show up in Saran wrap and the Saran stuff sticks to the wood for final transfer. Would also work for engraving.

- *Norman R. Bricker, Chambersburg, Pennsylvania*

ELECTRIC CHECKERING TOOL MMC

We received an order the other day from the Sumner Gun Shop, and on the bottom of it was this note: "Have given your electric checkering tool a real workout in the last year that I have had it. Anyone who doesn't have this tool in their shop is NUTS! Service, when needed, has been 100%."

So I wrote to the Wescotts (Mr. & Mrs.) who run the shop to get permission to repeat the above. Mrs. Wescott, (Virginia) who does the checkering wrote back she's called Ginnie and "You might add to my comments that even tho the cost of the tool might seem high, that with the man (woman!) hours saved with it, plus a lot of hard work, the tool pays for itself in a very short time. I make one pass with the MMC checkering tool, one pass with a Dem-Bart double cutter and the work is beautifully uniform with fine pointed diamonds." Ginnie and Stan (the husband) have been in the stockmaking business for 18 years and Ginnie does the checkering, finishing, sanding and book-keeping....

- *Sumner Gun Shop, Sumner, Iowa*

SIMPLE ELECTRIC CHECKERER

For those 'smiths' who do a lot of checkering but cannot justify buying an electric tool, here is an idea. We ground about 1-1/4" of a 2" piece of 7/32" drill rod to form 1/8" flats. The flat end was curved up to about 30 degrees and a Dembart cutter was attached. Used in the Burgess Vibro-Tool, it makes a handy electric checkering tool. With the S-1 cutter it is especially good for working in tight corners and for cutting full depth diamonds right up to border.

- Robin McDougall, Ft. Collins, Colorado

CHECKERING FINISHER

If you've an old Vibro-Tool, make an attachment with a Dem-Bart cutter on the end. Use for finishing up lines right at the border where it is so easy to make a slip when doing free-hand.

- Wayne Fleming - what works here and is the "right arm" of yrs. trly

CHECKERING RUN-OVERS

For folks who have troubles with run-overs in their checkering, have an extra checkering cutter and put the cutter in backwards. It can then be set at the border and pulled away from the border to finish up lines that are hard to reach.

- Healy Custom Gun Shop, Hampton, Virginia

HOME GROWED CHECKERING TOOLS

As the saying goes, even a blind sow can root up an acorn now and again, and by accident, I have rooted up one!

Like some of the boys, I make up checkering tools from cheap screwdrivers. Easy too, for all you do is bend to shape desired at the point, file into a "V" shape, and cut the teeth in the edges. Cuts out a lot of wood at a pass and can be resharpened many times.

But, the trouble is getting the teeth right. Started out by using a 30-line checkering file, which is fine except that the durned thing had to be resharpened often. So went to a 15-line file, and found it cuts too deep and the tool is too rough.

So, now I cut the teeth quite deep with a 15-line file and go over once lightly with the 30-line. Each coarse tooth then becomes two fine teeth. The deep cuts take care of the sawdust, yet the cut is very smooth even in very soft wood. Once the pattern is marked out with commercial tools, the wood can be hogged out in a hurry and be ready for pointing up with a finishing commercial tool. These save me a lot of arm work and cutter blades - and when the cutter gets dull, it can be resharpened with just a couple swipes with the 30-line file.

- Jim Carney, Orange Park, Florida

ELECTRIC CHECKERING WITH MMC POWER HEAD AND RECIPROCATING FINISHER

Bob Brownell asked me to write a little on the use of the Electric Checkering Tools. Indeed, I was pleased to do so, so went through my letters from MMC tool users and scratched around in my brain to check-up on my own experiences and came up with the following comments. Incidentally, I might add that it takes a liberal supply of guts to put some of this into writing, knowing that it will be subjected to some pretty knowledgeable criticism. So I hope any of you readers who have comments will let Brownells or me know and we can include them in the next edition of this book.

Wherever practical, the information has been arranged under headings so that it can also be used as a trouble-shooting reference. And, in order to keep things straight, I have tried to present the subjects in the chronology of an actual checkering job.

As those of you who have tried it know, checkering is the toughest, most exacting, exasperating, tedious, yet personally rewarding kind of wood working ever devised by the devil. Perfection is never attained because as you approach it you become more critical. I have yet to see a good checkerer who is satisfied with his own work. He may tell a customer that he is satisfied, but this is only to keep the customer happy. In actuality, the person who did the job is usually the most critical of it. He knows where the mistakes are - after all, he made 'em! But the old wood-scrapers still keep trying to do better.

Some of the tools of the trade - walnut scrap, thread-pitch gauge, brush, some hand checkering tools, flexible straightedge, scribe, veiner, pocket knife, grease pencil and the MMC Power Head and Reciprocating Finisher.

If you want absolute perfection on a checkering job, you can't do it *exclusively* with an electric rotary checkering tool. Hard to believe I'd say something like that? Well, dear reader, read on! Very good checkering can be done with it to be sure, and it takes a mighty critical eye to find anything wrong with the work done by a craftsman proficient in its use. But, the real place of the rotary checkering tool in really fine checkering jobs is to reduce the time-consuming job of getting the lines cut to depth in the first place. This it does rapidly, easily and accurately, leaving more time to do the fine hand-work required to properly finish an expensive custom job. If a person must sit and rub for hours just to get the line down to the point of being ready to finish them, he is probably about out of patience when he needs it the very most. So why not cut in the lines fast and easily, and save your patience and time for the "custom-finishing"?

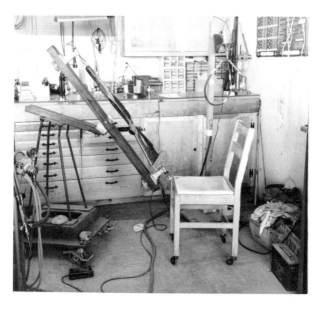

A view of my shop - especially cleaned up for the photographer - showing the free-standing cradle I use for full maneuverability.

Now don't get the idea that good work can't be done by the rotary tool - it can! Most of us in our efforts to make a living take on some jobs at a price that does not justify the time required to do our very best work. The customer understands this. After all, it is his pocketbook that has forced him to be satisfied with a job which can be done for less money. And, actually, he is getting much more quality for his money than a stockmaker could afford to give him if he had to do all the work by hand, because with a power checkering tool, the stockmaker can turn out more work in a shorter period of time.

So, electric checkering tools definitely have a place...but they don't "checker stocks". They just take almost all of the "ruba-ruba-ruba" drudgery out of the job.

About everything imaginable has been done to the basic diamond to produce different effects. Flat top or english, french or skip line in all ratios of lines to skips, rabbit track and combinations of checkering with stippling. The best to show up the grain, however, is the plain old repeated diamond - which also gives the best gripping surface. A plain piece of wood can really be dressed up with some of these fancy combinations, and believe it or not, these fancy ones are much easier to do than that plain diamond!

Stock Finish

I won't presume to tell anyone how to finish a stock, but do want to point out that in the interest of longer cutter life it is not advisable to use commercial wood fillers. The most common filler material is silicon dioxide (sand) which is very abrasive and will quickly dull any tool except those made of carbide. The plastic finishes are reputed to

Use standard machinist's thread-pitch gauge to set lines-per-inch.

be tough on cutters also, but probably not as bad as are the wood fillers. The nicest finish to checker, in my experience, is a varnish filler

A .45 Auto grip with center line drawn and master lines drawn and cut to it along straightedge with 32°s between master lines.

with a linseed oil finish. It isn't as waterproof as the plastic, but I think it looks much better.

Some workmen prefer to do their checkering on an unfinished stock. This will work, but seems to me like getting the horse a'hind the cart. It's difficult to keep the finish out of the checkering and almost impossible to fill the grain up to the edge of the checkered area. With french checkering, in particular, the little flat topped diamonds won't show up "shiny" to give the lace effect unless they are well filled

Tip head to left to cut first pass to depth from shallow master line.

and finished. It's also nice to be able to doodle on the stock with a wax pencil if you aren't sure what pattern to use, and this can't be done on an unfinished stock. All this seems to me to indicate that it's best to finish the stock before checkering it.

Layout

Basic pattern layout is covered more thoroughly in books on hand checkering, so read through a good one before starting with your power

By third pass full depth is reached. However, screw holes leave no groove for guide to follow - so must be cut in with hand tool.

Monty Kennedy's "Jointer" quickly cuts lines past screw holes.

Run-out lines develop as you work across the pattern. Do not let too many get ahead before extending with "Jointer" shown below.

tool. However, some points do come to mind that are worth mentioning here. On fill-in patterns (patterns where few or none of the lines are border lines), a template should be used to make sure both sides are alike. You can accomplish the same thing by outlining the pattern on one side with a wax pencil, scratching around it with a single-line hand-tool and then transferring strategic distances from a center line to the other side with dividers - which is my usual method. Said an old gunsmith in Columbia, Missouri, from whom I was seeking advice several years ago, "Hell! What you worryin' about? Nodoby can see both sides at the same time anyhow." Seems to me though, we should try at least to get the patterns similar on both sides. Fleurs-de-lis and other such frills are especially best done with a template.

Once a pattern is chosen, the master lines are scratched into the wood with a scribe and flexible straight edge. The angle between them should be consistent throughout the one checkering job at least. I use a 3-1/2:1 ratio which gives an angle of 32 degrees between the master lines. (I have used 30 degrees and it looks O.K. too.) Locate the master lines in the same place in each panel to be checkered. This is necessary because as the checkering goes around the distorted surface of the stock, the proportions of the diamonds will change which will result in an asymetrical pattern if corresponding diamonds on opposite sides of the stock are not of the same ratio. The location of the master lines is particularly important when the two panels come together as they quite often do in front of the pistol grip.

When the master lines are laid out to your satisfaction, they can be cut in. Use a single-line hand tool for this, cutting both lines fairly deep. It's more important to have them of a uniform depth than it is to have them at full depth. The visual practice here is not to cut the master lines to full depth. Sight along them to see that they are straight and if not, straighten them now before any irregularities are reproduced in the lines cut from them.

Setting the Guide for Depth

The MMC Power Head has a guide which is adjustable for width (pitch, lines per inch, etc.) and depth. First, the guide depth adjustment screw should be set so that the guide can be pushed up (against its torque spring) until it is even with the cutter. Test this by run-

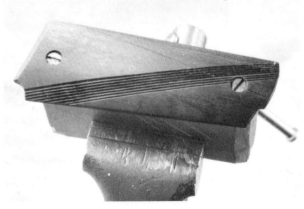

Lines cut to full depth on both sides of master line. Start guide in 3rd line (first one to full depth, see above) and work back.

All lines cut one direction. Recut other master line to full depth.

ning the tool over a flat board while holding it like a pencil so the plane of the cutter is normal to the plane of the board. The cutter should cut a groove the same depth as the fine groove made by the guide as it slides over the wood. Adjust the screw until it does. If the cutter is "tilted" to the plane of the wood, it will cut a groove which is shallower or deeper than the guide with respect to the wood surface - a situation which can be used to our advantage, as I will point out later.

Setting the Guide for Width for Standard Checkering

First, of course, decide how many lines per inch you want to cut. Then to set the guide, you will need a flat piece of wood, preferably the same as the stock to be checkered and a thread gauge or scale with inches marked accurately.

If you are using a thread gauge to set the lines per inch, cut a guide line with a hand tool, then cut 6 or 8 more lines with the Power Checkering Head and check with the gauge corresponding to the lpi chosen. If the lines on the board are too far apart, turn the guide nut counter-clockwise (looking at the right side of the Power Head). This allows the guide compression spring to push the guide out toward the cutter so that the lines produced will be closer together. Each click of this adjusting knurled nut is approximately .0007'' which ain't much. If you like to mess around with numbers, you could measure the exact number of lines per inch which were cut and calculate the number of clicks required to move the guide over to the correct position to produce what you want. But it seems much simpler to use the "cut-and-fit" method. Anyway, you now try it again, cutting 6 or

Good progress made on second pass. Shine disappears with finish.

8 more lines and checking with the thread gauge. If you moved the guide out too far the lines are now too close together. Remembering how many clicks you moved it counter-clockwise before, now move the guide nut clockwise half as many clicks. By continuing this process, you can bracket the correct position, working toward it until you get the guide set perfectly on the correct pitch. (Don't goof off on this, for if you ever want to duplicate it for additions to the stock or if the job is interrupted to do another, it's nice to be able to reset the machine accurately.)

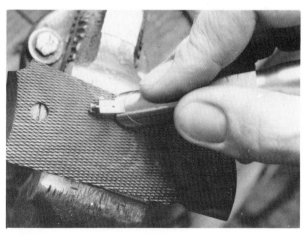

Reciprocating Finishing Tool used finishing-up the diamonds.

One word of caution - DON'T allow the guide to come in contact with the cutter, particularly while the machine is running...it's mighty rough on the guide!

If no thread gauge is available, it is almost necessary to cut a full inch of lines to get an accurate indication of how the guide is set. Cut a guide line with a hand tool as before. Now, with the Power Head, start cutting lines and counting them until you have cut the number of lines you want in an inch. Measure the width of these lines, from the guide line to the last line cut. If they measure more than one inch, the setting is too coarse and the guide must be moved closer to the cutter, etc.

While you are doing this guide adjusting you are also getting the feel of the tool. Note that if you tip the tool to the left, each succeeding line cut is deeper. This will continue until the cutter is in to the hub or you make corrections. Conversely, if you tip the tool to the right, each succeeding line is shallower. This might cause you trouble when working on curved surfaces, so best learn to keep the Power Head straight to the surface you are checkering.

Throughout all these contortions it is necessary to maintain some semblance of your "cool", so don't fight the tool. Too much tenseness will cause you to push down too hard, causing the guide to "bite" into the wood resulting in cuts of uneven depth - or, you will push the tool sideways, distorting the guide and causing variations in the lpi which the tool is supposed to be cutting.

All of this points to the hard fact that it's best to do a bit of practicing before you start on a custom stock worth many bux! It's hard to practice checkering because the incentive to do your best work just

Ebony grips are easy with MMC tools despite extreme brittleness.

Second pass master line transferred with dividers and scribed in.

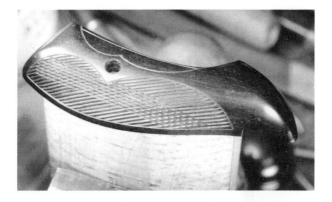

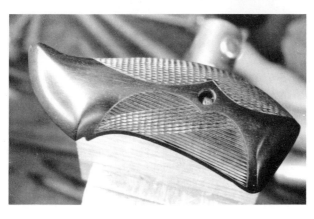

Before & After - note how much checkering dresses up the gun!

isn't there if you are working on a "scrap piece" of wood. Therefore, it's a good idea to work on a stock that won't be too much of a loss if the job isn't perfect. I have checkered such things as my son's .22 S.S., his Air Rifle, a camp axe handle, a nephew's Stevens Favorite and every scrap of walnut I can find around the shop. Most of the guns and the axe look pretty good but all the scraps are butchered. Incidentally, don't checker an axe handle if you intend to use it for chopping - it'll tear the hide off your hands!

Setting the Guide for Width for French or Skip-line

Some years ago a man wrote to me wanting to know how to do french checkering with the MMC Power Checkering tool. I advised him to set the machine for the number of lines to be cut and use a hand spacer for the skips. But I kept thinking about it until I came up with a better method which we call the D.C.A. (Dual Cutter Assembly). It is two cutters mounted on a mandrel with an integral spacer equal to the width of one line of the checkering it is made to cut. That's all there is to it, but this rig must be made very accurately or it's junk. Both cutters must be the same diameter, and the distance between the points must be the reciprocal of the number of lines-per-inch it is to cut. Also, in order to hold the radial run-out within acceptable limits, the mandrel-to-cutter fit must be very close. That's why the thing costs three times as much as a single cutter, but it's worth it if much french checkering of a particular pitch is to be cut. (It can also be used like a gang plow for standard checkering!)

Forearm well started on first pass. Note run-out extensions made every 3 or 4 lines to continue pattern smoothly across layout.

As mentioned above, each D.C.A. is made to cut only one lpi of checkering so it must be ordered for this lpi.

Let's assume the french checkering to be produced is 22 lpi with an 11 lpi skip. The D.C.A. for this will be made with the points of the cutters 1/22" or .0455" apart and the spacer will be .0455" wide. (The spacer isn't critical but is usually pretty close.) The reason for this spacer is to move the cutters out far enough to allow the guide to be spaced at 11 lpi from the inboard cutter. The machine was designed to

Use flexible ruler and scribe to run line behind the Fleur-de-lis.

give the shortest distance practical from the right side of the gear housing to the cutter so it can work in tight places.

The first step is to set the guide at the 11 lpi from the inboard cutter. This would be simplified if the outboard cutter wasn't there, but don't take it off...the idea is to set the guide by ignoring the presence of this outboard cutter. Eyeball the guide to about 11 lpi with the thread gauge or by pure guess if no thread gauge is available. Cut a guide line on a flat scrap of wood. Now, either of two methods will work: Make 11 passes and measure, cutting and adjusting until they

Cut in extended line with the "Jointer" to full depth.

are all exactly one inch across. Or, measure over one inch and cut until the inch is full. I'll describe the first method in detail. Cut a guide line on the flat board, set the guide in this line and make a pass. Now, put the guide in the groove cut by the in board cutter and make another pass, etc., until you have made 11 passes locating the guide in the inboard cutter groove each time. Measure from the guide line to the 11th groove cut by the inboard cutter. This will be the next to the last line cut. This measurement must be exactly one inch. If it's more than one inch, the guide is too far from the cutter. If less, the guide is too close. Make the necessary corrections and try it again until you get one inch in 11 passes of the inboard cutter. (This procedure has been described for setting the guide on a single-line cutter, but the presence of the extra cutter may cause some confusion.)

Back-fill behind the device with Power tool, working right to left.

There are several patterns that can be cut with the D.C.A. but it's a good idea to not burn any bridges behind you, which is why the guide must be set at exactly twice the width of one line. If you ever goof, you can salvage it by going back and splitting all the skips so that you end up with a standard diamond. If the guide had been set at some odd spacing, this "salvaging operation" would not be possible as the lines and diamonds produced by splitting the skips would not be the same as the other lines and diamonds.

In cutting standard french checkering - if there is such a thing - I think the most common method is as follows: cut five grooves and skip one. This makes four pointed diamonds and a flat the width of the base of one diamond. The procedure is to cut the master lines first.

They can be cut full depth, or only part way, but must all be uniform in depth. Set the guide in a master line and make a trial pass. If it's full depth there will be no "shiny" line between the two grooves cut by the cutters. It probably won't be deep enough, so if not, make another pass over this same line and this time tip the tool slightly to the left. It should be full depth now. Put the guide in the groove made by the inboard cutter and make another pass. Four grooves have now been cut, but one more is required. Move the guide to the left one groove

Ripple has developed, so tool tipped to right to cut shallow line.

Hold page up and sight down the last line. Crooked, ain't it?

Bring down to full depth with "Jointer" and ripple disappears.

and make another pass. Note that only the outboard cutter is cutting this time. Now move the guide to this last groove and make another pass. This makes the skip and two more grooves which puts us back where we started. Repeat this procedure on across the stock. Naturally, there will be point rows where you must reverse the stock and extend the lines so there will be a place for the guide to run. (See "Point rows" below.) Also, the two cutters will leave little under-run spots when a border is approached. This is because the outboard cutter must stop at the border, leaving the inboard cutter back a little ways. This is no problem to take care of later by using a standard single-line cutter with the guide set on 22 lpi, or a hand tool, or the Reciprocating Finishing Tool.

If the motor tends to bog down when using the D.C.A. just give it some more throttle with the rheostat. With two cutters sawing away, you are loading the machine twice as heavily if you are moving the tool at the same rate. Also, there is more tendency for the machine to heat when using the D.C.A. which is not due to internal friction but rather is due to the heat generated by two cutters being fed back to the machine for dissipation. This heating usually doesn't give any trouble as the operator must stop more often to extend lines anyway...'cause you're cutting across the pattern twice as fast! While we are on the subject of heat, it should be pointed out that a dull cutter will generate much more heat than a sharp one.

As mentioned before, the D.C.A. costs three times as much, but I think it is well worth it. First, there are two cutters so each is cutting only about half as much. To be exact, the outboard cutter does 3/5 of

Back-fill point rows, taking each group as unit. Don't jump around.

the cutting while the inboard does 2/5, so the thing has about twice the life of a single cutter. The rest of the story is the bonus in time with the actual cutting time a little more than half that taken by a single-line cutter. Money in the old pocket.

I haven't said much about using the D.C.A. for standard checkering. Well, there isn't much to say except that it works fine! Setting it for standard checkering is about the same as for french except that the guide is set one space from the inboard cutter instead of two. This is not really necessary but it gets the guide closer to the cutters and reduces the effects of sharp contours mentioned above. It is practical to do standard checkering with the D.C.A. set up for french as I have proved by going to sleep and forgetting to skip a line at the proper time. Boy, this really moves you across a pattern!

Standard Checkering

The layout and cutting the master lines has been discussed briefly, and setting the guide for both depth and width has been described in detail, so now it's time to do the actual checkering. This work can be done without the use of a checkering cradle, but if you are serious about checkering, a checkering cradle is at least desirable. There is no point in handicapping oneself. The stock must be free to rotate on its longitudinal axis, but some resistance to turning should be provided - though not so much that the rotating motion is jerky.

There seems to be about only two techniques available for manipulating the tool: (1) rotate the stock so as to keep the cutter normal to the surface as it traverses the line, or (2) hold the stock still and tip the cutter to keep it normal to the surface. Number 1 seems to require co-ordination capabilities which are beyond me, and number 2 would require me to be an accomplished acrobat - so I have come up with a combination of the two methods which works just quite well.

I hold the stock firmly with my left hand and cut as far as I can (pulling the tool toward me) by tipping the cutter to keep it normal to the surface. Then I rotate the stock slightly, start back a little ways in the groove, compress the guide, pull the tool toward me and start tipping the cutter to the left until it starts cutting. It's somewhat

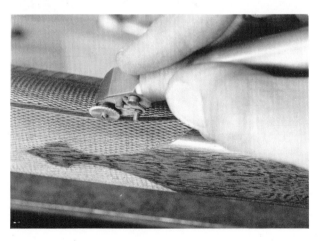

On "bright-line" patterns put spacer between cutter and head so can put guide on one side, cutter on other, and cut to exact width.

With Reciprocating Finishing tool you can cut perfect borders.
I use with F-I cutter with cut on forward stroke at slow speeds.

like a "brushing" motion in that the cut starts gently, blending with the previous cut and proceeds on its own. This blending is very important. If you simply sock the cutter down at the approximate end of the interrupted cut, there is a good chance of making an abrupt change in the depth of the line. This step will then be reproduced in the succeeding lines and the accumulation of all these steps can create quite a mess. Since the name of this game is Repetition, we don't want these irregularities flarin' up!

It's a good idea to start with the forend panels which are usually closer to a flat surface than the grip panels and therefore much easier to do. Set the guide in one of the master lines at the far end. It's a little safer to pull the tool toward you than to push it, although both methods will work. Cut this line all the way across the panel to the near end of the master line. If the master line has been cut to full depth, this new line, just cut, will meet it at the surface of the wood and no shiny finish will remain between them. However, and this is usually the case, if some of the shiny finish still shows between the lines, the master line and therefore the new line, are not to full depth. So, make succeeding passes with the cutter while holding the machine tipped slightly to the left so that the lines get deeper. Do this tipping until the last line is to full depth as indicated by the disappearance of the strip of shiny surface between the last two lines cut. This deepening process is usually accomplished in just three or four lines, but it actually depends on how deep the master line was cut and how much the machine was tipped to

Finished except for pointing-up corners done best with veiner.

the left. This is also a good time to see how uniform the depth of the line is. If the shiny surface between the lines shows variations in width, the depth is also varying. Some variation is inevitable but should not be abrupt, indicating a jerky tool movement. Long, graduate variations will not be noticeable in the finished work except as slight waviness in the rows of diamonds as viewed from their side. This is the same technique followed by professional hand checkerers to control depth of all diamond cuts. It is explained here for the benefit of those of you just getting started. Really, it is quite easy!

Now that full depth has been reached, the job can proceed with the machine held normal to the surface. Keep alert and check yourself often. A hard spot in the grain may not have been cut to full depth but, if caught early, can easily be corrected with the machine by going over this spot again. If you don't catch it quickly, it will develop into quite a mess as the situation is self-aggravating. (We talked about this earlier.) These hard spots are particularly bad if the cutter is dull - so keep it sharp. Another thing to watch for is crooked lines. These seem to come about as a punishment for the operator's sins - I can't find any other explanation. Keep sighting along the lines fairly often so you can catch them early. When you see a crooked line developing, cut a shallow line with the machine by tipping the cutter to the right. Then take Kennedy's "Jointer" and work this shallow line down to depth.

I use soft brush with half-&-half Lin-Speed and turpentine. Saturate then pat off excess with cloth. Put on second coat sparingly.

Air jet on tool clears sawdust from guide's path for uniform depth.

This will straighten out the kinks...No sweat.

Cut all the first-pass lines in the one panel in one direction before starting the cross lines (second-pass lines). Finish all the point rows as close to the border as possible with the rotary tool. It isn't necessary to completely finish these lines but it helps to do so. I usually don't because I'm in too much of a hurry to see what it's going to look like, but the checkering does suffer as a result. It is important that all

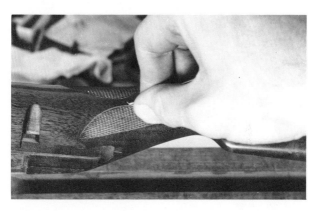

A veiner is indispensable for tight curves on devices or borders.

the first-pass lines are to uniform depth because the second-pass lines will camouflage the fact if they are not. It is easier to see the uniform depth when all the first-pass lines are cut by looking for the shiny surface between the lines. Work these lines down with a hand tool or the Reciprocating Finishing Tool until they are perfect from border to border. Regimentation is important. Don't jump around from one area to another. This is most important when finishing a job because it's harder to tell "where you been from where you ain't been".

Now it's time to cut the second-pass lines, but the master line you cut earlier has usually almost disappeared. You can find it by brushing the area with a stiff tooth brush. Incidentally, keep the tooth brush handy for an accumulation of sawdust in the lines will cause the guide to ride high and not allow the cutter to cut to the right depth. Most of this you can blow out but not all of it. (Tobacco chewers should use caution so as not to stain the freshly checkered area!) Work the master line down to the depth of the first pass lines with a hand tool. This is a lot easier to cut now because the first pass with the Power Checkering tool has removed most of the wood. Now, start cutting the second-pass lines being careful not to cut deeper than the first-pass lines. It's better to cut these slightly shallow than to cut too deep. If you over-cut these now, all the time spent finishing the first-pass lines is wasted

Extending second pass run-out lines can be tricky - don't fake it!

because they have to be worked down to the new depth. Go over the panel in this direction, finishing out the point rows and working as close to the borders as possible. Now go over the second-pass lines down to the same depth as the first-pass lines. The diamonds should be pointed up nicely at this time if all the lines have been cut to full depth and no more.

The only thing left to do is remove the little piece of wood at the end of each line where the Power Checkering Tool cutter couldn't reach without running over the border line. The border must also be brought down to full depth. I prefer to deepen the border first before final clean-up, but not quite to full depth (save some wood to clean up small nicks). During the main part of the checkering I like to leave the border lines very shallow so I can move them a little to cover a blunder if neces-

Tape stiff plastic around curve, cut line with knife then "Jointer".

sary. After deepening the border line the Reciprocating Finishing Tool really shows its stuff. I use the Dem-Bart F-1 cutter with the teeth pointed forward and the machine set for a short stroke. I run the machine at about 2,000 rpm but this is a matter of personal preference, and I am still learning its capabilities. Carefully guide the cutter on the Finishing Tool gently into the groove and move it forward until it is against the border. As the cutter approaches the border line it will break out the small partitions of wood that are left. At this point it is being used as a battering ram. Watch it, as it's easy to cut too deep, especially if you are accustomed to using a hand tool for this job. Don't try to run the Finishing Tool too slowly or it will dig in and the tail start wagging the dog. I have noticed too that this tool is somewhat

These extensions are tricky too, but trick with plastic works fine.

sensitive to wood texture. Hard brittle woods, like ebony, cut so easily that it is difficult to start the cutter in a groove. Also, if it's the least bit to one side of the groove, it will cut right there before it's down in the groove. But handled carefully, it does a fantastic job of finishing up the panel - really melting the wood into dust - and what's left is pure gold.

Point Rows

As I recall from my farming days, a point row is the result of a row approaching a fence at some angle other than 90 degrees. This applies to checkering in much the same way - if the lines approach the border at some acute angle, and this is most often the case, we have point rows. They are no problem when the lines are getting shorter but when they are getting longer at either end the Power Checkering Tool can't go where it has no previously cut line to follow. The solution is to extend the last line out to the border with a hand tool. But you must be careful for there is a strong tendency when extending this line, to curve it toward the border. Monty Kennedy's "Jointer" helps by giving a long bearing to keep the tool cutting straight. It's a good idea to cut this extension line lightly first and check for straightness. If it is straight, then cut it down to depth. It is very important that this extension be exactly in line. It's going to serve as a guide line for subsequent lines so must not be crooked. Now that the guide line is available the Power Checkering Tool can go back and finish the little patch.

I see that most of the pictures are concerned with the use of hand

Ready for finishing. Do the many abrupt contours with hand tools.

tools. Have got to admit that this wasn't intentional - it just worked out that way. Strangely enough, when you are doing a checkering job with the MMC Power Checkering Tool and the Reciprocating Finisher, you do spend a bigger share - relative share - of the time using various hand tools. That's because you can get so much of the big areas in the pattern done so quickly with the power tools that the time you spend with hand tools laying out the master lines and finishing up some of the points and borders seems to take forever, they move wood so slowly! But let's face it, the reason any of us buy a Power Checkering tool or a Reciprocating Finisher is to turn out as much top quality checkering as possible in the shortest amount of time...and with the MMC Tools, you can do it!!

- *Bob Sconce, Inventor & Manufacturer of the MMC Power Checkering Tools, Deming, New Mexico*

CORRECTING "STAMPED" CHECKERING

Here is a service I have started for those customers of mine who are disappointed with the stamped checkering in their new guns: Set up the stock in a checkering cradle and follow right down the middle of the lines, using a V or fine 3-Sq file. Go mighty lightly at first for guide lines, then increasingly deeper. Job should be complete in three passes. On the first pass be careful not to hurry! What you have when you finish is a first-class job with something to hang onto... attractive (because of the relief effect) and relatively easy.

- *Art Finney's Gun & Repair Store, Mankato, Minnesota*

CLEANING AND POINTING CHECKERING

By the way, I've been checkering gun stocks for 40 years and your needle files are the finest thing I have ever used for cleaning out and pointing checkering...

- *Charles W. Crowe, San Bernardino, California*

FINISHING & CHECKERING THE CUSTOM GUN STOCK

(Note: Stan is the artist who designed and perfected the Decal Checkering Patterns. He is, without doubt, a leading authority on the subject and his ability to explain the work is proof of his knowledge on the subject -- BB)

Making a custom stock, whether you do it as a profession or as a hobby, is a fascinating pastime. Transforming a rough, unfinished piece of wood into a useful thing of beauty requires both skill and patience, but the hours spent on such a project are usually highly rewarding.

With a great many low-cost military rifles and actions still available it is possible to turn out excellent hunting rifles at moderate cost. In addition, if the conversion is correctly made the owner will have a rifle that will fit him much better than most run-of-the-mill factory guns and will be superior in appearance besides. Not that we have anything against regular store bought guns because we don't. But let's face it; the finish and checkering on all but the "custom grade" factory guns leave much to be desired, for these are quality features that just can't be mass produced. Then too, factory-made guns are of necessity a compromise design intended to fit most any hombre whether he is thin, fat, short, tall, medium build or whatnot. It's like making slacks in only one size and expecting them to fit everybody.

Actually quite a few things should be considered in designing a stock so that it will fit the individual perfectly. The length of the stock should be governed not only by the length of the person's arms who will be using it but also to some extent by the type of clothing that will

Stan deTreville with one of his beautiful checkering jobs -
and Elk, of course!

be worn for most of the shooting. If you are all bundled up for cold weather a stock that is too long can hang up on your clothes when you bring the gun to your shoulder in a hurry. Or if you do a lot of hunting in your shirt sleeves you won't want a stock that is too short unless you enjoy being kicked. The choice of sights also has a very important bearing on the design of the stock, 'scope sighted rifles requiring a much higher comb on the stock than a rifle with open or peep sights. A stock correctly designed for the individual will rise easily to any position and in addition will minimize the effects of the gun's recoil.

And speaking of guns that kick brings up the question of whether a recoil pad should be used on a fine custom gun. Some fellows like 'em and some don't. The well known stockmaker Thomas Shelhamer used to voice his views on this subject with the remark, "A good rifle with a fine custom stock having a recoil pad looks like a man in evening clothes wearing rubber boots." Then on the other side of the fence the late Lindsey King, another fine gunsmith, used to point out that "Rubber boots have their place too and if you just want a gun to look at there is no need for a recoil pad, but if you are a shooter and not just a looker you can do a lot MORE and BETTER shooting with a gun that is a pleasure to shoot." Personally I'm a rubber boot man myself and have recoil pads on most of my high-power rifles. Contrary to Tom Shelhamer's views I think that a good looking recoil pad improves the appearance of a fine custom gun for, by implication, it shows the gun is a real he-man's weapon and not just a BB gun.

Opinions vary widely on the shape of gunstocks too, and a lot of you fellows probably won't agree with what I have to say on this subject and that's good too, because this would be a pretty drab old world if we all liked the same things. My preference is for a stock with a pistol grip that is well curved and long enough so that the hand is not cramped, but not too large in circumference so that it won't feel clumsy. The comb should be high enough to support the cheek so that the eye is in perfect alignment with the sights. This is especially important with a 'scope sighted rifle, for if the eye isn't exactly centered the image will black out and can cause you to miss a shot. For best results in shooting from any position the top of the comb should be straight and parallel with the line of sight. With a stock that has a comb sloping to either front or rear the sights may align properly in the offhand position but black out entirely in the prone, kneeling, or sitting positions.

Even in shotgun shooting a stock that is properly fitted to the individual can make a whale of a difference in a person's shooting. In most cases where a shotgunner consistently undershoots the target it's because the comb of the stock is too low. This is probably the most common fault of guns used for trapshooting or for quail or pheasants which are usually rising targets. Raising the comb on a shotgun stock is accomplishing the same thing as raising the rear sights on a rifle; the shooter will see more of the barrel and the gun will shoot higher.

A good way to check to see if a shotgun stock fits is to set up a large sheet of paper at 40 yards and shoot at it, throwing the gun up and shooting in a hurry as you would on game. If the shot patterns low make a pad of several layers of cloth and tape it to the comb of your stock and try shooting again. Add or remove thicknesses of cloth until the comb is exactly the right height. A lace-on pad of this height can then be used but a better looking and more permanent solution is to restock the gun with a stock that fits correctly.

If you are not a pro and hesitate tackling the job of inletting a new stock to the gun there are a number of reputable manufacturers that can supply semi-inletted stocks for most standard rifles and shotguns. These stocks are available in a wide variety of woods and in grades ranging from plain to ultra fancy. Some of these stocks are semi-finished and require only a minimum amount of work in order to get them to fit the individual. Judicial use of a fast cutting wood rasp makes shaping the stock comparatively easy. If you don't do enough stock work to warrant getting a whole set of stockmaker's double-end rasps you can probably get by with the No. 352 which has a flat rasp on one end and a tapered curve rasp on the other end. In working over the stock be sure to leave sufficient wood to allow for sanding out all the rasp and file marks.

One of the best sandpapers for this purpose is the Durite No-fill Silicon Carbide Paper, starting with the #3/0 and working progressively through the #6/0 and #8/0. After the stock has been sanded to the point where it is smoother than a well oiled eel, take a wet cloth and rub over the entire surface, then dry the stock over a gas flame until all traces of moisture have been removed. This will cause the grain in the wood to rise and feel "whiskery" when you run your hand over it. Using the #8/0 paper go over the stock thoroughly, sanding with the grain until all of the whiskers have been removed. Repeat the wetting, drying and sanding operations four or five times or until the grain stops rising when dampened. Some stockmakers use steel wool for this purpose but tiny particles of steel are apt to imbed themselves in the wood causing some staining when the stock is dampened.

After all the whiskers have been removed the stock is ready for finishing. Space doesn't permit going into all of the different types of finishes used on gunstocks but most experts seem to prefer a hand rubbed oil finish on their best stocks. For a finish of this type I usually start with the G-B Lin-Speed, or Tru-Oil finish diluted 1 to 1 with turpentine and without any filler. Most fillers are highly abrasive and will dull your checkering and carving tools in a hurry so stay away from them. Rub the thinned-down oil into the wood thoroughly and then go over the stock again with the #8/0 finishing paper plus lots of elbow grease, always working with and never across the grain. The next coat of Finish can be a little thicker, about 2 parts of oil to 1 of turps and again repeat the sanding operation. From here on you can use the Finish undiluted, applying a coat and sanding after each application until the pores of the wood are completely filled and the surface of the stock has taken on a lustrous sheen that brings out all the graining. A final going over with the Finish rubbed in with the palm of your hand completes the job. It's a lot of work but when you're through you'll have a stock that will make an ordinary factory job look rougher than a cob.

At this stage the stock is ready to checker or carve, but if you have the time it is a good idea to set the stock to one side for a couple of weeks to let the finish age. The reason for this is that the finish will be less apt to clog up the teeth in your checkering tools if it has a chance to dry thoroughly.

While the stock is drying you can be choosing the design to use on it. Actually the most important part of the checkering or carving job is coming up with a good design and unless you have a great deal of artistic talent you had better stick to patterns designed by experts.

One method of doing this is to make a tracing of a design from some other gun that has a stock that is similar in shape to the one you plan to checker or carve. If the forearm design is symmetrical you only have to draw half of the design, then fold the pattern along the center line and trace the other half. A flexible plastic rule and a couple of French curves are useful in improving the rough tracing or in designing new patterns. Make frequent checks with the tracing on the new stock to be sure that it will fit correctly. A diamond template made from thin plastic or cardboard is useful for laying out the master guide lines in the pattern. One measuring 9" long and 3" wide at the widest part of the diamond is about right.

When you are satisified with your design rub a heavy coating of white crayon or grease-pencil on the back of the paper pattern, position it on the stock with scotch tape and trace off the design, making sure that you have drawn all of the lines before removing the tracing pattern. Some stockmakers lay out their design directly on the stock without the aid of a tracing. They determine the center line of the forearm and use the diamond template, flexible rule and dividers to draw in the rest of the points in the design. On the pistol grip they use the flexible rule or French curves to draw their design, being careful to see that the designs on each side of the grip line up perfectly. This method is all right for comparatively simple point patterns, but trying to lay out a complicated design in this manner is about as fast as a tortoise with bunions, requiring several hours work at best.

Still another method of applying the checkering or carving pattern is by the Stan de Treville decal method, and this is much the fastest and easiest way of all. Based upon the familiar water transfer process and tough enough to stand considerable shoving around, the Decal Patterns simplify the difficult layout problem so that anyone can prepare a stock for checkering in a matter of minutes. The decal method has a number of other advantages too. Unlike most pattern material the decal will adhere to a compound curved surface without forming wrinkles which distort the pattern. As the decal material is only about .001 of an inch thick you can checker right through the pattern if you wish without dulling the checkering tool. The patterns are also much easier to see, being printed in dark brown on a yellow background, and there is no danger of the design being smudged or rubbed off while working over it. Then too, there is a wide choice of designs to choose from so that you can satisfy most any customer's taste.

The checkering job should be the last thing you do to the stock before installing the hardware. A few wood whittlers in the business prefer to finish the stock after the checkering is done, but trying to get a good rubbed finish right up to the edge of the checkering without taking off half the points in the process is about as easy as playing tennis while wearing snowshoes; it can be done but it's a mite awkward.

Another awkward practice is trying to checker a gun without a checkering cradle. I checkered my first gun that way, trying to hold it steady in my lap and still get my head close enough to see what I was doing. After having that dern stock slip out of three half-nelsons and a toe hold I decided there must be an easier way so built me a checkering cradle. You used to have to pay 25 or 30 bucks for a checkering cradle and I used to recommend that you make your own, but the bottom must have dropped out of the checkering cradle business because you can get a pretty fair one now for about one fourth what they used to sell for, so building your own is hardly worth the effort.

The same holds true with checkering tools, and unless you have an awful lot of spare time it doesn't pay to make your own. There are several excellent machine-made tools on the market that are of such precision manufacture that changing blades in the middle of a job presents no problems as all the cuts will be uniform. The tools shown in the catalog are of this type and are available in 16, 18, 20, 22, 24, and 28 lines per inch. In addition, 10 or 12 line spacers are available for French or Skipline checkering. The skipline blades are made with cutting teeth on one side only, the other side being smooth to act as a guide. For this reason two skipline blades are required, a right and left hand blade for each size. Skipline checkering is achieved by using

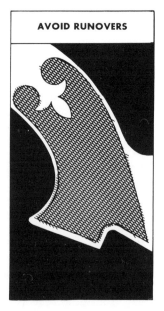

AVOID RUNOVERS

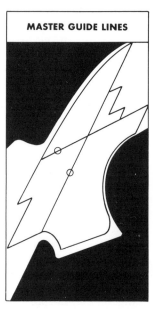

MASTER GUIDE LINES

two different width spacers, such as a 20-20 regular spacer and a 10 line skip spacer. Two lines are usually cut with the regular spacer, then one with the wide spacer two more regular lines and so on. Sometimes 3 or even 4 regular lines are cut followed by the wide space. Skipline checkering is more difficult than regular checkering and the skipline blades cost twice as much so the price charged for this type of checkering is usually from one third to one half more than for the ordinary variety.

Having a border around the checkering is a matter of choice, but the real pros who pride themselves on their steady hand and eagle eye tend to sniff when they see a border used on a fine stock, maintaining that it was probably just put there to cover up the runovers. The border tool looks somewhat like the spacer except that it cuts a rounded ridge instead of a pointed one, and as the pros point out it IS useful for hiding runovers around the edge of the design.

In checkering, whether you lay out the design yourself or use the Decal method of applying the design, the actual checkering is done in the same manner. First cut one line in each direction to serve as the master guide lines. These should be cut only deep enough to act as a guide for the spacer tool to follow in making the next cut. After both guide lines are cut it is better to complete all of the rest of the lines in one direction before cutting the other series of lines which will form the diamond shapes. Keep just enough pressure on the tool so that it cannot jump from the guiding cut. Remember that easy does it and don't fight the tool. Use a short back and forth sawing motion and blow the wood dust away as you proceed so you can see what you are doing. If a line wavers and is not absolutely parallel with the preceding line it should be straightened out with a 90° bent needle file before going on to the next line. Be sure to work where you have plenty of light to see what you are doing. If you plan on doing very much checkering it will pay you to get a pair of 3-D magnifying binoculars as they are real eyesavers and make the job of checkering a lot easier. The No. 3 which provides 1-3/4 X magnification at 14 inches is about right for the average eyes.

In cutting the lines particular care should be taken to keep from running over the edge of the design. It is better to stop a little short of the edge and then using a block of wood as a stop, work up to the border with a small cutting tool such as the Dem-Bart S-1 Special tool. The S-1 is also just the thing for working down into the points of the design or between carved areas where the regular spacing tool is too long. Don't try to cut your lines too deep. It is better to put all of the lines in lightly and then go back over them two or three times until the cuts are of the right depth, finally pointing up the diamonds with the V tool or a 90° needle file. Some stockmakers use a 60° V tool for pointing up the diamonds but these are more apt to chip out. After the checkering is completed apply a light coat of Lin-Speed or Tru-Oil with the aid of a toothbrush, brushing the oil thoroughly into the wood so that none remains on the surface to collect dirt and fill up the checkering.

In recent years carved designs on gunstocks have become increasingly popular and the custom stockmaker who can't provide this type of work is missing out on a good source of income. Carved patterns have long been favored in Europe and highly skilled German and Austrian craftsmen can carve anything you might want on your musket, from hounds chasing a stag down to more sophisticated designs depicting a couple of sexy sirens nestled on the stock and wearing only a hand-rubbed finish.

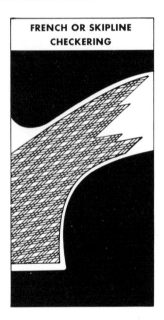

FRENCH OR SKIPLINE CHECKERING

GOUGE USED FOR SHORT RADIUS CURVES

While some carving can greatly enhance the appearance of a fine gun it is sometimes carried to such extremes that it ceases to be functional. I once saw a .30-60 rifle that a Marine picked up in Korea that was one continuous pattern of pagodas and oriental figures. It was a beautiful piece of carving, but the only trouble was that everytime the poor guy fired the rifle he ended up with a 3-dimension imprint of a grinning Buddha on his cheekbone.

Some of the most impressive looking decorations for gunstocks are those that combine both carving and checkering. These usually make use of sweeping leaf designs with carefully executed checkering between, the contrasts in textures complimenting each other. Old August Pachmayr, the father of Frank Pachmayr who manufactures scope mounts and recoil pads, was a past master at this type of checkering and some of the masterpieces that he turned out are now collector's items valued at $1,000 or more. The No. 4 Decal Pattern while not an actual copy of a design by August Pachmayr, was inspired by the design on the rifle.

Carving isn't as difficult as it appears provided you have a good design to start with, and in some respects it is less tedious than checkering. Good carving can be done with nothing more complicated than a sharp pocket knife, but a good set of carving tools can make it a lot easier. A small patternmaker's riffler and a Swedish needle file are also very useful in shaping-up the carving. Some of your wife's sandpaper sticks that she uses to manicure her nails can be used for this purpose too, as they can be trimmed to most any contour. If you are inexperienced in carving, select designs with long sweeping lines rather than those that have a lot of tricky curves. Study the carving on fine furniture to gain a better idea on the techniques used to make the design stand out, the shaping of the leaves, stems, etc.

In starting the actual carving use a sharp knife and carefully cut all of the outlines, holding the blade vertically and cutting only about 1/16" deep. A short bladed knife of the Exacto type is good for this work. On designs that have very sharp curves straight gouge chisels such as those put out by J. A. Henckel are very useful. Select a chisel that fits the curve, hold it vertically in place and tap the handle lightly with a wood or leather mallet until the cut is of the right depth. Then the surrounding wood can be carefully cut away to give the desired raised effect. This method is particularly useful on a design like the No. 4 Decal Pattern where there are a number of small circles to cut. On these the No. 77/6 gouge for the small inner circles, and the No. 77/10 gouge for the outer circles are about right.

Some carving makes use of a stippled effect as a background for the rest of the design. Decal Patterns No. 20 and 21 make use of this stippled technique. Stippling can be done with a sharp center-punch, tapping it lightly with a mallet as you carefully move it over the area to be stippled. Many beautiful effects can be achieved by combining stippling, carving and checkering. Inlays of wood, plastic or silver can also be used to good advantage in giving your guns that expensive custom look. Fashioning fine gunstocks is not easy and it requires lots of skill and patience but it can be fun if you go about it in the right way. And remember, if you can turn out some really outstanding guns they too might become collector's items worth $1,000 or more!

- *Stan deTreville, San Diego, California*

EXOTIC WOOD INLAYS

(The following was written for us by Lee Estes, Portland, Oregon, stockmaker, gunsmith and woodworker. One of his guns above gives an idea of the unlimited possibilities with the inlay forms and colors shown on these pages.)

Inlays of exotic wood give that final and distinctive touch which sets off a custom stock.

There have been few masters in this specialty. Most of the blemishes result from not having a precision cut inlay!

Now, for the first time, we offer a remarkable array of inlays created for us by Lee Estes, Portland, Oregon, custom stock maker. They are precision cut in five basic patterns and three sizes. See illustration. Each inlay is precision cut regardless of density of wood or thickness of inlay. This is vital in working up compound inlays. Every inlay is machine cut with a five degree taper on the edge for ease of installation, and perfect fit to the stock wood. Our wide assortment of wood gives a variety of shades and patterns to contrast or harmonize with any type of stock wood.

With three tools and sandpaper and four quick steps, any gunsmith or serious gun hobbyist can be a master at inlaying when he uses these inlays. Tools needed to inlay with our precision cut patterns are: 1- Scribe; 2- Skew chisel such as No. 70-12 Twin Brand not over 7/16th inches wide and, 3- A file to dress down the inlay before sandpapering.

To start an inlay, place the pattern at the center of the mass of wood which has been marked off as shown in illustration below. The large design is centered on the butt stock and the small design on the forearm. - Figure 1.

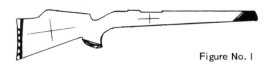

Figure No. I

To install a single inlay pattern, simply center, place inlay - small side to stock - scribe, chisel out wood from the stock to a depth of about half the thickness of the inlay. Use care to cut precisely along scribe lines. Apply glue, press in inlay, clamp and allow glue to dry. Dress inlay to contour of stock and sand for finishing.

Here are steps to finished compound inlay like that illustrated in Figure No. 2:

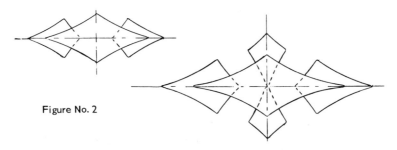

Figure No. 2

1- Take base pattern, in this case large diamond, and draw around with pencil; space other parts of design around base (center) inlay and mark around each with scribe...In this case four kites were arranged around a large diamond. 2- Cut out recess for each kite with the skew chisel, using caution not to over cut the scribe line, and carefully remove wood from the stock. 3- To set in inlays use same procedure described for single inlay. 4- Dress down four kite background inlays; overlay large center diamond, mark with scribe, chisel out recess, inset, let glue dry, file down, and sand whole compound inlay. As an added attraction to this pattern, the small contrasting diamond can be set in the center of the large diamond.

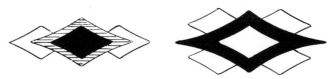

Figure No. 3

In creating designs a great deal of true beauty and interest can be had by studying the various woods offered and the colors that characterize them. To some, the contrasts of dark and light woods are desirable, to others the use of different colored woods but of the same general tone, add a great amount of "richness" to the finished stock. In any event - with the large number of patterns, the interesting color combinations and the unlimited possibilities of design potentials it is now possible for each inlay to be "different" - a personal characteristic of your own individual workmanship. Never will your inlays be just black, white or red plastic with no character and no real beauty.

Figures 4, 5 and 6 further demonstrate that the only limitation on the number of designs is the individual's imagination...As a final touch, single inlays can be placed in the center of the pistol grip cap and on the bottom of the fore end tip.

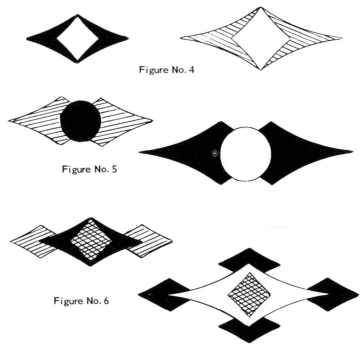

Figure No. 4

Figure No. 5

Figure No. 6

Study the following color descriptions of the popular woods available. It will be a great help to you in determining the ones you will want to use in making your own personalized inlays.

TULIP: Rose and White stripe. The two colors are so sharp that they appear to be almost laminated.

ZEBRA: Brown and Yellowish stripe. Stripes are wider than Tulip and softer. Give smooth contrast.

LACEWOOD: A very unusual wood. The Yellowish and Brown grain of the wood is such that the pieces appear to be of fine lace. Interesting and most attractive.

VERMILLION: A bright Red wood with faint grain pattern. It works well in a lot of different patterns for contrast.

PURPLEHEART: Un-treated, a muted Purple color. If a torch flame is passed over the final sanded inlay and the wood heated (being careful not to scorch) it turns a brilliant Purple that always attracts attention if carefully worked into the inlay pattern.

ROSEWOOD: One of the real standby woods in stockmaking. Deep Reddish/brown with swirling black designs. Rosewood is a very "rich" wood when used in either block or inlay.

EBONY: Black - used for accent.

HOLLY: Snow White wood - used for accent.

OSAGE ORANGE: Attractive Yellow wood, fine grain & hard.

BLACK MYRTLE: Greenish Black. A contrast wood that will work very well with any color you wish to match.

MYRTLE: Grayish Yellow with unusual grain and appeal that makes Myrtle popular with many for gun stocks.

- *Lee Estes, Portland, Oregon*

PROFESSIONAL METHOD OF ATTACHING ATTRACTIVE FOREND TIPS

Perhaps Alvin Linden was right when he questioned the sanity of cutting off a hunk of wood just to put another in its place. In spite of the logic on the practical side, there are those who like to see their pets dolled-up to take them out of the strictly utilitarian class and kindle a glow of appreciation, or perhaps even envy in the eyes of their friends. The following is a variation of Linden's method of attaching a forend tip. I have found it to be reasonably simple with several features to recommend it.

1. This series was done starting with rifle blank. Working with a shaped blank presents a little more of a problem in making an accurate layout but the same thinking goes into it. With the top and two sides

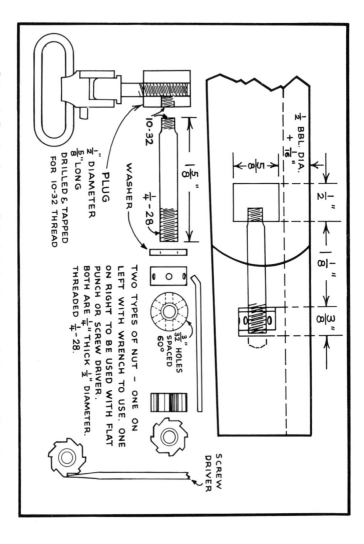

Schematic Drawing for James B. Meek Professional Method of Installing Forend Tip

PLUG
½" DIAMETER
⅝" LONG
DRILLED & TAPPED
FOR 10-32 THREAD

10-32

WASHER

1 ⅝"

¼-28

½ BBL. DIA.
+ 1/16"

⅝"

½"

1 ⅛"

⅜"

TWO TYPES OF NUT – ONE ON
LEFT WITH WRENCH TO USE. ONE
ON RIGHT TO BE USED WITH FLAT
PUNCH OR SCREW DRIVER.
BOTH ARE ¼" THICK ½" DIAMETER.
THREADED ¼-28.

3/32" HOLES
SPACED
60°

SCREW
DRIVER

of the rifle blank square and the forend blank square we are ready to start. This picture shows the squared blank and block laid out and sawed. Before sawing you will of course have determined what length forearm you want, where you want the sling swivel and work from there. On this particular stock the forearm was to finish 10-1/2 inches ahead of the receiver, the swivel 14-1/2 inches ahead of the trigger. The reasons for the curve are that it gives more glueing surface and it does away with the side pins usually used to prevent any turning of the block, as the curve itself prevents any turning. At this time I smooth the inside of the curve on the tip material as it will be fitted to the curve on the end of the stock and it is easier to do the final fitting on the exposed end of the stock.

2. I put the tip on when the barrel is almost down to its final position. This shows the layout on the stock and the blank set up in the drill

press locating the center with a center finder or wiggler. With the barrel diameter known at this point it is easy to find half the diameter. It is now ready to drill.

3. The first hole is drilled all the way through the forearm with a #21 drill for the sling swivel screw. Then, from the barrel channel, redrill and bottom the #21 "pilot" hole with a 1/2" drill to the exact depth of the layout on the side of the stock. This hole is for the plug shown in the drawing, and I like it to fit a little tighter than you can push in by hand. Although I make my plugs on the lathe, see #4 below, it could be cut from any half-inch bolt or available stock and set in the

hole with some stock bedding compound. When done, it must sit tight with no play.

4. The plug was then made in the lathe. The dimensions are given in the drawing. While it was in the lathe it was also drilled and tapped for a 10-32 thread, into which the Michaels forend swivel screw will attach. At this time a screw and nut with washer were also made. Dimensions are also shown in the drawing. On this particular job I used a nut with the holes already drilled. The wrench I made to fit (as shown in the drawing.) However, I think that the ratchet type nut is the better and is easy to make. You can take a hack saw and saw directly toward the center to about one sixteenth inch depth, making a series

of saw cuts around the circumference of the nut and then relieving the one side of the notch as shown in the drawing. Make sure that you file off the correct side of the notch so that you have the flat side of the notch to drive against when installing. I prefer this type nut as it can be tightened while the pressure is on from the stock clamp. This is done by setting the clamp slightly to one side so that you can get a slim screw driver or flat punch past it.

5. The drill press table was turned vertically with the stock held in the vise and centered accurately to the layout. It was first drilled with a number 28 drill clear through the wood and into the center of the plug which has been already inserted. This hole was then opened up with a number 21 drill also to the center of the plug. Then drill down to the plug with a letter drill "D" (.246 of an inch) which should let your quarter inch drill rod screw fit tightly.

6. The quarter inch hole has been drilled and the block turned on the side to be routed out with a 5/16th inch router bit to a slot 3/8 inch wide and 15/16th of an inch deep. Stay about 3/32 of an inch away from the barrel diameter at each end of the slot. Finally, with a chisel

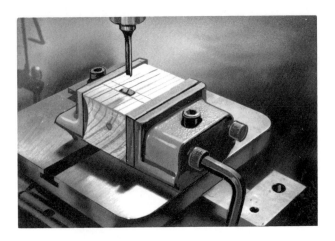

square the corners of the slot toward the joint, leaving the radii as they are on the opposite corners.

7. Showing the plug in the stock with the hole drilled and the plug being tapped for the attaching bolt. Tapped with a 10-32 tap.

8. In this view a steel "fitting pin" has been made that fits the block securely with the exposed part of the pin taken down a little smaller to a slip fit in the hole of the stock. I do this so as not to make the hole in the stock any larger, as I usually must put these together an ungodly number of times before getting the fit that is final. Using some 10 cent store chalk I chalk the concave block and spot and remove the high spots on the stock until I reach that aforementioned

final. You will note a penciled indication of the finished stock dimensions. I do this in order to be SURE of a good tight fit in these areas as it is very disappointing to do a lengthy fitting job and then find that when you take the stock down to the final shape you open up a sizeable crack where you thought you had a perfect fit. The areas outside this line I just keep cleared.

9. This is the final step in attaching. I put a small amount of cement (I use Weld Wood casein glue) into the hole in the stock, insert the bolt and set it up tightly by screwing it into the plug in the stock. Clamping the stock in the vise I get everything all set by assembling the stock clamp. For this I always insert the trigger guard and magazine into the stock so that plenty of pressure can be used safely.

The picture shows the clamp assembled with the glue applied generously. The forend tip is pushed onto the bolt to a point where the screw is extending into the slot in the fore end tip that the washer can be put on. The nut in the picture is being held in a pair of tweezers ready to be attached. When I have lowered the nut into position I push the tip on far enough that the nut cannot come off. I then proceed to screw the nut on and push the tip on until it is in place, securing it

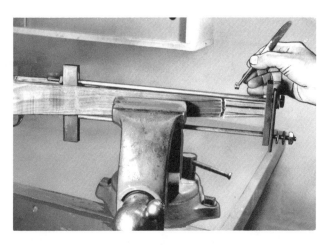

with the clamp.

In using the notched nut you can place the clamp so that you have room to get the flat punch or screw driver past on the right side. Also if you use the notched nut be sure that you have the correct side started on the bolt so that the flat side of your notches are exposed to your punch (I speak from experience). With your clamp set up tightly you can at the same time set up the nut tightly. When using the nut with the holes drilled in it and the wrench, I tighten the nut as tightly as I can after the clamp is taken off. If the holes tighten up anywhere near close you can further tighten it by using a round flat end punch against the edges of holes. This doesn't make as neat a job, but as Linden would say "Hell Fer Stout".

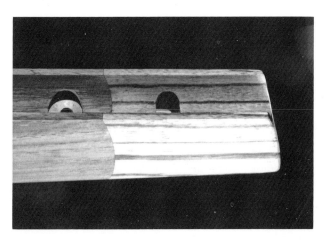

10. Shows the finished job minus the stock finish. You may wonder if it was worth it but you just wait until some of your friends express varying degrees of appreciation and I know that you'd do it again. GOOD LUCK.

- *James B. Meek, Newton, Iowa*

THE WAY THE JOB IS HANDLED IN THE PROFESSIONAL GUNSHOP OF CHAM OSBORN AND LAUREN GROOVER

Attaching a forend tip on a stock is a very interesting part of the stocking job. Good design, good fitting, selection of grain and color contrast are the basic practices to follow and will enhance the appearance of a good rifle.

We prefer to completely inlet the barreled action and be sure the top surfaces of the forearm are straight and even with the horizontal axis of the barrel, before attaching the fittings.

In custom rifle work the length of the barrel will determine the length of the forearm for good design. Another factor which must be considered is the physical requirements of the person for whom the stock is being made.

For example, we will decide on an eleven inch forearm, from the front of the receiver ring over the tip, with tip measuring two inches in length on the top surface.

Please note: We work everything from the top of the forearm. As

Layout with a square the 45 degree angle from the top surface, saw along your line, then sand this angular cut flat.

we related in the beginning, this is the finish line of the forearm.

We now measure out nine inches from the receiver ring on the top surface of the forearm and mark on each side of the barrel groove. Being sure the marks are at right angles to the barrel groove and with a machinist square, we carefully mark our 45 degree line on the sides of the forearm and cut close to the line. Then on a disc sander, we sand the angular cut smooth and perfectly flat.

Now, the forend tip may be cut in the same manner. We prefer the rough tip size to be approximately one-eighth inch larger on all sides than the forearm measures. Select the side of the block to be the top of tip and sand straight.

The best grain and color should be on the sides and bottom.

Check the angle cuts by placing them together in their proper

location and if they are right, the top surfaces of the forend tip and the forearm of the stock should be in a straight line. If there is any rock in the tip, when the angular cuts are held tightly together, the surfaces are not flat and the finished tip will show a glue joint; correct this now.

Contrasting wood spacers are very attractive if properly fitted. We prefer 1/32 inch thick spacers, and cut them to the width of the tip and the length of the angular cut on the tip. Holding them against this surface, we sand the tops flush with the top surface of the tip, now we are ready to drill the stock for the dowel.

Our simple drilling set up is a small vise bolted to a piece of hardwood, fitted, of course, to hold the stock in a straight, vertical position for drilling the dowel hole.

Place a one-eighth inch thick hardwood shim on the top edge of the forearm and place in the vise as shown in picture. With a three-eighth inch flat bottom end mill, we bore a flat on the sloping surface so the drill will not walk. Then with a Letter "V" .377 drill, we drill 1-1/2" deep, slowly to avoid charring the wood.

Remove the stock and one-eighth inch shim, place the forend tip in the vise as shown, without the shim. This will allow the top surface of the tip to be one-eighth inch above the top surface of the forearm when doweled together. In drilling, use the same procedure used for the stock.

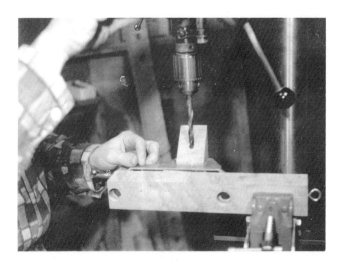

Before removing the tip, place the spacers on the sloping surface in their respective order, and holding them firmly in position with the 3/8th inch end mill, cut very lightly through, into the dowel hole.

For dowels, we use 3/8th inch, hard maple and cut to bottom in both forearm and tip when placed together dry, without the spacers in place.

Next we take the dowel on the edge of a disc sander and by rotating, we cut a thread like spiral groove about 1/32 inch deep, the entire length. This tends to hold a good distribution of glue in the joint.

We prefer "Weldwood" plastic resin glue in powder form and mixed as directed on the container. Now mix as directed with cold water and let stand for a few minutes and it will become very smooth.

With a one-eighth inch drill, put a vent hole in the forearm from the bottom of the barrel groove into the dead end of the dowel hole, and likewise in the tip from the top surface on center to dowel hole.

Now all parts are cut, ready for a dry fit as a final check, and ready for the glue.

Our clamping vise is simple, but does a good job. Please note the top surface of the clamp is straight to hold the top surface of the stock perfectly flat, and notched one-eighth inch deeper to permit the top surface of the tip to fit flat and in alignment with the forearm.

Remove all sawdust and chips and put a smooth even coating of

The completed job - well worth the effort to do it right!

glue inside dowel holes and coat entire dowel, also both sides of each spacer as well as the sloping surfaces of forearm and tip. Press dowel into forearm, place the spacers over the dowel in their proper sequence and position. Press on tip, put the assembly in the clamp and tighten forearm down on clamp firmly, being sure the front of the magazine cut out is against the block, to avoid moving rearward. When the tip is being tightened, check alignment of spacers and tip, then tighten firmly. All excessive glue that has squeezed out is removed to be sure pressure is sufficient to assure tight joints. This is the last chance to correct it and even now it would be a lot of extra work, so work carefully on each operation as you go.

- *Cham Osborn & Lauren Groover, Sheakleyville, Pennsylvania*

OUR LEADER

A group of tourists were being guided through an historic battlefield, when the guide stopped them at a bronze plate on the ground, took off his hat and said: "On this spot our glorious leader fell." One of the lady tourists remarked: "I can understand that! I almost tripped on the damned thing myself!" (Note: To which little yarn I might add: A whale of a lot us darned near trip and fall flat on our faces over the remains of someone else's efforts!)

- *E. A. Bixby, Gun & Saddle Shop, Mt. Pleasant, Michigan*

GLUING ROSEWOOD TIPS

In order to get as much wax as possible out of the surface of rosewood, saturate the surface with alcohol and wipe several times before gluing.

- *James B. Meek, Newton, Iowa*

WANT TO INCREASE YOUR SLING SALES?

I always put one of the Latigo Slings on one or two of the best looking rifles in the shop. Gives the rifles lots of class and also advertises the sling at the same time. Then for every rifle sale, show the customer the sling on the fancy rifle and try to talk him into one too. And be sure you have a good supply of swivels to fit the rifle the guy just bought!

Have found that the Win 100 front swivel doesn't have enough clearance, so I just squeeze it in a smooth-jawed vice and bend the bow slightly. Sometimes you'll need a spacer between the base and swivel. I use a regular front swivel and run the stock nut tight and cut off the excess length. Can also use a European type detachable with the loop pinned so it can't bend. This holds it off the right distance (works especially well for the 760 Rem) and gives room for the Latigo to work right.

- *John Dicks, Saline, Michigan*

FORE-END GROOVES & SLING SWIVEL CENTERING

With just a little grinding of a small broken tap, one can make the dandiest tool for cleaning out or recutting the grooves in fore-ends on shotguns. The size tap would depend on size grooves, of course. I use the 6x48 on standard M/12 fore-ends - one size we have plenty of! One of those needle file handles in the catalog is a must for this tool and job.

Another thing. I tried for a long time to figure some way to install swivels on a rifle stock and know they were centered. I finally came up with the idea of leveling the stock, top side down, in a well padded vise.

- *Vernon Dodd, Crossville, Alabama*

LATIGO SLINGS

I wanted to tell you how much I like your Latigo Sling. Guess this is no news to you, but have carried this for two years in the elk country of Idaho and a big hunk of Alaska. The thing that impresses me is that it is so damn fast and handy. When you want to stick it in a full-length saddle boot, give it a yank and it fits as slick as a cat's tail in his hide; another pull and it is ready for use. Quicker than I can tell it.

- *Bob Hagel, Gibbonsville, Idaho*

TOOLING LATIGO SLINGS

Your Latigo slings tool very nicely if soaked for 5 minutes in warm water.

- *Miles Baker, St. Simons Island, Georgia*

LATIGO SLINGS

I have just purchased one of your Latigo slings for my own pet Model 70 and have arrived at the conclusion that it is the best damned gun sling that a poor old Texas boy could ask for, including the rest of the foreigners outside the Beautiful State of Texas. All kidding aside, it is an excellent product and I highly recommend it...

- *Lawhons Engraving & Bluing Service, Beaumont, Texas*

SLING KEEPERS FOR LATIGO SLING

A kink for your Latigo slings: Punch a hole in the front sliding leather keeper and put the brass stud through all three pieces. Works real fine.

- *Chris Christensen, Ventura, California*

LATIGO SLINGS

We found Latigo slings much improved by putting a slit, 1/4" plastic tube on swivel band to act as a roller. Increases radius of leather and reduces friction. Real slick...

- *Eck Sports, San Luis Obispo, California*

MAKING A SANDING DRUM TO FIT GERMAN BUTT PLATES

When cutting off the butts of stocks to put on fancy butt plates in the Germanic style, frequently had trouble getting the thing shaped right. So now, I cut the curve into the stock with a coping saw - or a band saw if you are fortunate enough to have one. Then carefully keeping the stock at right angles to the shaft, smooth and true up the end with a 1-1/2" diameter sanding drum.

You make this drum by turning one end of a hardwood dowel to a 1/4" shaft and then slotting the other end to take sandpaper strips. Just be sure the end you slot is long enough to do the full thickness of the stock in one pass (don't make too short!). The whole job takes about 45 minutes and is going to save you hours of sweat.

- *Robert G. Wilson, Wichita, Kansas*

BUTT PLATE FITTING FIXTURE

We have one of the 3" diameter drum sanders with a 2" face in our shop. We inlet out a flat piece of wood - 2x6x12 - to hold the butt stock

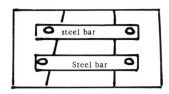

Don't blame this rather crude drawing on Herman - it is some of my FREE handed work! -- Just hew out a hunk of 2X6 soft wood to fit stock into -- drill four holes and insert 1/4" carriage bolts - use two metal bars of about 1/4" X 3/4" flat stock and shim with thin cardboard to level up and you are in business. Just scribe a line and work to it -- and protect the stock by putting felt on the steel bars

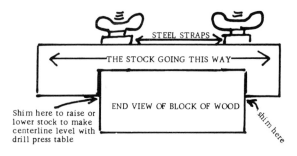

STEEL STRAPS

THE STOCK GOING THIS WAY

END VIEW OF BLOCK OF WOOD

Shim here to raise or lower stock to make centerline level with drill press table

shim here

in place and fit four bolts through with felt covered clamps to hold the stock in the piece of wood. Use this on your drill press table. Makes the dandiest thing for fitting curved butt plates, and used with a face plate sander, it is the "best" when it comes to fitting recoil pads to level and smooth the stocks. The holding fixture - as per the drawings - has been used by us for nearly 20 years now.

 - *Herman Treptow, Milltown, New Jersey*

ACRAGLAS CASTINGS

Fred Davis brought in a couple of identical looking butt plates, some cast copies of beautiful engravings and some copies of other stuff. The butt plates you couldn't tell one from the other...both seemed to be original Mauser. One was - but the other was cast with Acraglas that had been made black with the DuPont black stain we show in the catalog. He made his moulds from Dow Corning "Silastic RTV 501". The beauty of this stuff is that after being cast it is just like pure rubber but reproduces the finest detail - and can be used over and over again for making reproductions of whatever you want. We would carry it in the catalog but it does not have a long enough shelf life for that. If you are interested at all, write to Dow Corning Corporation, Midland, Michigan, and ask for literature. They will also advise you their nearest office and prices. A guy could have a lot of fun making things with this stuff.

 - *Fred Davis, Falls Church, Virginia*

INSTALLING RECOIL PADS WITHOUT MARRING THE HOLES

Just use your Magna-Tip Screwdriver with one of the extension bits. The round shank of the bit won't tear the rubber, and works especially well with a little grease or spit.

 - *Sports & Recreation, Hampton, Iowa*

ATTACHING THE RECOIL PAD

Anyone can attach a recoil pad to a shotgun or rifle. The finished job can be beautiful or strictly utilitarian. Here we shall forget about the less fortunate jobs and start at the top with a high grade gun. It being a fine gun we will do everything necessary to complete the job so that our work does not detract from the original excellence.

1. Here are some of the items that will be needed. The recoil pad with instructions. These instructions call for a glue. The glue shown here is a Goodyear product called Pliobond. It makes a good bond with the end grain of the wood as well as a good bond with the pad. An Exacto knife with a pointed blade for slitting the holes in the pad through which the screws can be pulled without tearing the rubber. I

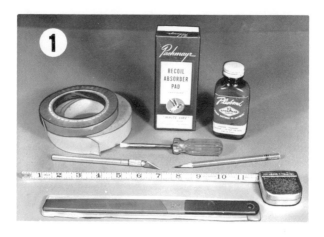

keep a new file with a protective plastic cover that I use for these jobs only. Also two rolls of Minnesota Mining tape; one roll of clear tape and the other one masking tape. A good soft pencil, a ruler and a screw driver that has received some special attention complete the important necessities.

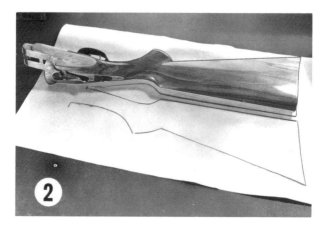

2. I am a member of the old "Stitch-In-Time" school and a charter member of the "Ounce-of-Prevention" club so I take a piece of heavy wrapping paper and laying the stock on it I make a tracing of each side. You can complete the whole job of covering the stock in a matter of minutes. It can save you hours of refinishing should the stock get scratched. Of course, you will handle it carefully because it won't stand KNOCKS that could dent the wood through the paper.

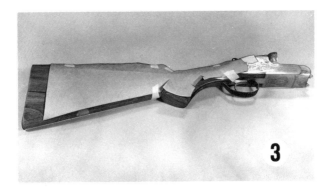

3. On this particular job the stock length and the pitch are to remain the same. The paper was cut to a length that would allow the
one-inch masking tape to hold the paper and still accept a pencil line
that would mark the cut-off line. See illustration number six. By making a few slits the paper will drop around the stock like a glove. Tear
off a few small pieces of masking tape and apply to hold it in place until
the final taping.

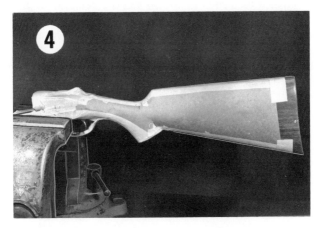

4. With the receiver fully covered with tape you can hold the stock
in the vice and proceed to tape the paper firmly to the stock. I left a
gap in the tape to show about how much of the paper is secured by the
tape. Now press the tape firmly to the wood with the flat of your finger
nail all around the stock on the cut-off line. There should be good contact as this will prevent the wood on the bottom side of the cut from
slivering out.

5. This is an adjustable carrier that I made to take care of the taper in the stock when sawing it off. Using this or some similar method will assure that the recoil pad will be square with the stock center line. Figure six shows it in use.

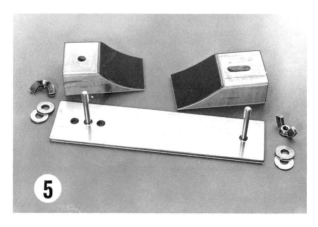

It is made of one piece of cold rolled steel 1-1/2x6-1/4x1/8 inches. There are four 3/32 inch holes drilled and countersunk on the bottom side. Two 3/16 inch bolts with flat heads and 1 1/4 inches long are used with two washers and a wing nut on each bolt. The outside holes are bored 5/8 inch from the ends and on one end two additional holes were bored on 1/2 inch centers. This allows the slotted segment to be adjusted for wider or narrower stocks. I made the blocks from hard maple. The stationary end is 2-1/2"x1-1/2"x7/8". The movable end is

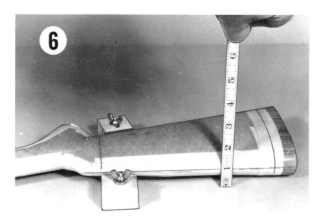

2-3/4"x1-1/2"x7/8" with a slot 3/4" long. The curve was laid out with a segment of a French curve and is not critical. The black covering shown is a piece of a rubber blanket from an offset press. It could be covered with whatever is most convenient but I like the rubber as it helps to hold the stock with no tendency to slip.

6. A top centerline has been established along the comb to the butt. Also the cut-off line that will give the proper length and pitch has been drawn. Now lay the stock on a flat surface and with your ruler adjust the carrier so that the centerline measures the same at the comb and the butt. When everything is squared up tighten the wing nuts. After it is properly adjusted, mark the paper on the stock so that you can locate the carrier in its correct position.

7. My stocks are cut off on a table saw. This shows the adjusting of the mitre gauge so that the cut-off line is straight and parallel to the saw blade.

(Editor's Note:-A great many gunshops do not have table or band saws readily available. The best possible way to insure a good, straight cut is to use a miter box. Be sure that the centerline of the stock is absolutely parallel to the bed of the miter box and perpendicular to the saw ways so that the cut made across the butt of the stock will be square. Carelessness here can result in the butt pad being canted to one side of the stock or the other.)

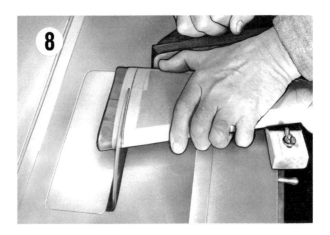

8. Here is the actual sawing off of the stock. With one hand holding the stock firmly in the carrier and against the mitre gauge, the other hand pushes the whole assembly over the saw with ease and a feeling of security.

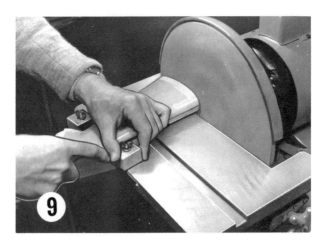

9. This step I don't usually need. If the table saw is good and sharp it generally comes off with a perfectly flat and smooth surface. - However, if you are forced to cut it off by hand or some other means that leaves an uneven surface this Delta Sanding Disc will true it up beautifully in seconds. For taking down a recoil pad it is tops. Here again the carrier is used to maintain that square end.

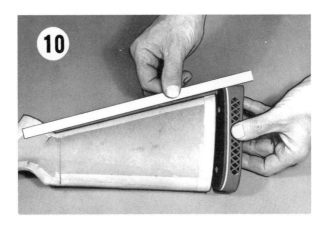

10. After preparing the stock for the pad, the position of the pad on the stock must be determined. This shows the locating of the pad so that there will be sufficient room to carry the bottom line of the stock all the way across the full thickness of the pad.

Check the bottom screw hole to be sure that you have plenty of room at the toe. Observe the top of the pad so that there is sufficient material to clean up. When it is in the proper location mark the location at the top hole.

11. You did determine the position of the top hole in illustration number ten. Now draw a center line from top to bottom. Measure the distance the holes are between centers and lay out on the center line.

Check the holes in the pad to see that they are centered from side to side. Read the instructions that came with the pad. The main objective is to see that the pad is centered when it is screwed down. Having located the hole position drill and insert the screws to not quite final depth. The reason that I like to do it this way is that I know the screws will go in properly and I intend to put the screws through the pad ONCE only. With the stock prepared I now apply the Pliobond glue according to instructions.

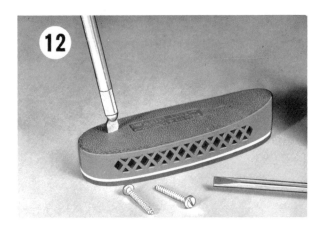

12. There are two details here to note. To locate the place where the knife is to be inserted, lay the surface of the pad into which the knife is sticking face down on a board (without the knife). With a sharp punch that fits the hole, force it through until it penetrates into the board. Without removing the punch, turn it over and using the point of the punch to locate the position insert the Exacto blade. Make the cut the long way of the pad. Insert the back of the blade against the side of the punch and force it in until you have cut a distance about 1/16" more than 1/2 the diameter of the screwhead. Now remove the punch and knife. By placing your thumb and finger on opposite sides of the cut you can force it open slightly. Reverse the direction of the knife and open the slot an equal amount in this direction. We want that screw head to go through the rubber without tearing it. After both slots are made apply Pliobond to the pad and let it dry.

The other item is the screw driver which is ground to fit the slot and is also ground straight back with all the edges rounded (except the blade) and polished.

With the glue on both the stock and pad, the pad with the screws inserted is put into place and screwed down tightly. One of Bob Brownell's News Letters had an item about using a silicone lubricant on the screwdriver blade. It works.

13. This is a simple and fast operation though certainly one not to be done carelessly. It requires only a few minutes to rough off the excess pad, being careful to maintain the straight lines of the stock.

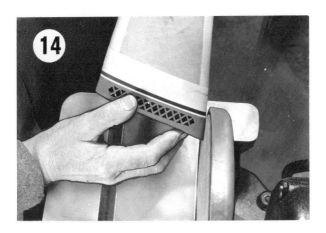

14. In front of the pistol grip place a good light so that it shines directly down on the pad and sander. You have a good clear view of the edge of the sanding disc and the black of the recoil pad. You can sand the pad until you almost touch the tape protecting the stock. If you are a good craftsman take it down to the tape. I take it down as

close as possible without touching the tape. From now on it is hand work.

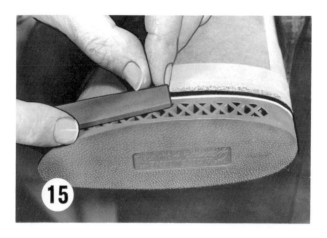

15. With that good sharp file take the edge of the pad right down to the tape. The tape is about .005 thick so I keep on filing until I rough up the tape. You KNOW that you are now getting close.

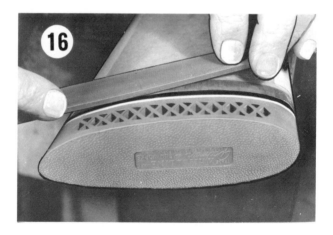

16. We will now take off the masking tape and apply our clear tape right up to the pad. This tape is a few tenths over .001 thick and you can see the surface that you are approaching. With just a little care you can take it down and actually see when you are starting on the tape. From here on you are the judge.

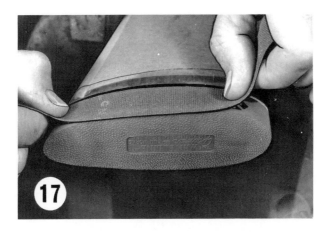

17. With some of the abrasive grit strips and using short sharp strokes you can smooth out any unevenness that may have resulted from not making a perfect, uninterrupted pass around the toe or heel of the pad when it was sanded. This also cleans up the white strip and leaves it sparkling clean.

18. Well, that cleans it up except for removing our "paper" insurance and polishing off the wood with a clean cloth. It should look just the way it did before you started except for that glittering new pad.

If your job requires a refinish on the stock before you attach the pad, that simplifies considerably the job of attaching the pad itself. Many of the precautions and care then are not necessary.

Some of the gunsmith's jobs are high in "nuisance value" and this is one of them. I hope that I have reduced at least a few of them.

GOOD LUCK.

- *James B. Meek, Newton, Iowa*

(Who in my opinion, and if such a classification is possible, quali-
fies as a true, non-professional, Master Gunsmith! - Bob B.)

RECOIL PADS AND STOCK DAMAGE

Before putting on masking tape, spray stock with powdered
graphite and the tape will come off but won't remove finish when pulled
off.

- *R. J. Williams, Saginaw, Michigan*

REMOVING MASKING TAPE

To take off the masking tape after installing the recoil pad, just
paint a little turpentine on the tape and it will soak loose in 10 to 15
minutes.

- *Stewart's Gun Shop, Riverside, California*

TO PULL OFF MASKING T/ ?E

When using masking tape around recoil pads on the new plastic
or polyurethane finishes, I saturate the tape with kerosene or any
similar petroleum agent when I am ready to take it off. Let it soak for
about 15 minutes at least, and then remove it by starting at the forward
edge of the tape and pull back over itself toward the butt. Has always
worked like a charm for me.

- *Hal Dowling, Bainbridge, New York*

INSTALLING RECOIL PADS WITH NO FINISH PEELING

All you have to do to stop finish peeling when taping around the
butt stock to finish off a recoil pad, is to squirt some oil on the stock,
smear it around, then wipe off the surplus with a rag. You'll find that
the masking tape will stick to the stock but it will come off without
pulling the finish with it.

One Caution - use good masking tape only. Some types of tape
have too good a stickum on them for this job. The oil I use is called
"White Oil" and I get it from one of the bulk dealers here. Costs about
a buck and a half a gallon - so cheap you can squirt it on a stock, squirt
it on the floor, squirt it on the lathe or the wall. Sure a lot of
little squirts in a gallon!!

- *Paul Westphal, Austin, Minnesota*

TO KEEP THE TAPE FROM PEELING THE FINISH

I take some regular gun grease and grease the first inch of tape
I put on, and overlap the other end onto this end when I get back to
the start while wrapping the tape around the butt. To take off, peel

back the overlapped piece, take the greased piece which will lift easily off wood, fold it back over the tape in the direction of wrap and keeping it down close to wood, just "unroll" it back over itself off the wood. Just be sure not to pull straight up - keep the bent-over piece you are pulling on close to wood at all times and it won't lift the finish.

- *Pete Hess, Omaha, Nebraska*
- *T. R. Taber, Deerwood, Minnesota*

STOCK FINISH PEELING

We got a lot of fine letters from a lot of you on this. Most of you came up with the same darned good idea. Boiled down it amounted to this: pour kerosene or turpentine on the masking tape you wrapped around the stock butt prior to cutting off for pad mounting. Let soak for a few minutes and then peel off, starting at the top and working towards the butt!

- *Bob B.*

INSTALLING A RECOIL PAD - WITHOUT TAPE

Been having trouble with the factory finish lifting when I pull off the masking tape, so now, I don't use any tape at all. First I lay out the correct pull and pitch and with a flexible ruler, draw the cut-off line on the stock (after the screws and factory plate have been removed, of course.) After cutting off the stock and filing smooth and square, I mount the pad on the butt, and with a small, thin knifeblade, scribe completely around the butt onto the pad, giving me a perfect outline of the butt.

Next, grind away most of the excess pad while it is installed on the butt to be sure to carry the lines of the stock into the pad. Remove the pad then, and very carefully finish grinding it to shape, using the scribed line. You'll almost always get a near perfect fit. After reinstalling the pad, smooth up any hangovers that are left with a flat mill bastard file. Be careful with the file, and you won't touch the factory finish, and when you're done, there is no chance of lifting the finish off the wood.

Finally, put a seal coat on the butt stock and around the new pad and you'll get as tight a fit as momma's drawers!

- *David Wyer, Muleshoe, Texas*

LOOSE BUMPERS, ANYONE?

About a week ago a very buxom young lady walked into our shop. Being rather short, she had someone cut off the stock of her 20 ga. Ithaca and install a recoil pad. She also had the same job done on a .257 Mauser. Now, I don't know what part of the country she came from, but wherever it was they apparently refer to recoil pads as 'bumpers'. At any rate, one of the pads had come loose and looking me right in the eye she stated "I'm having trouble with one of my bumpers." Right about then I tried like hell not to even get a twinkle in my eye, but I'll bet I looked like a long-tailed cat in a room full of rocking chairs!

- *Stanton L. Sperl, Waukesha, Wisconsin*

BUFFING RECOIL PADS

I take my haul-around belt sander and lay it over on its side. Then handhold the stock with the pad mounted. Take the pad almost to the finish size with a coarse belt and finish with fine. Make a couple of strokes in the opposite direction with a hand sanding block to knock off the burrs, blow out the dust and you're finished. Be sure, tho, you have a hard flat backing plate behind the belt. Takes me only about 15 minutes to turn out a thoroughly professional job this way.

- *Harry Hickel Jr., Silver City, New Mexico*

FITTING RECOIL PAD

Use the H386 Surform Drum tool to cut butt stock to install recoil pad. If you are careful and watch what you are doing, this works quite well and saves perhaps 15 minutes time.

- *Bob Wilson, Wichita, Kansas*

INSTANT MATCH STICKS

From Bob B. - After doing the last Newsletter, some character sneaked in and goofed up a bit of it! It surely couldn't have been me who made the misteak!

From Robert G. Wilson - You got my kink just a wee bit kinked up. I suggested you use the surform tool to cut down the recoil pad, NOT the gun butt stock. I don't have a heavy enough grinder to do a good fast job on pads, so I surform the pad to within 1/16" then use a hand sanding disc on a 1/4" drill to come to fit. Just to see what would happen to a cheap butt stock if you stroked it across the grain with the surform, I tried it on a junker. Wow! Instant Toothpicks!

- *Bob Wilson, Wichita, Kansas*

INSTALLING RECOIL PADS

Here's a small kink I found installing recoil pads that makes for a much neater job: I take a double edged X-Acto knife and cut a small 'X' over each hole, through the outside, and then just before the screw head is buried in the pad, I take a sharp scribe and lift up the four pointed edges formed by the cross-cut and go ahead and turn in the screw until buried. (Note by Bob B: you can also spit on it! This lubricates the rubber and lets the screwhead turn in without marring the rubber.) When the screwdriver is withdrawn, if one is reasonably careful, it is nearly impossible to detect the spot where the screws were put in. Incidentally, I've been using Phillips head screws as they create less torn edges than the conventional kind.

- *Blackburn's Custom Gun Stocks, Fort Worth, Texas*

RECOIL PAD HOLES

I use a silicone lubricant on the screw heads and screwdriver blade, after first cutting a small criss-cross X cut where the holes are located on the pad. You can install a pad using this silicone lubricant and hardly leave a trace of the hole entrance. Just works beautifully!

- *Leslie M. Lindahl, Central City, Nebraska*

STOCK PINNING

Put some coarse threads on some pieces of 1/16", 3/32" and 1/8" brazing rod. Drill stock through crack with minor diameter drill and tightly clamp the stock together and screw pin in with a hand drill. With good wood and 1/8" pin, you cannot pull the crack apart by hand.

- *Willy's Gun Shop, Wadena, Iowa*

STOCK CLAMP

For years now I have been using a strip of inner tube as a stock clamp when working on gun stocks. Cut them about 1" to 1-1/2" wide and about 18" long. Then powder inner side with talc to protect the stock finish, and wrap it around the wood under tension, tucking the end under the wrap to hold it tight. Best clamp I've ever found. Just vary the width and length to suit the particular job.

- *David Christen, Wadena, Iowa*

BROKEN STOCK CLAMP

Here is a little trick I use for gluing cracked or broken stocks, or adding on combs or grip caps of wood. Take an old rubber inner tube and with a pair of scissors go around and around the tube, cutting a 1" wide strip 6' to 10' long. Prepare your surface to be glued and join with epoxy and then wrap the rubber strip around the wood. Stretch the rubber as much as possible as you wrap. When completely wrapped, let set up until glue is set. This makes the best possible clamp on all irregular shaped pieces of wood and will leave no clamp marks. Pass it along for the trade...coating the rubber with a good paste wax will prevent the epoxy from attaching itself to the rubber.

- *Beacon Gun Works, Wilmington, North Carolina*

GUN STOCK CLAMPS

When it comes time to do some gluing wood pieces together, I almost always use a piece of 3/4" inner tube for my clamps. It always has the same tension, which you can control by how tightly you stretch it when you wrap it on. And the tension does not slack off as it sometimes does with a metal clamp. Works especially well on gun stocks where you have odd shapes and angles to go around and you don't want to scratch the wood.

- *John Turnbull, Toulon, Illinois*

A HAIRY DOG

A young lad of about 16 came into my shop the other day with his Stevens crack shot. He'd taken the gun down and re-assembled it himself and had the stock upside down. I told him that the "comb" should be Up and not Down. "What's the 'comb' on the stock?" asks the kid. "It's got no hair!"

- *Ralph Gripe, Craley, Pennsylvania*

MIXING SMALL AMOUNTS OF ACRAGLAS

Use a small plastic pill bottle. By sticking a strip of masking tape on the side of the jar, it is a simple matter to measure off the 1/4 ratio with a ruler!

- *T. E. Daw, East Lansing, Michigan*

CRACK PATCHING

"Had purchased a stock blank," says Jim Horton, "with purty figure in it, but as sometimes happens, there were several cracks thru the figure. Mixed up some Acraglas without flock and spread it on the surface over the cracks. As the Acraglas settled into the cracks, I'd push in more until it started to set. After it was completely set, I sanded the surplus with a power sander and then finished it with elbow grease and fine garnet paper...Makes best filler I have ever seen for cracks. No fall-out either!"

- *Jim Horton, Trenton, Missouri*

ACRAGLASSING A BUSTED STOCK

Spread Acraglas in a cracked stock with compressed air! First spread crack apart then pour plenty of Acraglas around. Point air at it - 100-175 psi. Wipe off glasses, face, walls, floor, ceiling and stock before it dries. Works good and gets Glass clean to bottom of crack!

- *David Christen, Wadena, Iowa*

REPAIRING CRACKED STOCKS

The crack must be completely free of oil and grease. If the stock does seem oily, flush thoroughly with some form of degreasing agent. Regular lighter fluid works fine, but be sure to handle with care. If wood is in two pieces, wipe the break with fluid-saturated cotton and dry with clean patch. If wood is still in one piece, flush with fluid and blow out thoroughly with your compressed air.

Mix up a dob of epoxy glue. With a thin piece of metal pry crack slightly open but not to the extent of widening or lengthening the crack. If the wood is in two pieces, coat each piece with a thin, even coat of glue.

Strike a regular kitchen match and hold the flame one inch from the glue for about 15 seconds. This will turn the glue watery and thin, and it will flow down into the tiniest crack. Wipe off the excess glue carefully.

Secure the wood with C-Clamps if possible. If the wood is odd shaped, which it is more than 90% of the time in gunstocks, press the joint closed with one hand. With the other, press a strip of SCOTCH FILAMENT TAPE across the crack at right angles. Add additional pieces of tape. When done correctly, the tape will hold as good as any C-Clamp. (Be sure to use Scotch Filament Tape. The others tried stuck to wood or glue and would not come clean. This one won't for some reason and holds like a clamp.)

Let the glue dry 12 hours regardless of what it says on the tube. Remove the tape which will not stick to the glue. Apply a small amount of stock compound and rub the glue joint down, finishing with a coat of stock finish to blend with the rest of the stock.

- *Ralph Walker, Selma, Alabama*

CHAPTER 2

ACTIONS & RECEIVERS

RESHAPING MILITARY RECEIVERS

Looks to me as tho the following is the best gun shop method yet offered for taking care of reshaping military receivers to any radius desired.

My method of turning to radius: Use a bar (B) of strap iron of sufficient length to cover distance of tang holes in receiver and be handled on the drill press table. Drill 3/8" holes (blind holes) in strap iron centered to match distance of tang holes in receiver. Cut & thread two stud (A) screws to be used in place of tang & recoil lug screws in the receiver.

After the bridge has been rough ground to near radius (as in my case, 721 Rem which I recall as 2" radius) the stud screws can be cut and fitted to the proper length for racking on a 2" radius under a cup

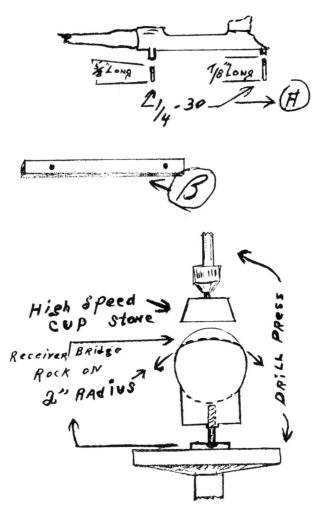

wheel on the drill press. The strap iron bar "B" is to be used as your racking plate. This I find gives a truly fine finish and you might pass it on to the boys for what it is worth. (Observation by Bob B: If you do not have a lathe, then you could purchase inletting guide screws and carefully cut them to the proper length for the stud screws. Also, using the above method it would be a simple matter to get the rear bridge to exactly the same height as the barrel ring, or any other height desired. And, best of all, have it really true!)

- *E. J. Richter, Shenandoah, Iowa*

ROTARY BOLT FACE CUTTER

Use Tungsten Carbide Cutters shaped like #194 in your Catalog but 1/4" dia. (These are not bought with cigar store coupons - $6 or $7 and $2 to re-sharpen.) They have to be used in a tool like Dumore grinder or better. Must be used in tool-post with bolt in lathe....a little tip: UNPLUG your lathe motor and rotate bolt by hand. I say unplug because if you don't, you are very apt to hit the switch automatically - or without thinking - and if you do, Brrrrrr...there went the teeth off the tool all to you know where...

The small amount to be removed for feeding can be done free-hand if you use the proper caution. Like everything else, my Pappy used to say "Nobody ever does anything right the first time..." So, I suggest a surplus Springfield bolt to practice on.

- *Jim Winton, Gaston, Oregon*

BOLT FACING WITH BORING BAR

Tip a boring bar with carbide and use your boring bar holder to feed straight into bolt face. Feed the bit across the bed and turn the work by hand. This is a scraping process and works fine....To preclude chipping the carbide tip, soft solder a filet to the extractor slot in the left hand bolt lug....we have to have this rig ground elsewhere as the carbide is hard to sharpen...have tried on everything and works best.

- *Muse Davis, Starkville, Mississippi*

CARBIDE BOLT FACE LATHE CUTTER

Take a piece of carbide - I use a throw-away bit or anything about 1/16" thick - silver solder this to a lathe bit and grind to the desired angle. Keep the flat side so you will have as much of the carbide supported by the lathe bit as is possible. Make a pilot that will just fit inside the bolt and long enough to chuck in the lathe. Slide the bolt on the pilot and tighten to the chuck. Use a steady rest on the end of the bolt next to the lugs. I use two pieces of flat iron and a bolt to clamp the bolt handle to the jaw on the chuck. This makes for a right rigid lash-up. I turn the head-stock by hand and feed by hand....will take a cut off anything but carbide and it doesn't take long.

- *Dick Turgeon, Sioux Falls, South Dakota*

BOLT FACE POLISHING

When opening the face of bolts on standard bolt actions to take a Magnum case, here is a trick to make 'em look better: - While bolt is still in lathe, seat a bullet backwards in a magnum case and chuck up the case neck in the tailstock. Using base of case, apply a little lapping compound & polish the face at hi-speed. This can be done in a drill press also if care is used - but after all, aren't all good "smiths" care-

ful?!
- *J. D. Sayers, Pasadena, Texas*

ENGINE-TURNING TIPS

You can roll your Bright Boy engine-turning tips in glue and let them dry--you will find that they do not break down as easily as before....

- *Murray F. Ruffino, Rutherford, New Jersey*

BOLT JEWELING JIG

Here is a drawing of the bolt jeweling jig we used in our shop for many years.

- *Bob B.*

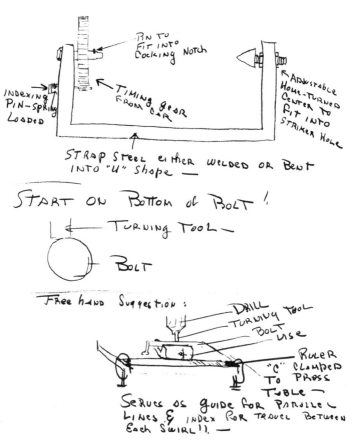

MAKING SWIRLY-GIGS ON ROUNDED RIFLE BOLTS
(that's Jeweling to you, Baby)

It had been a long, hard day. Exhausted, I leaned back in my chair, put my feet up on the desk and lit a cigar. Finally, I thought, I have time to read my new issue of *GUNsport*.

Just as I was getting really settled down I heard an unmistakable dissonance outside the shop window; rock and roll through a transistor radio. A miniature silver poodle ran through the door, made one long jump and landed in my lap. "Oh, hi, Brandy!" I said.

The transistor reached a shattering crescendo in the shop doorway as my niece Pam made a grand entrance carrying, besides the radio, a mysterious cardboard box. "Hi, Baby," she shouted between pirouettes. "You working on anything special? I have something I want you to do for me." She fished through some oiled paper in the cardboard box and produced a very ordinary looking Springfield bolt. "Will you put some of those little swirly-gigs on this crank handle?"

"Oh, you mean rows of spot polishes...I'll tell you what, Pam; put on this apron and you can pro-tem for your poor, tired uncle this month."

"But, I haven't even been initiated into the gunsmith's union," she giggled.

The proper method of jeweling a rifle bolt is illustrated in the photos. Bolts from commercial rifles are usually ready for jeweling when the striker assembly and the extractor have been removed, but blued or parkerized military bolts have to be polished before jeweling can be started. There are several practical and comparatively rapid methods of removing most of the parkerizing.

Cut strips of emery cloth 1" wide, the length of the sheet, and use them in a shoe shining motion. If you have a grinder or buffing arbor, a rubber drum with slip-on abrasive bands like the one in the photo will accomplish the same task in a fraction of the time. Abrasive cloth flap wheels work equally well. The principal consideration is to remove as much finish as possible in as short a time as possible without leaving deep tool marks.

Polish the knob, handle, bolt body, safety lug and locking lugs, but do not remove metal from the cocking or extracting cams or the locking surfaces of the lugs.

After most of the parkerizing has been removed, finish the bolt with successively finer grits of prepared buffing abrasive compounds, such as Brownell's Polish-O-Ray. Hold the bolt at about a 20° angle to the axis of the wheel and use the old metal finisher's trick of reversing this angle from side to side at every change of grit. Be sure to remove every mark from the preceding grit before going to a finer compound.

An average amateur's buffing equipment consists of one stitched muslin wheel, which he cleans between grit changes with an old file. It will finish a bolt, but a much better polish, bright and ripple free, can be obtained by using soft felt wheels for the grits from 140 down through 500 and using a hard felt wheel for the 555 grit.

There are several kinds of tools designed to make circular polishes on metal, but the two most practical ones and the only ones that will make full, deep circles on a rounded bolt body are the pencil eraser-like abrasive bonded in rubber and the tiny wire brushes shown in the photos. Both styles of tool will eventually make a spot polish if they are used dry, but for professional looking results they must be

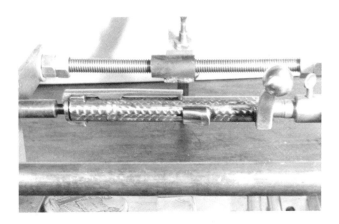

used through a film of coarse valve grinding compound. Oil mix compound works better than water mix on rifle bolts.

Mount the bolt between centers in the index fixture with the bolt handle up so that the first experimental rows of polishes will be underneath the bolt when it is in the closed position. Next, align the fixture and clamp it in a position where the spots will be exactly centered for the entire length of the body. Then run the advance screw in until the brush is as close as possible to the bolt root, with the advance knob straight up.

Grip a wire brush in the drill chuck. A piece of 1/4" drill rod 3" long will make a simple brush extension that will allow jeweling right up to the bolt handle.

Spread an even layer of valve grinding compound about 1/16" thick over the top surface in line with the first spot row. Set the drill press to top speed setting, switch the motor on and bring the wire brush into full, firm contact with the bolt body. Do not apply much force, since pressure will spread the circles. Set the depth stop to repeat the position and insure uniform sized circles.

Bring the brush down into contact with the bolt for seven full seconds, then raise the quill. Turn the advance screw two full turns and stop with the knob pointing straight up. Make the second circle in the same manner and repeat the process until the first row is completed.

To make the second row, back up the advance screw one complete turn, stopping with the handle's knob end pointing straight up. Rotate the bolt in the fixture one index stop. Spread a layer of valve grinding compound as before, bring the quill down to make the first

Hand drill powers wire brush in amateur fixture. Works well, but unlike Pro practice of using drill press with double cross slide vise to obtain accurate indexing.

circle in the second row and continue in this manner until the entire bolt body is jeweled.

If you take care not to turn the extractor collar from its original position, it can be jeweled with the bolt body. Some gunsmiths jewel the sides of the safety lug, but this is optional. Carry the rows out in unbroken sequence everywhere they will be visible.

When the jeweling is completed, remove the bolt from the fixture and immediately wash it in solvent or gasoline. Use a 1" paint brush to scrub away the residue of abrasive. Remove the extractor collar and clean the groove thoroughly. When the entire bolt body is clean and grit free inside and out, coat it lightly with a film of gun grease or vaseline.

The extractor can be jeweled quite easily the same as any flat part: Clamp it tightly in a drill press vise, bring the brush down into full firm contact for about seven seconds, lift the brush, advance the

vise so that the circle overlaps about halfway and repeat the process. Leave a half step between rows to match the offset of the bolt body jeweling.

The rubber bonded abrasive sticks can be chucked directly in the drill chuck or attached to an extension tool. Buy the coarse abrasive grits, since these cut faster, and use them through a layer of valve grinding compound exactly as the wire brush was used. The rubber is soft, and will conform to the rounded surface of the bolt body. Do not let the tip "fin" or spread out into a wide circle. Cut away the flared portion of tip as it forms and when the rubber is worn away close to the chuck or tool extension, replace the tip. Using the bonded abrasive in this manner, with valve grinding compound, makes the tips last several times as long as using them dry, and the quality of spot produced is several times better.

I slipped the finished bolt into a Springfield from the rifle rack and held it up for Pam to see. "Say, that looks all sparkly...like a new poodle collar." She glanced up at the clock. "Oh, oh! Look what time it is. I have to go home and do my 'rithmetic." I handed her the bolt and she switched on the radio. The rock and roll took up right where it had left off. "So long, Baby, and thanks for this." She lofted the bolt, threw a quick kiss and disappeared around the corner. I heard her footsteps patter down the concrete walk. Brandy barked at an imaginary rabbit. The sound of the transistor faded into the distance and the shop was plunged into silence.

I wasn't tired anymore, but I felt restless. I walked over to the drill press and wiped down the fixture. Suddenly I felt very much alone.

> - *John G. Lawson, Reprinted by special permission from* GUNsport, *April, 1968*

HE WHO KNOWS NOT...

When someone comes in and starts giving you that old line of stuff and he's so far off-base you nearly blow a gasket keeping your mouth shut - just think of these words of wisdom from Bob Albrecht: "He who knows not that he knows not, is a Not Knows!"

- *Bob Albrecht, New Brunswick, New Jersey*

BOLT JIGS FOR SPEED

Have changed two bolt handles with the fixture I received. It now is a pleasure from start to finish, Bob. Very EXPERT idea...

- *Paul Miner, Waterloo, Iowa*

Like to compliment you on the bolt jig (welding, that is). I'd made up one myself but yours is faster and more accurate.

- *Harry McGowen, St. Anne, Illinois*

PROFESSIONAL WELDING TECHNIQUES

When low mounted telescopes are installed on most military rifles, it is necessary to alter the bolt handle so that it will clear the eye piece and tube of the scope. Forged bolt knobs provide an easy method of doing this, and most gun cranks prefer the pear shaped knob and the pleasing lines provided by the forged bolt knob over the method of forging or cutting off and welding the original military bolt handle. The following instructions apply to the acetylene welding method, but with the exception of the dimensions of the stub left on the bolt from the original bolt handle and the welding itself, similar methods are used with electric welding.

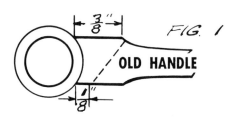

Cut off the handle of the military bolt, leaving a stub of the shape and dimensions in Figure 1. If you have an abrasive cut-off wheel, the cut is easily and quickly made. If it is necessary to make the cut with a hack saw, in most cases you will have to anneal the bolt handle. To anneal, polish the bolt handle at the point of the cut with coarse abrasive. It is not necessary to produce a smooth surface but a bright surface is required so that you can watch the temper colors develop. With an acetylene torch, heat at the point of the cut, playing the flame on all sides of the bolt handle, until the temper colors have passed through the blues and turned almost gray. Heated to this color and allowed to cool, even the A-3 bolt handles can be cut off with a hack saw, using very slow, steady strokes and considerable pressure. On A-3 bolt handles and on some others, if the heat is carried through to a dull red, the material will re-harden itself from the quench effect of the nearby unheated steel or from the air.

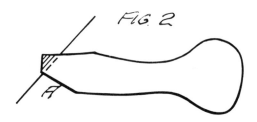

FIG. 2

File the lower edge of the cut at the 1/8th dimension so that this section is parallel with the axis of the bolt. Clean up surface A, Figure 2, of the knob and file off the shaded section. The sharp edge should be a straight line and when this edge is butted against the edge of the stub remaining on the bolt, the position of the rear surface of the knob should be 7/8" from the rear side of the stub as shown in Figure 3. Filing the stub and the bolt knob underneath next to the bolt body is difficult and if these surfaces are properly dressed and properly mated before welding, the only thing necessary will be to polish off the scale and time will be saved.

Plug the bolt body with wet asbestos. This should be packed down into the bolt body past the threads and into the cocking cam notch. It is possible to properly position the bolt body and the forged bolt knob in the correct relationship with one another by using mounds of wet asbestos on a firebrick, but if you have more than one or two bolts to do, it will pay you to buy Brownell's Bolt Welding Jig. If you do not have a jig, lay the bolt body flat on the firebrick with the bolt locking lugs horizontal and the handle stub vertical. Pack wet asbestos around the rear 1/3 of the bolt to hold it. Build up a mound of wet asbestos to position the bolt knob as shown in Figure 3 and 4. With the bolt welding jig, the parts can be located in their proper relationship much faster and easier and the parts are locked in relationship so they will not be accidentally moved by touching them with the welding rod or torch. In either event, pack wet asbestos well around the bolt body and up next to the stub of the bolt handle.

If you have never done any welding work, get one of the simple textbooks on welding which are available from any of the welding equipment manufacturers and after you have studied it, go to your local welder and pay him for an hour or two of his time to instruct you in the simple welding techniques required for such things as bolt knobs. Also, at the present time, it is possible to buy surplus military bolts at a very low figure and experience with a couple of these might be a good investment before you start working on your best customer's favorite gun.

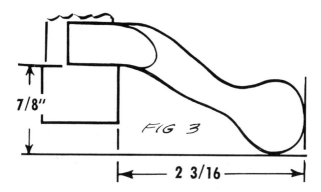

FIG 3

7/8"

2 3/16

Most manufacturers of welding equipment sell an aircraft size blowpipe which is ideal for most gun work. These come with a variety of tip sizes. A tip with an orifice the size of a #50 or #53 drill is about right for bolt knob work. With the materials that are used in most bolts, it is best to use a flame with a slight excess of acetylene. You will find instructions in your welding manual on the techniques for adjusting the flame.

5/16

1/8"

FIG. 4

The material of which the forged bolt knobs are made is very easy to weld and because of this and because of the mass of the bolt stub, plus the cooling effect of the wet asbestos, your flame should be directed principally against the stub, manipulating the flame to bring the knob up to heat at the same time as the stub. The first weld is made at the bottom and middle of the V. Use 1/16 diameter welding rod and add material from the welding rod until the added material has flowed out to both ends of the V and has built up at least half way to the top of the V. When you stop adding material, the blowpipe should never be pulled away quickly as the flame is used to protect the molten material from scaling and pitting. Rotate the flame slightly and slowly pull the torch straight back away from the molten puddle until the puddle loses its look of wetness. Move the flame to the front side of the V and add in material and shape until you have bonded in this section and carried the added material completely to the top of the V. Do the same on the back side of the V. Then move the flame to the top and fill in the rest of the V. Watch out for scale which will form pits and inclusions in the finished weld. In the molten metal, scale glows with a yellowish glow instead of the red of the rest of the metal and it can be floated out of the way by the pressure of the torch flame. The metal added must be solid leaving the scale off to one side or on top in sections which are dressed off in shaping and finishing. The faster you are able to work, the less heat will be transferred to the bolt body and the less problem you will have with scale in the weld. Pour water on the asbestos fore and aft of the bolt knob and stub to reduce the heat flow. Do not allow the water to strike the welded joint. Allow the whole bolt to cool and clean all of the asbestos from the outside and the inside of the bolt. A brass rifle cleaning brush will help in getting the asbestos out of the inside threads of the bolt. Chip the scale from the weld by striking it with a dull cold chisel or any similar tool. This will save on tools and time in finishing.

If you have a lathe, the shaping of the front and rear sides of the bolt, welded section and part of the handle can be done with hand fitting.

Make up a threaded and centered plug to fit the rear end of the bolt body. Chuck the front end of the bolt in the lathe chuck and support the threaded plug with the tailstock. This is shown in sketch No. 5 together with the tools and holders for facing the bolt stub. When facing the right hand side (in the illustration), feed the lathe tool outwards. Use a left hand tool holder on the left side and feed in. Note that the tool bit must be ground to provide clearance for the safety lug on Mauser bolts. Match the cuts to the stub. On the rear side of the Springfield bolt stub, there is a milled notch which provides clearance for the end of the safety. This notch is unnecessary and a neater job is obtained by facing the stub and the forged bolt knob to the bottom of notch.

Next, file the radius on the top of the stub and bolt knob to provide proper clearance for the scope eye piece, round up the forged bolt knob and match the lines with the lathe cuts. Use a half round bastard file

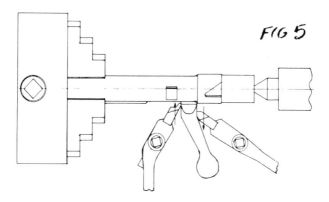

FIG 5

and after you have obtained the desired lines, take a finer file and smooth up the scope radius clearance. Polish the extractor cam, maintaining the original lines, and chamfer or slightly radius all square corners. Re-harden the extracting cam surface; and the cocking cam surface, if the temper of this has been drawn. Use the same tip that you did for welding and play the flame along these surfaces so as to quickly bring the surface to a cherry red. Quench in oil as a water quench may be too drastic for some alloys. Properly done, only 1/16 to 1/8 of an inch of the surface is heated up and hardened.

The band sander sold by Brownell's is ideal for polishing the knob and bolt shank. Use an 80 to 100 grit belt for roughing, semi-finish with about a 150, and then finish with a 320. Hold the bolt shank loosely between the thumb and forefinger of the left hand and rotate the bolt body to polish the knob; then cup the knob in the fingers of the left hand and rotate again to polish the shank. You will soon develop a technique which will almost eliminate hand polishing. The polishing of the scope radius clearance and the square sides of the stub must be done by hand. If you desire, final finishing can be done either on a buffing wheel to produce a high polish or by wire brushing to give a satin finish.

The final operation is cutting the clearance for the bolt shank in the receiver and in the stock of the rifle. The above technique leaves a bolt shank with a flat underside so the receiver cut is a flat bottomed slot at right angles to the bottom surface of the receiver. Many receivers have to be spot annealed in order to make this cut. The slot can be cut on a milling machine or by hand with files. Make sure that the back side of the slot shows a little clearance for the bolt handle when the bolt is in place and the locking lugs fully locked. On Springfield actions, the slot is cut deep enough to allow the safety lug to contact the bolt raceway. On Mauser actions and Japanese actions, the depth of the slot governs the point at which the bolt is fully locked. This must coincide with proper operation of the safety and cocking cam. On the Mausers, cut the slot deep enough so the original military safety can be fully rotated into the safe position with the bolt fully locked. There should be a slight amount of play in the bolt handle after the safety is fully turned. On the Japanese rifles check to make sure that the straight side of the cocking cam notch lines up with the sear slot in the receiver.

The original military safety on the Springfields and Mausers will have to be replaced with one of the commercially manufactured scope type safeties.

The above basic instructions apply to the 1917 Enfield and the model 54 Winchester except that in the case of the Enfield, the forged bolt knob is welded to the end of the bolt stub, while on the model 54 bolt, it is welded so that the bottom edge of the knob shank is even with the bottom edge of the safety lug. On both of these rifles, the forged bolt knob should be shortened as otherwise the finished bolt handle will be too long.

- Creighton Audette, Springfield, Vermont

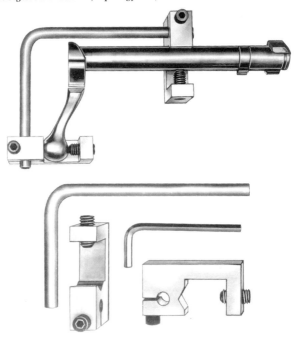

Commercially made Bolt Welding Jig complete with all necessary accessories and detailed instructions available from Brownell's Inc., Montezuma, Iowa

BOLT JIG FOR EGG-SHAPED KNOBS

I take one of your bolt jigs and put a little bend in the rear arm about half-way along its length so that it will hold the egg-shaped handles better. The bend puts the knob holder at about a 15-20 degree angle past perpendicular, so that the locking screw is able to get a better purchase on the off-square centerline of the egg-shaped knob. I think once you try it, you will see why it does a better job.

- *E. P. Barber, Portland, Oregon*

DON'T MAR THE KNOB

To keep from burring the checkering on bolt handles when holding them in the welding jigs, put a drop of soft solder on the end of the holding screw that tightens down onto the knob. Will stay there a long time and hold better without marring the checkering.

- *Bob Blackburn, Ft. Worth, Texas*

CLEANING UP BOLT WELDING JOBS

I was trying to clean up under bolt welding on a forged handle. On the 12" Atlas lathe the locking lugs prevent proper alignment. The answer is easy. Chuck between centers. With an 8 power glass, no deforming of the firing pin hole could be seen. (Commercial: May we call attention to our Bolt Welding Jig?)

- *A Lynn Case, Chief Infantry Marine Gunner, Miami, Oklahoma*

PEANUTS

A drunk staggered into a phone booth and dropped a dime into the phone. The operator promptly replied, "Number please" and the drunk exclaimed, "I don't want any numbers, where the hell are my peanuts?"

- *Art Schwedler, Northport, New York*

TRIGGER ADJUSTMENTS

I've seen elaborate hints on how to make a fixture to adjust trigger and sear angles... I use the gun frame itself and its pins or screws. The trick is to assemble on the outside of the frame. Trigger pressure can be substituted for springs and the action is easy to observe. Good on a lot of doubles, too!

- *James C. Hall, Flint, Michigan*

TRIGGERS FOR BULL PUPS

Have been building bull pups here for varmints and have had a DXX'# time with push rod trigger assemblies. Stumbled on to the old idea of Bowden Cabel (Auto Choke Rod to you) using modified Timney trigger and own front assembly. Makes about 2000% easier to inlet.

Use stainless tube & piano wire around magazine box. Works like smooth oil...

- *Bob's Gun Shop, Moses Lake, Washington*

ABOUT TRIGGERS

A fact that many gun owners fail to realize is that their gun, in practically all cases, is capable of shooting much finer groups than the shooter is capable of holding. Other than the natural wobble all of us have in any shooting position there are many factors that cause us to open up our groups or, on long shots where point of impact is very critical, cause the bullet to hit "where we wasn't lookin".

The two chief offenders for causing misplaced shots are sights and trigger pull. There has been enough advertising and editorial publicity in the magazines about sights that practically all shooters are aware of how much they can improve their shooting by the installation of good telescopic sights. However not enough emphasis has been put on the values to be derived from installing a top quality specialized trigger on any rifle - especially military arms which have notoriously poor trigger pulls for sporting use.

Many a good military trigger has been ruined when its owner has attempted to follow the instructions in some magazine article on how to "improve the military trigger". These articles, if followed exactly, do give the right instructions. But, too often, a slip is made by the gun owner and a dangerously unsafe trigger is the result.

Nothing can be more disconcerting when, after you have been stalking a particular trophy for hours (or days!), you end up having to take a longer shot than you'd hoped for and, to confound the issue, have to fight a trigger pull that is either full of jumps and jerks or has a habit of letting off just when you don't want. The same is true when sighting-in before the hunt or the hundreds of shots you will take with the same gun during your off-season shooting....and thousands more shots are fired at paper and rocks than at living game.

So! Why not give your gun the chance to prove itself to you that it so richly deserves? Install a trigger that co-operates rather than one that fights back.

Barn door actions are wonderful on barns - NOT on triggers.

With the exception of the German Mauser Double Set triggers, all triggers are accompanied with excellently detailed instructions - if special instructions are needed for installation. Adjustment setting instructions are carefully explained and the screws making those adjustments are pointed out. You must remember that good triggers are precision pieces of fine equipment, built and designed to give precision results when the shooting is critical or just plain "plinking". Fine craftsmen have assembled and adjusted them before being sent to you -- don't tear them down just to see what makes them "Klick" any more than you would a good watch.

- *Bob B.*

USE GUNS OWN PARTS TO ASSEMBLE THE GUN

Noted that in one of your newsletters, you showed a bent wire shell holder for assembling the Remington Model 11-48 guard into the receiver, with the wire tool holding the shell latch in place when inserting the guard.

Now, why go to all the trouble of making up a tool to do a special holding job on a gun, when the required tool is frequently one of the component parts of that same gun.

For instance, on the 11-48, put the shell latch into the side wall of the receiver. Stand the guard at right angles to the receiver and slip the guard down into the receiver ahead of the front crosspin hole. Keep the guard at right angles to the receiver and slip the front crosspin from one side and only into the receiver until it is flush with the shell latch. The pin will hold the shell latch in place while you rotate the guard down into proper position, and you can slide the pin home.

On the Winchester Model 12, use the carrier spring to hold the hammer spring onto its guide rod while assembling the hammer with spring and guide rod into the guard. Remover the carrier spring after the hammer pivot pin is in place.

On the Savage-Stevens Model 87, .22 rifle, use the firing pin to slide out the breechbolt assembly.

I could go on and on...but the whole point is to take a good careful look over the gun as you assemble it and you will find in most cases that the tool you need for assembly is one of the other parts of the gun.

- *Al Zalud, North Platte, Nebraska*

INSTALLING SPRINGS IN THE "MEAN" DOUBLE BARRELS

Clamp the receiver in the Drill Press vise. Take the largest Allen head wrench that will clear in the spring slots and chuck it into the drill press. Compress the spring with the drill press by cranking down the handle and lock it in place. Now you can use both hands to line up the pin hole and tap in the pin.

- *Richard A Turgeon, Sioux Falls, South Dakota*

PUTTING IN THE EJECTOR SPRINGS FOR AUTO EJECTS

Have had trouble with these until started squeezing them about flat in the vise. Then slid about a 5/16" or 3/8" open end wrench over about half the spring width. It will now slide right in place with no fuss and you can slip off the end wrench.

- *Richard A Turgeon, Sioux Falls, South Dakota*

SLAVE PINS

Round wooden toothpicks make good slave pins for assembly of parts. Just insert the toothpick and break off. (Note by Bob B.: You will find the term "Slave Pin" used many times in The Encyclopedia -- it is a pin used to hold parts in place when assembling a gun but is NOT used otherwise. The "Slave Pin" is removed when an assembly is in position and the regular pin - or pins - then inserted.)

- Rawar Gun Shop, Long Beach, California

THE MIGHTY VW

The guys in the shop want to know if you guys know what is harder than getting a pregnant elephant into a Volkswagen? Answer: "Getting the elephant pregnant in a Volkswagen."

- Gun and Saddle Shop, Mt. Pleasant, Michigan

REPLACING FIRING PINS SUBJECT TO EARLY FATIGUE

Material:	Crucible Steel Company's LaBelle Silicon 2
Remarks:	Leave ample radii when permissible
	Polish to remove all tool marks which act as stress concentrators

Pre Heat:	1300/1350 F.
Harden:	1600/1650 F.
Quench:	Light, clean quench oil. Use rapid agitation, figure 8 motion. Water quench for large parts ONLY.
Temper:	700 F. 10/15 minutes; 500 F. 25/35 Minutes.
Rockwell "C":	54/55

Note: hold part in boiling water if tempering furnace is not available - at once. This material does not lend itself too well to easy machining due to silicon content, but has excellent shock & wear resistance. Small parts such as these are difficult to properly heat treat and require a good knowledge of metalurgy.

Second Suggestion: Purchase factory pin & give same a good tool draw prior to insertion in customer's gun. This will not anneal but will relieve stress. Give 300/350 F. for 30 to 40 minutes. Cool to room temperature with no quench. I would suggest using liquid heat (liquid heat salts) if the LaBelle steel is used to fabricate new firing pins as this helps to control decarburization.

Note from Bob B.: Crucible Steel Co. has addresses in 35 larger cities. Their home office is located in "Department TR," Oliver Building, Pittsburgh, Pa. I believe that if you-all were to write them asking for address of your closest distributor they would send it to you. It would be well worth your time as gunsmiths to have a small quantity of such steel on hand for shop use.

- *Bill McDonnell, Denver, Colorado*

CHAPTER 3

BARRELS & BARREL WORK

BARREL REMOVAL

For someone who does a little barrel removing and does not need a big special vise around the shop for the job, I came up with this trick. It works real well. Place the action in a padded vise (I use aluminum padded jaws); use 3 feet of 1/2" diameter nylon rope with an eye tied or braided into one end. Wrap the rope towards the action, wrapping it around the barrel in the direction of removal rotation. Let the eye overlap the rope just ahead of the action. Put a 2-foot long piece of 1" pipe through the eye and resting one end on the rope wrapped around the barrel, start cranking with the other end and the barrel will turn itself off.

- *J. Alvin Wayne, San Rafael, California*

BARREL VISE BUSHINGS - ACRAGLAS

The formula I used is 1 oz. resin with 1/4 oz. hardener and half the glass fibers in the kit. I made the mold by using a cardboard liner in my barrel vise. I took a 1/4" plywood board and bored a hole in it the exact diameter of the barrel. Then I centered the plywood hole in the barrel vise hole and glued the plywood to the back of the vise... I then greased the barrel with wax base die lubricant, stuck it through the hole and poured in the Acraglas...I had made up only half enough Acraglas, so mixed up that much again and added to that in the vise hole...

To eliminate holes and voids, I tamped the mixed Acraglas and turned the barrel to get out all bubbles. This I left overnight to cure. Next day I tamped the barrel and it came out easily. I have used this bushing many times with no failures. Next one I make will be in a wooden mold so that the outside will be exactly the same size as the barrel vise.

- *Jerry Klein, Knoxville, Iowa*

BARREL BUSHINGS IN BARREL VISES OF ACRAGLAS

Nearly everyone has difficulty with barrel bushings in barrel vises. I have several metal bushings (store bought) and for a while I used lead (too soft), then lead and tin mixed, but still involves quite a lot of extra work to mold. Here is the secret: Make them with Acraglas - a cinch! Works beautifully and easy to make, perfect fit on barrels and most factory and service barrels are pretty close as to sizes and tapers.

My second tip also involves barrel removal. Most gunsmiths use powdered rosin in their sleeves for non-slippage. You can scratch a barrel, though, if you don't happen to be cinched up tight enough. I dissolve lump rosin in turpentine and either paint it on the barrel or in the bushings. Works fine and is easier to keep a supply in a small bottle. Anyone trying this can just about tell how much rosin to put in. It doesn't take too much to make a real non-skid surface...

- *Gene W. Taylor, Wolf Creek, Montana*

BARREL VISE BUSHINGS OF ALUMINUM

...and I have long since quit fighting the battle of the barrel vise with the wood block and rosin bit or the steel inserts...Pick up a bar of dural aluminum at the local scrap yard and cut into suitable lengths. Bore each block .0312" undersize for each barrel size. Polish internal surface well and hacksaw thru along one side. Using Dural blocks of this type, well polished, does not damage bluing or gall the steel. Blocks may be spread with a wedge to obtain slip fit on a large barrel. No more rosin, cracked wooden blocks or lost bushings.

- *Eldorado Gun Shop, Sunnyvale, California*

CERROSAFE BUSHINGS FOR BARREL VISE

I use Cerrosafe to make special bushings for my barrel vise. Use a form for external features of bushing that is in two pieces. Use the barrel you want to remove as internal form. By putting aluminum shims in on each side, bushing can be split if desired. Dam the ends with modeling clay. This Cerrosafe bushing, along with a little rosin, will grip any barrel it is cast to fit without damage to the barrel or to its finish.

- *R. L. Watkins, Seattle, Washington*

BARREL VISE SHIMS

Use copper pipe 1-1/2", 1-1/4" and 1". Get this from your plumber. Use two types of wall thickness. Type "L" High Pressure is heavy wall. Type "WDV" is light wall. The different wall thicknesses give you many different I.D. sizes to choose from...

- *Wayne M. Koch, Twin Falls, Idaho*

TIGHT BARREL REMOVAL

"For those mean military barrels that slip in the barrel wrench no matter what you do when you tighten up and apply the power... just get some of that 'double-backed' tape that has adhesive on both sides of the tape. Wrap a piece of this around the barrel, tighten up the wrench and give it the works. Never had one slip this way yet..."

- *Bill Webb, Kansas City, Missouri*

FOR U.S.M1 RIFLE RECEIVER CLAMP

I had the enclosed jig made up to solve the problem of supporting the U.S. M1 Rifle receiver while removing the barrel. Just clamp the pieces around the receiver in a vise, or drill & tap for clamp screws, and use a big monkey wrench on it. If you want to pass this on to the rest of the boys, go right ahead - sure saves me a lot of time and trouble.

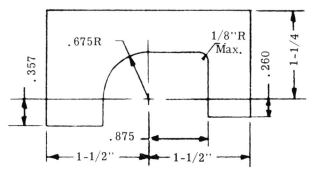

PIECE NUMBER I

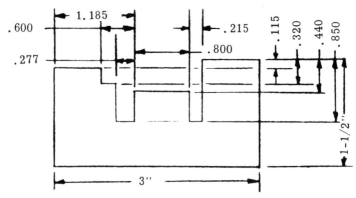

PIECE NUMBER 2

MATERIAL - Aluminum T-60. Notes: 1) Both pieces 3/4" thick - 2) All tolerances Plus/Minus .005 except fractions.
- *David M. Laston, Royal Oak, Michigan*

REMOVING SHOTGUN MAGAZINE TUBES

When I was there visiting you I meant to tell you a little trick I stumbled on. Being a plumber, I have a few pipe tools in my shop. The one I use most is a strap wrench, the kind you charge with resin. It really works on those hard-to-remove Model 11 magazine caps and stuck magazine tubes. I have even pulled barrels on 22 rifles with it and no marks! Anyone can buy them in a plumbing shop.
- *Eugene E. Judas, Charles City, Iowa*

FIXING NICKS IN FIBER GLASS BARRELS

Mix up some Twin-Weld and add a little bone black. Will look a little dull when first put into the nick, but will shine just like the rest of the barrel in a few minutes and after it has set up. Will probably take two applications for very deep nicks.
- *Richard A. Turgeon, Sioux Falls, South Dakota*

RENEWING .22 CHAMBERS

Those of us in the fix-'em-up-and-make-'em-work business are often called upon to put a new chamber in a .22 barrel that has had too many shorts shot thru it. Go to the local garage and pick up a worn-out push rod out of a 1957 Chevy. Take it to the shop and grind off the round ends and by polishing a little inside with a piece of 220 emery paper, you will find that a .22 round will fit it perfectly. Cut off a piece the proper length. Put the barrel in your trusty lathe and bore the chamber out to about .002" under the O.D. diameter of the new chamber. Heat the barrel and slip in the new chamber. When the barrel cools you will have a shrink fit and a finished job that will never come out.

- *Elmer's Gun Shop, Carrollton, Missouri*

INSTALLING BARREL LINERS

Instead of soldering in a barrel liner, drill out the bore to 3/8" and counterbore the breech. Silver solder a ring around the breech end of the liner to fit the counterbore. Grease up the liner with heavy gun grease and slip into place. Drill and tap a small set screw under the flat spot on the underside of the barrel to keep the liner from backing out when ejecting.

Beauty of this system is that no heat or glue is required, so if the liner wears out or gets rusty, a new one can be easily installed by merely loosening one set screw and tapping the old liner out.

- *Leonard Goff, Batavia, Iowa*

"SOLDERING" BARREL LINERS WITH ACRAGLAS

We have had a number of customers that use our barrel liners write us and say that they have been using your Acraglas to "glue" the 22 rifle liners in the barrels instead of solder - and are having excellent results. I tried it, also, and got on the average, better groups. The only thing that worries me is what to do to get the liner out, if for some reason it has to be removed...

(Answer from Bob B.: Heat the barrel up to around 212 or 240 degrees F. and it should come with a bit of persuasion.)

- *Harold Hoffman, Bucklin, Kansas*

BARREL LINER "GLUE"

I've used Acraglas for barrel liners with excellent results. One has been in a pistol for over three years - a .38 Special.

- *Benny Newman, Agency, Iowa*

BARREL LINING WITH LOC-TITE

Sure does simplify the job over soldering. Some of the tubes have been in place over a year and are doing just fine. Loc-Tite is easier than epoxies and seems to better fill any voids because of its capillary action. To use, clean the liner and reamed hole to remove all oil. Swab in some Loc-Tite and coat the liner. Set the barrel vertical and start in the liner. Deposit a film of Loc-Tite at the barrel-liner junction and keep it wet as you push in the liner. If the liner is pre-chambered, chamber an unfired (bullet pulled and ignition composition wet) case and close the action gently. Lightly push on the liner to insure correct headspace. Set rifle aside for a day or two. Cut off excess liner, file in the extractor slot, and you are ready to shoot.

 - *Baker's Gun Shop, Marshall, Texas*

GUNPOWDER

 The selfsame Fred M. tells about the gunsmith who did his work on his farm. He also had an expensive Hereford bull that had fallen into the doldrums and had become delinquent in his family duties. The owner was no little worried, so he contacted a vet. The veterinarian provided a supply of large tablets and prescribed that one be given every 12 hours for four days in the bull's food. After three days the bull quickly resumed the fulfillment of his obligations, even to the extent of crashing through a fence to visit some of a non-shooting neighbor's cows of a different breed. The gunsmith/farmer was telling some of his shooting pals about the treatment. "What did the vet give him?" asked one old trigger puller. "I don't know," was the reply, "but it tastes like black gun powder..."

 - *Fred Moulton*, The American Rifleman

VENTS

 And lots of people know just exactly how to do things too...Like the guy Wm. Pryor writes about: "So help me, the following is true. A gunnut (?) called me last week and wanted to know if he 'vented' his old twist barrel shotgun, could he safely shoot it? I asked him what he meant by 'venting' and he said, 'Oh, I figured to bore a 1/16" hole in the throat on the left and the right side of each barrel!!!' I told him if he did it, to read the fine print in his insurance policy real fast. He then asked me if I would test fire it for him after he had worked on it!!! I told him, 'Only by proxy.'"

 - *William M. Pryor, San Jose, California*

HYDRAULIC DENT RAISER

 Among the other things that are new is the damndest thing I've ever seen. It works like a ding-boned dream, does it fast, saves hours of time, simple to operate and service. It is a HYDRAULIC DENT RAISER, made in Europe by one of the old, old gun houses and for which we were lucky enough to get the U. S. distributorship. Available in 12, 16 and 20 gauge. We took a piece of Model 50 barrel, laid it on the vise, put a piece of drill rod on that and beat the rod into the barrel. I then stuck the hydraulic affair into the barrel, twisted the handle with finger tips and Presto! the dent came up like magic. Utterly Fantastic! A baby could do it! When you think of all the time it takes to iron out a dent with the regular dent raiser, and what you have to charge a customer - this thing is going to revolutionize that little job overnight. Two or three jobs will pay for the thing and from then on it

will be a blue-eyed pleasure to own. And after you get the dent up, you can twist the instrument and burnish the dented area on the inside!
  - Bob B.

HYDRAULIC DENT RAISER

Of all the various gunsmithing tools I have purchased from you, I believe the greatest time saver, temper saver and cussin' eliminator is your hydraulic dent raiser. When I think back thru the years of all the confounded troubles I've put up with raising dents! This tool is wonderful, especially on raising dents in the choked portion of a barrel.
  - Harry Y. Haight, New Preston, Connecticut

MUZZLE STUFFER DENTS

By way of additional copy for the hydraulic dent raiser, you should include the information that being completely operable from one end of the barrel, it is additionally useful for removing dents from muzzle loading shotguns too.
  - Dave Ballantine, West Hurley, New York

AND AS A BORE MICROMETER

What I did was slide your fine hydraulic dent remover up the bore from the chamber end. Tightening the allen wrench to just a good touch, I slid it out and miked the dent remover across the anvil-back. This gave the bore diameter. Next, I cranked the anvil back down, slid it into the muzzle end and again turned the wrench until I had just a snug feel, out again and miked the anvil-back. This gave the choke dimension.

If you cannot measure bore diameter at the breech, you can do it all from the muzzle as follows: On the back of the dent remover is an octagon nut that holds the handle assembly in place. The allen wrench is also octagon in shape. All you do is mark one of the points of the allen wrench. When you take the reading at the choke, line the marked point on the allen wrench up with one of the points of the octagon retaining nut. You have a reference.

Now insert the tool down into the bore. Slowly turn the wrench, counting each point of the octagon nut as you pass. Let's say a total of five points passed. Multiply this by two. You have a total of 10. This is 10 thousands. Each point of the octagon nut passed is .002" ...or, half way of a flat of the octagon nut is equal to .001". Add the total to the reading at the choke and you have the bore diameter to a "T". In fact, if one does not have a mike, take the reading at choke and let it be "X". Now slide it into the bore and count the points passed. This will give the points of choke. Say it is .007". This would be improved cylinder in a 12 gauge.

(Note from Bob B.: If you will check page 32 and 33 of the December, 1965 issue of *The American Rifleman* you will find a complete listing of bore and choke diameters to use in conjunction with the above information. As Ralph says in his letter: "This, old hoss, is ten times more accurate than any of the so-called "choke Gauges" I've seen advertised.)

- *Ralph Walker, Selma, Alabama*

SHOTGUN CHOKING

V. M. Starr, well known gunsmith explains shop method of choking shotguns for any pattern.

(Editor's Note - For many years V. M. Starr of Eden, S. D., has been known for his ability to choke shotguns. Because of the many requests for such information from our gunsmith customers, "Starr" was good enough to pass on the following:)

Friend Bob: -

So you want me to tell the trade how to choke a shot gun? Well, I will say this for a start: 'Taint easy to do or tell, but here goes -

My first experience in choking a shotgun was in the old blacksmith shop on the farm in north Ohio where I was born. I was about 16 at the time and Dad and I took a shot-out muzzle loading rifle and bored it out to about 24 gauge and worked a choke into it. The thing shot surprisingly well. Dad used a long bit with the choke taper on the end and used a wood shim under it to make it tight in the barrel. Turned it with a brace until he got the pattern he wanted. He kept adding paper shims under the wood shim as he cut and the tool loosened up. I have no idea how much choke was in the finished barrel, but when I got it pointed right it got the job done in good shape.

Some 24 years later, after I'd moved here to Eden, South Dakota, I had a 45-70 Springfield Model 1873 and needed a gun to shoot varmints around the place. Money being nearly non-existent I decided to work over the old Springfield.

A neighbor had a blacksmith shop of sorts and I went over there to see what we could do. I welded a drill on to a 3/8" rod that would just about take the rifling out. I then made a long bit like I had seen Dad use and reamed in some choke and smoothed up the barrel. Using the 45-70 cases with all the powder and shot I could cram into them, I had a gun that would do just about as much as the 2-1/2" .410 loads would do - using black powder, of course.

A few years after that I became dissatisfied with the open patterns I was getting with another gun and decided to try to choke it for longer range. I made up a choke reamer like the illustration in Fig. No. 1 and worked a recess choke into the barrels about 10 inches

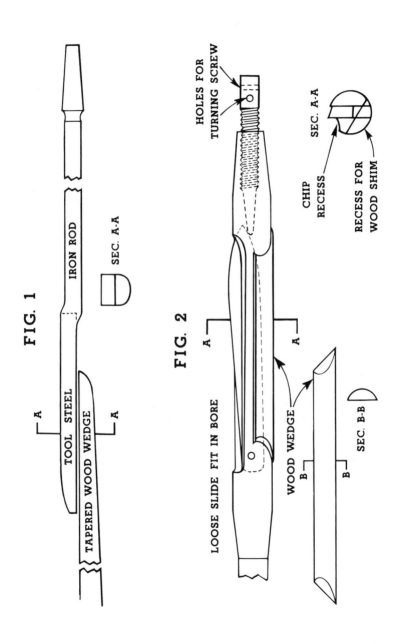

FIG. 1

A

TOOL STEEL   IRON ROD

TAPERED WOOD WEDGE

A

SEC. A-A

FIG. 2

HOLES FOR TURNING SCREW

CHIP RECESS

SEC. A-A

RECESS FOR WOOD SHIM

A

A

LOOSE SLIDE FIT IN BORE

WOOD WEDGE

B

B

SEC. B-B

long. With this I managed to improve the patterns quite a bit.

Shortly after War II, Miller Bedford of New London, Ohio, and his wife came out to visit and hunt in So. Dakota. I'd met him at Camp Perry in 1941. When Miller saw what I could do to the tough old rooster pheasants with my home-bored-and-choked muzzle loading charcoal burners, he insisted that I put an ad in "Muzzle Blasts" and tell the boys I could choke their muzzle loaders to shoot good patterns and I have never been caught up since!

With this crude device I managed along with a lot of sweat and worry to turn out a lot of guns that shot very good patterns. To operate the reamer I inserted it from the breech and put a stop on the rod to keep from cutting closer than about 1/2" from the muzzle. I then inserted the tapered wood wedge from the front end and tapped it gently until it tightened the reamer against the barrel. Then, worked the reamer back and forth as I turned the reamer to the length of the recess, cutting the recess to the depth required to give the desired patterns. A recess of .015" depth usually gave about 60% patterns and .020" to .021" was about right for full choke.

Make the recess about 10 inches long and only remove enough metal back of the recess to smooth up the rest of the bore. Remove as many pits as possible but never make the bore below the recess larger than the recess. If I got the balance of the bore as big as the recess and there were still pits left, I had no choice but to leave the pits. You are always limited to the amount of metal you can remove from between the breech and the choking recess as you can take out in making the recess.

In recent years I have been using the tool shown in Figure No. 2. The original of this tool was given me by Lyman Blank after he and his wife had visited and hunted with me.

When your readers go to make up one of these choking tools the following will be of help: The head of the boring tool should be about 7 inches long and of a size that will just pass thru the bore easily. The wood shim should make the tool a tight fit in the bore. As the bore enlarges paper shims should be placed beneath the wood shim to keep the tool as tight in the barrel as possible. If this is not done the tool is liable to hog and cut rough and remove too much metal.

By taking light cuts and keeping a rabbit's foot in your pocket and a horse shoe hanging over your head and a bunch of 4-leafed clover in your bench and a fervent prayer to Lady Luck and your tobacco in the middle of your mouth, work out a recess 8 or 10 inches long and about .015" deep for modified and about .021" for full choke. If Lady Luck sticks around and smiles on your efforts, you will get good patterns. But, don't be surprised if you don't as anything can happen - and often does! Then all you can do is test fire and keep trying until

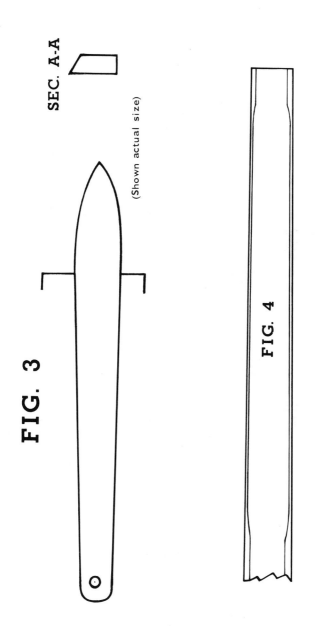

SEC. A-A

(Shown actual size)

FIG. 3

FIG. 4

you find out where you have gone wrong - and, Brother, that ain't easy.

I have bored many barrels that needed cleaning up the full length by putting them in a clamp on the compound rest on the lathe and running the lathe at about 75 rpm. The feed should be 40 turns per inch. Cut them full length to 1/2" of the muzzle. During this operation I insert a plug in the muzzle that is attached to a hose from an oil pump and keep a steady flow of cutting oil going thru the barrel to float the chips out as the cutting goes on and to keep the barrel cool.

In boring muzzle loading barrels the breech plug threads are often smaller than the bore. It is a must to have a reamer that can be expanded in the bore after it is inserted in the barrel. I do not think it advisable to do any damage whatever to the threads in the breech under any circumstances.

Another important thing to keep in mind is never to bore a barrel so that it is any thinner than .030" at any point. I have found that that is the absolute minimum thickness that can be expected to stand up and I would much rather have it more than that. I always make it a point to remove as little metal as possible and still get the desired patterns - even if it means leaving some of the deeper pits in the bore. If the barrels are cut thinner than .030" they are liable to resemble a blunder-buss rather than a modern gun after the first shot. On barrels that are too thin to take the choke wanted, I bore in as much recess as possible and quit - this usually improves the patterns somewhat over the original cylinder boring.

Very important to the cutting qualities to the tool shown in Fig. No. 2 is the shape of the cutter - especially the curve on the end that forms the choke cone. I am attaching a full size outline to be followed. This will give the proper shape to the cone. See Figure 3.

The above system works well on both modern shotguns and old-timers. I have choked a lot of modern barrels that have been blown off at the muzzle and have managed to restore the patterns in many of them to as good or better than original at much less cost than a new barrel or a choke device.

To anyone wanting to choke a barrel or two, I would advise using the tool shown in Figure No. 1. It is easy to make and while it will cut slow and needs a lot of elbow grease, I have been able to choke many barrels with it that shot very good patterns. To get the pattern desired is just a matter of cut and try until the desired results are obtained. If everything has been done right you will get just what you want...

A section thru a properly bored barrel should look like Fig 4.
- *V. M. Starr, Eden, South Dakota*

SHOTGUN BARREL STRAIGHTENING

Found another use for your hydraulic dent remover! I straighten a lot of bent shotgun barrels that customers bend over dogs, rabbits, mother-in-laws, etc. Have to be careful with the thin wall bending. I insert the tool up to the bend, leaving it in the down position, then tighten just a bit. The barrel is placed on the barrel straightener and sprung slightly back toward the correct straightness. Then tighten up on the tool. I keep repeating, working the tool in until it is just opposite the bend. From then on, I spring back, tighten on the Allen wrench, repeating until the barrel is straight.

This keeps the inside of the bore smoother than if the dent remover is not used and prevents buckling the inside of the barrel. The most important thing is to place the anvil facing the INSIDE of the bend and tighten about 1/2 a point of the octagon nut on the tool handle rear for each springing of the barrel back into place.

You should see my barrel straightener! Built it out of an old machine that riveted brake linings on. Foot operated. I can sit down (naturally) and holding a barrel, spring a barrel back into line pronto. Have straightened a couple that were bent 25 degrees out of line...!

- *Ralph Walker, Selma, Alabama*

STRAIGHTENING BENT SHOTGUN BARRELS

Turn out two close fitting plugs the inside diameter of the bent barrel. Then soft solder one in the breech end of the barrel, fill the barrel full of very fine silica sand (or powdered rosin) and solder the second plug in the muzzle end. Now, go ahead and straighten, and there is very little danger of ending up with a kinked barrel!

I've used this trick many times...even had a 11-48 barrel come in which was bent down to one side at least 30 degrees. (A fox hunter clubbed a cripple by hanging onto the barrel while the gun was still loaded yet!) When I got this one straightened by this method, the people who have seen it before and after, accuse me of replacing the barrel. Learned this little trick, by the way, way back when I still had pin feathers and short spurs while bending aircraft tubing. (Note from B.B. A fellow was in the other day telling me about how one of the companies bend pipe into coils...they fill them full of water, freeze it solid and bend away. Don't know if it would work on a shotgun barrel or not!)

- *Cliff Kroll, Lanark, Illinois*

STUCK/BROKEN CASE REMOVAL WITH SCREW EXTRACTOR

The best broken case extractors I've found are the #4 and #5 Cleveland type broken screw extractors. These are the full circle type

- not the four cornered type - and these two numbers will cover all calibers.

Braze them onto a 5/16" steel rod long enough to reach through a bolt action plus enough length to make a right-angle bend for a hand grip. One twist to the left removes any case I've ever had stuck in the rifle chamber.

To use on lever actions, use the broken screw extractor without the brazed on handle, turning it with a small wrench or pair of pliers.

- *W. F. Vickery, Boise, Idaho*

BROKEN CASE REMOVAL WITH CERROSAFE

When I have a case stuck in the chamber with the head broken off, I push a patch down from the muzzle on a button tipped rod. Stop the patch about 1/2" ahead of end of case and leave rod and patch in place.

Then melt Cerrosafe and pour the chamber full. Use a long necked funnel to get it into the chamber, if the gun has a long action. As soon as the metal hardens, use the rod and patch which is already in place to knock out the chamber cast and your ruptured case will come with it. I have never had this method fail in the great many times I have used it.

The beauty of it is, it is almost impossible to do any damage to a chamber when using this method. Even if one spills some metal into the action it is easy to get out and with any care not to overflow the chamber this shouldn't happen. I even carry a piece of Cerrosafe big enough to do this job in my hunting kit!

Note: - You should have at least two Cerrosafe Buttons for the job. Cerrosafe melts between 158-190 F. It should be melted in a clean iron ladle. Source of heat should be removed as soon as the alloy is completely melted, at which time it is ready to pour. The solidified casting should be removed from the chamber before or when it cools to room temperature. If allowed to remain in the mold over an hour it will grip the chamber walls and be difficult to remove. - Bob B.

- *Gordon Bess, Canon City, Colorado*

REMOVING A LIVE STUCK CARTRIDGE HYDRAULICALLY

When you have a live one stuck in the chamber and simply cannot get it out, first remove the stock. Then break the seal of the bullet in the cartridge by carefully and gently driving the bullet back into the cartridge about 1/8". Fill the barrel with motor oil and stand in the corner for 24 hours.

Make up a steel polished rod some 6" long to fit close into the rifle barrel. Drill and tap the end of it for a small screw and attach 2 leather disks to fit the barrel grooves tightly. With the receiver on a wood block, put the "piston" rod in the barrel muzzle on top of the oil and strike with a 4 lb. hammer. Three blows will usually bring out the primer or the entire cartridge.

The primer should be caught in a rag, for even after soaking in oil, some of them fire. Now, with the primer out, it is possible to drill and tap the cartridge for a threaded rod and to jack out the stuck cartridge.

- *Roy Lewis, Lakeview, Oregon*

STUCK CASE REMOVAL WITH DRY ICE

Next time you have a stuck case and you're out of Cerrosafe, just pack the chamber and case full of dry ice. It will shrink the brass and it just drops out. In really stubborn cases, tap the barrel lightly in the chamber area with a rubber mallet.

- *Charles Summers, Franklin, Illinois*

CLEANING OUT SHOTGUN CHAMBERS

Go down to the local Army-Navy store and get a couple of the 20MM BRASS bore brushes. Use one of them as is for double barrels, M-12's, etc. Take the other one and slip a piece of copper tubing over a 1/4" drill rod and drill through both of them, pinning together, leaving about 1-1/2" of tube extended past the rod core. Insert end of bore brush into the tubing collar and flow in solder around the sides to hold it there. With this brush you can now do all the Brownings, etc. with barrel extensions.

To use, chuck the brush in the electric hand drill and insert the brush into the chamber. Press the button in short bursts, releasing contact just as drill starts to get up to top rpm's - sort of "on-hesitate-off", "on-hesitate-off". This will prevent twisting and overheating. Digs all that nasty stuff out of the chamber, and definitely will not damage the chamber or bore. Specially effective against the rust and crud buildup from plastic shells that we get down here with our climate. And takes all the wax and residue out of the forcing cone too.

- *Ralph Walker, Selma, Alabama*

A MATTER OF SCENTS

Three moles were burrowing along under ground, Momma, Poppa and the Baby. They came to a wall, and Poppa Mole said, "I smell food." Momma Mole said, "I smell good food, too." And Baby Mole said, "I smell molasses."

- *Harold Rose, Grinnell, Iowa*

DRAW FILING

This may be old stuff to users of a bandsander, but when I have a rifle barrel that needs extra work like draw filing - I don't! I put on the grit belt I think best for the job and hold the barrel between two live centers from the lathe and press against the belt, moving it back and forth from muzzle to breech. Follow with finer grit until the barrel is finished...little buffing is required...if you are "spinning" the barrel it moves out at many rpms so HANG ON.

- *Eugene M. Spencer, 3rd Army Adv. Marksman Unit, Fort Benning, Georgia*

BRASS CROWNING BALLS

I see by one of your Newsletters that you are having a heck of a time getting brass muzzle crowning balls. Weep no more! I know you can't sell the durned things but for your own use the next time you want to do some muzzle crowning just stop in at the iron monger's (hardware store) and get a hand full of round headed brass wood screws ...large ones in assorted sizes. To use these, just put the threaded part in a small crank type hand drill, dip the round end in your grinding goop and forget about round brass balls. The slot in the screw helps by holding compound. I have been using these things for many years and wouldn't give you much for all the brass balls ever made. If the screw seems to be a little too hard, just soften up by heating with a torch. When one gets worn out just throw it in the scrap box - brass is worth ???? per lb.?

(Note by Bob B.: Wonder why in blazes I keep printing such as above and talking myself out of sales??? Humphhh!)

- *James L. Winton, Cherry Grove, Oregon*

BARREL BAND

...nice ones can be made from the rear sight base sleeve from the Model 98 WW II Mauser. A bit of grinding and shaping, drill a cross hole at the bottom and slit so it can be drawn up tightly.

- *John Weaver, Grand Rapids, Michigan*

BARREL MARKING

To make the caliber or gauge stampings on rifle, pistol or shotgun barrels more visible or pronounced, I use white crayola. First clean the stamping with alcohol or lighter fluid on a small gun patch; then wipe dry. Now, rub the crayola back and forth across the surface of the stampings and wipe off excess. Result, a crisp white print which is easily seen. I do this upon completing all re-barrel and re-blue jobs. Try on the optic bell of rifle scopes and windage and elevation turret... Now, this doesn't mean you gotta steal the crayola from your kids! (Note from BB: Of course, we'd rather see you buy that purty gold kit or lacquer stik.)

- *Rudy's Custom Gun Shop, Cedar Rapids, Iowa*

BARREL LUBRICANT

Do-Drill makes a real good lubricant for barrel threads on re-barrel jobs. It withstands heat, allows the action to be pulled up as tight as possible, and stays there after the bluing is done. Also, it smells just like the tarry stuff on old Colt, Rem., etc., that has been there for years. Why use a lubricant? Some other damphool may want to remove the barrel 15-20 years hence and we have all seen rusted ones.

- *Dick's Gun Shop, Mandan, North Dakota*

RIB ENDS

Save the ribs from the ends of shotguns you cut off to install comps. The ribs make very nice looking ribs on pistols. I find that the Simmons and the late Win. ribs that slip onto dovetails work the best. You can turn new posts in your lathe to suit height needed...

- *Garry R. Newell, Lewiston, Idaho*

BARREL TURNING

Barrel turning is a rather tricky machine operation. It is seldom that any ordinary machine shop technique will work. It requires a special ground tool and a somewhat different technique than is applied to ordinary machine jobs. A round nosed tool is definitely not in order. One of the best ways to grind a tool is shown in the accompanying sketch. It will be noted that the tool is ground with an extremely sharp point, with plenty of rake. It is necessary to rotate the work from 200 to 250 RPM and use a rather fast feed. The main objective is to reduce the barrel blank in size, not paying a great deal of attention to the smoothness. A follower rest cannot be used because barrels are always tapered and the use of a steady rest is not recommended, and it is not necessary because barrels up to 32 inches can be successfully turned without it.

Any good bench lathe or floor type engine lathe is suitable for barrel turning. Young gunsmiths who are planning to set up their own shops do not need to buy a heavy lathe. A light machine, such as the nine inch South Bend workshop lathe, will turn barrels almost as fast and just as good as a $10,000 Monarch. One of the main considerations is sufficient distance between centers. The small South Bend with all the necessary attachments can only be considered in the longest length, which is 54 inches, giving about 34 inches between centers. These little machines have a direct speed of around 220 RPM which is just about right for barrel turning. A little practice will determine the proper feed to use, but as mentioned above, the general rule is a slow rotation plus a rather fast speed. From .0043 to .0056 is about right.

Before starting to turn the barrel it should be cut to 1/2 inch of the desired length, then make sure that both ends are square. Set the

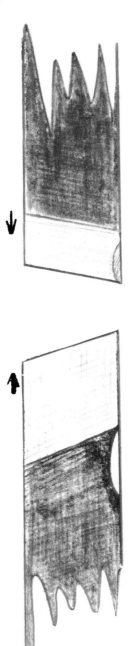

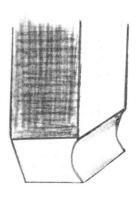

P. O. Ackley's Lathe Cutting Tool, described in the accompanying article, is specifically designed for taking barrels down to desired size quickly.

lathe up between centers using a lathe dog and driving plate instead of the chuck. Always make it a rule to do everything possible between centers, which will insure concentricity with the bore. This rule applies to all kinds of lathe work, as well as barrel turning. After the job has been set up, including setting over the tailstock for the proper amount of taper, the barrel can be cut down to sporter size by making a series of cuts - usually it takes five or six cuts to get it down to a light sporter size. By setting the tailstock over, the proper taper will be maintained throughout the length of the barrel up to a point where the contour of the breech end begins. At this point it is necessary for the operator to contour this portion by hand, and with a little practice he will get very proficient in getting the contour he desires.

One of the main obstacles in barrel turning is warpage or distortion. Many authorities will credit this to the heat generated by the turning process. However, a barrel blank which contains stresses will warp, regardless of how cool it may be kept, so it is imperative that the gunsmith obtain blanks which are made of a material that is absolutely stress-free. Barrel blanks as obtained from various makers, especially those from some of the larger factories, are extremely bad about warping while turning. After a few cuts have been taken over the barrel and distortion shows up, it is necessary to straighten the barrel. (Straightening will not be gone into here because it is an art in itself.) If the gunsmith cannot be assured of barrel blanks which are absolutely stress-free he will be much better off to purchase the blanks pre-turned to approximate dimensions. He should insist that the barrels be turned to within a few thousandths of the size that he wishes the barrel to finish, which will leave only a very slight finish cut for him to make after the barrel has been fitted.

If it becomes necessary to straighten a blank, which was warped while turning in order to save it, there are several books available which describe the straightening process, such as the *Modern Gunsmith* by Howe. The difficulty comes, however, from the fact that the barrel has been rifled and the shadows are broken up by the lands, making it necessary to have a great deal of experience before rifled barrels can be successfully straightened, which can be gained only by long practice.

- *P. O. Ackley, Salt Lake City, Utah*

ELEPHANT TALK

Son Frank called the other night and among other things wanted to know if I knew the difference between a barroom and an elephant's petard (original Latin meaning). One is a barroom and the other is bar-ROOOOOM. Put a lot of emphasis on the last syllable and it is sorta funny even saying it to yourself.

- *Bob B.*

BUEHLER LATHE SHOP TIP

A little gadget that is a real necessity for accurately chambering, threading or crowning barrels is the little ring on the rear end of the lathe spindle. Made to carry four screws for centering anything run thru the spindle. Easy to construct. Bore it 1/16" or so larger than spindle hole and attach it to lathe spindle adjustment nut or any other convenient way - great strength is not required as there is no strain. 10x32 screws work fine. A mount for a dial indicator is an excellent addition to speed up adjusting.

For a Super accurate barrel job, indicate to a plug that has been turned to a push-fit in the gun's bore. Many times the outside dimensions of a rifle barrel and inside dimensions are not concentric, with the result that if you align to the outside of the barrel the finished job is not true. The little gimmick described and shown above will correct this and improve the job.

- *Maynard Buehler, Orenda, California*

CENTERING THE BORE ON A LATHE

Anyone ever mention how easy it is to line up a barrel on a lathe for chambering or muzzle crowning by using the spuds from your collimator? Just insert the spud in back side to (with the uncut end first) until the spring is about 1/2" away from the muzzle. Be sure not to put the spring wire into the barrel as will cant the spud; and don't force it or you'll ruin your spud. And be sure the burrs are all removed from the muzzle (if you're crowning the muzzle). I use a case deburring tool for the purpose, and leave it right at the lathe.

My spuds have proven accurate to .001", which I consider quite ample for this job.

- *Doug Hough, Pittsburgh, Pennsylvania*

TO DRILL OUT A BORE

For those who don't know - and there are a lot of good tool makers and metal workers who don't - all you do is take a drill the size of the liner you want to install and grind a pilot an inch or so long, the exact size of the original bore. Or if no grinding equipment is available, anneal an inch or so of the drill and turn it to size on the lathe.

To do the drilling, I chuck the barrel in the lathe so it would turn and the drill was stationary. This gives the bore a chance to correct any error that might occur in drilling.

   - *Leonard Goff, Batavia, Iowa*

THE TECHNIQUE OF CHAMBERING

   This is a short article on fitting and chambering a rifle barrel. This is not for the finished gunsmith because each man develops his own methods through trial and error. This is just an outline to help a novice or to give a newer gunsmith some ideas. Everyone may not agree with the methods used, but as long as a good job is turned out any method is correct.

   There are six steps as follows:
1. Getting headspace figures from the action.
2. Preparing the barrel for turning, threading, chambering and polishing.
3. Reaming.
4. Headspacing.
5. Chambering and polishing the chamber.
6. Test firing.

   1. To check for barrel fit and headspace prior to chambering a barrel, strip the bolt and make sure the action lug recesses and bolt face are clean and free from dirt and oil. Look at the locking surfaces in the action and check for lug contact and set back. Check the action ring for burrs - this is the portion of the action that butts against the shoulder of the barrel. If any burrs are found on action ring, drag a stone across the ring. Hold the stone flat so it will be even. If the action ring is burred up too badly to get a reading, a cut must be taken on the lathe to smooth the ring. To take a cut from the face of the action ring you must make a mandrel to fit the action so it can be put between

centers of the lathe. Facing Action Ring between centers will keep the face of the action ring concentric with the bore.

The figures below were taken from an action off the shelf - do not go by these figures. Each action and bolt will vary. You must take the headspace figures from the action YOU will use.

With the micrometer held flush across the ring of the action, measure down to the inside shoulder (mauser type action). This comes out about .630"; next, mike from the same place on the action to the face of the bolt. This will be about .740". Substract .630" from .740"; this leaves .110"; substract .002" for compression of the metal, and .108" is the amount the headspace gauge protrudes from the breech end of the chamber.

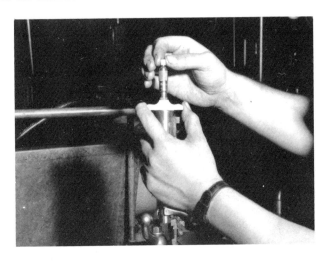

Make sure your barrel has been fitted correctly to the action you are using. In this case the length of the threaded portion of the barrel would be .630".

On a Model 70 type, mike from the action ring down to the bolt face; this should be about .700". Your barrel should be threaded and cut off to about .760" from the breech end to the shoulder. Subtract .700" from .760"; this leaves .060"; add .002" for compression and you have .062". This should be the distance from the breech end of the barrel to the headspace gauge.

On a U. S. Model 98 30-40 Krag, mike from the action ring to the inside shoulder. This comes out at .753. Then mike from the action ring to the face of the bolt. This comes out .817. Subtract the .753 from .817 and you have a figure of .064. Subtract .002 from this figure for metal compression when the barrel and action are screwed together. This would give you .062 as a minimum breech space. With the barrel properly fitted to this action the headspace gauge should protrude from the breech end of the barrel a minimum of .062 to a maximum of .067.

It does not matter if you are chambering for a Rimless, Rimmed or Belted case. Headspace is the distance from Bolt face to the base of the cartridge. The examples above should cover the different types of actions.

2. Make sure the lathe is true, tail stock centered; the chuck should be clean and free of burrs. Put the barrel in the lathe between centers with the muzzle end to the tail stock. Lathe dog clamped on threaded end. Turn a short portion of the muzzle end of the barrel true to the bore. Most barrels are an inch or two too long so there will be no loss. If your barrel has been turned between centers, leave as it is, it should be fairly true.

The threads on the barrel should be turned between centers as this leaves both ends true to the bore.

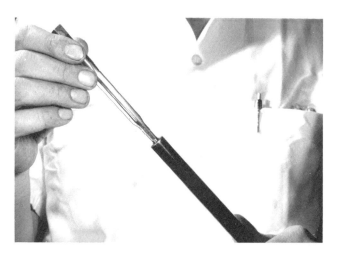

Get your chamber reamer out and check the pilot of the reamer in the bore, make sure it does not bind. If using a roughing reamer, check the distance on a case or headspace gauge from the edge of the shoulder angle to 3/16" from the base of the case or gauge. Take this distance and mark your reamer or put a piece of tape around the flutes. This is the distance the reamer will go into the barrel. There will be about 1/16 of an inch left to cut with the finish reamer. If no roughing reamer is used do the same procedure with the finish reamer. It is best

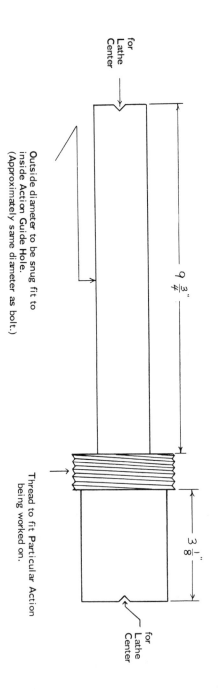

ACTION MANDREL

for Lathe Center

Outside diameter to be snug fit to inside Action Guide Hole. (Approximately same diameter as bolt.)

$9\frac{3}{4}''$

Thread to fit Particular Action being worked on.

$3\frac{1}{8}''$

for Lathe Center

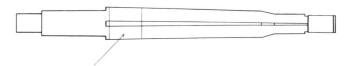

Cellophane tape wrapped around reamer for "Stop Mark"

to have a roughing reamer; this will take a big load off the finish reamer. You will then have smoother chambers and the finish reamer will stay sharp longer. If you are just cutting a few chambers then it won't be necessary to have a rougher reamer.

Put the 3 jaw chuck back on the lathe and chuck the muzzle end of the barrel, line up the breech end with the center and put the steady rest on the threaded portion of the barrel. Be careful when you snug the rests against the threads. With the barrel turning slowly, tighten the rests against the threads finger tight, then lock. Remove the center from the bore. The barrel should be running quite true. Take the center out of the tail stock and install a 3 jaw Jacobs chuck or a rubber flex tapping chuck. Put a T handle on your chambering reamer leaving about 1" of reamer shank protruding. Slip a large flat washer over the shank of the reamer so it rests against the T handle. This will give you a flat surface for the Jacobs tail stock chuck to push against.

3. Put the reamer into the Jacobs chuck and tighten until you have about .010" play between the shank of the reamer and the chuck jaws. About one inch of shank is all you need in the Jacobs chuck. This depends on how long the shank of the reamer is; more or less shank will not matter as long as you have a bearing surface. This set-up gives you a floating reamer and it will follow the bore. Set the lathe speed

at 30 to 40 RPM. Start the reamer into the bore, feeding in .020" to .040" before clearing. Use a pressure oil can with good grade of cutting oil to squirt oil into the chamber and on the reamer before you start the cut. Any good grade of cutting or threading oil will do.

The reamer determines how much feed you can take, so watch the flutes of the reamer and do not overload. You can feel the cutting from the T handle. You will get a certain amount of pull from the handle as the reamer is cutting. This is normal. Also you can feel any reamer chatter that might develop. Make sure your T handle is short enough to turn with the reamer without hitting the lathe bed. If the reamer ever hangs up, let the wrench go, it will rotate with the barrel. This way there is small chance for a broken reamer or a galled chamber.

When you remove the reamer from the barrel, blow the reamer off with compressed air. Blow chamber free of chips and oil. Always use air if possible on reamers and chamber. If no air is available use solvent to clean the reamer and a bristle brush to clean the chamber. If the chips are left in the chamber you may pick one up on a reamer flute, and cut a ring in the chamber. Oil chamber and reamer freely and take another cut.

4. When roughing reamer is into the barrel to the mark or tape on reamer, change to finish reamer and recut until you get chips showing on the shoulder of the reamer. Then check with headspace gauge. Using a depth micrometer, get the distance the gauge must go into the chamber to make the gun headspace correctly. If the lathe tailstock has a dial gauge you can use this to get close to the finish. If you have no dial gauge you must ream small amounts from the chamber and check with your headspace gauges often. When you get within a few

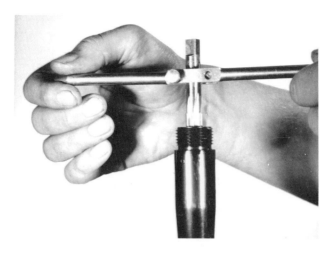

thousandths of the finished chamber, take the barrel out of the lathe and ream the last few thousandths by hand. You must figure on going .002" over the minimum chamber. When the barrel is screwed into the action the shoulders of the barrel moving against the shoulder of the action will compress the metal about .002" or .003". When the correct headspacing figure is arrived at, put the barrel and action together. Barrel in a barrel vise and an action wrench on the action. Tighten and loosen the action a few times to make sure you are seating the barrel all the way in. Then try the headspace gauges. A stripped bolt should just close on a minimum gauge. Bolt should not close on a maximum gauge. If bolt does not close, never force it - it will ruin the chamber.

If the bolt handle does not drop down to a closed position under its own weight with the minimum gauge in the chamber, then the chamber will have to be reamed deeper. If the bolt handle lacks about 1/2 inch from closing, you have .002" to .003" to ream from the chamber.

Remove the action from the barrel and take the barrel out of the vise. If the barrel is left in the vise, and you try to ream the barrel in the vise, you will end up with an egg-shaped chamber because of the vise jaw pressure over the chamber.

5. Ream out by hand the proper amount and assemble again. If the gages check out and the headspace is okay, remove action from barrel and barrel from vise. Put the barrel back in the lathe in the same set-up you used for chambering. Get a small 3 cornered file and grind the file marks off the first inch of the point - use this for a scraper. Turn the lathe on and chamfer the base end of the chamber about

SCRAPER

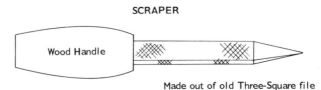

Wood Handle

Made out of old Three-Square file

1/16", which should be enough. This will help the feeding and the edge of the chamber will not scrape brass from the cases as they enter chamber.

Next, loosen the rests on the barrel about 1/4 to 1/2 turns each. Lock rests again. Change the lathe speed to 5 or 7 hundred RPM. Get a piece of rod 3/16" in diameter and 8-1/4" long, cut a 3/4" saw cut in one end and bend the other end at 45 to make a handle. Wrap some 320 grit abrasive cloth around the rod and put a bit of cutting oil on it.

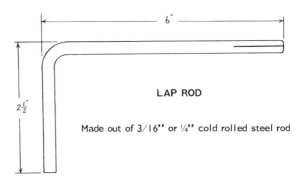

6"

LAP ROD

2½"

Made out of 3/16" or ¼" cold rolled steel rod

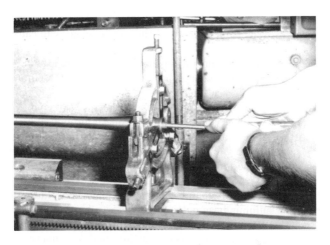

Turn on the lathe and polish the chamber. Run the cloth into the chamber evenly in and out a few times. This will take a very small amount of metal out and give a nice smooth job. Repolish with some crocus cloth for a mirror finish. A smooth chamber gives much better extraction. Do not use any cloth coarser than 320. Clean the barrel and tighten back into the action.

6. Test fire the rifle with a factory round or a good hand load. Do not try to make up proof loads because you have no way of checking pressures. Check the fired case for rings around the case caused by tears in the chambers. Check for a protruding primer, caused by excess head space. Check the shoulder and base dimensions of the fired case - a chart on case size will be found in any hand loaders manual.

If all of these things check out okay then you have a good chamber. From here on it is a matter of experience and your own ideas of improvement.

- Fred Huntington & Don Tucker of R.C.B.S.

CARE & USE OF CHAMBERING REAMERS

(Note from Bob B. - Anyone associated with working on guns, as is our trade, usually appreciates additional information on how to use their tools. This is especially true if that information comes from an authority. It is our feeling Max Clymer, the man who makes the reamers, has as complete a technical knowledge as will be found. Whether you be an old time gunsmith or a novice - the following will be of value to you during the years to come...)

Care in handling the Chambering Reamer is one thing we can not stress too often. A nick on one of the cutting edges will cause more trouble than anything else.

When putting the reamer away after a job, be sure it is in its shipping container or a small wooden box, so it cannot nick itself on another reamer.

The only time we suggest you stone a reamer is to remove a small burr or nick.* A reamer which has been properly ground and checked, should last for 20 or more chambers. If the reamer gets dull from use, we suggest you send it back to the manufacturer to be reground and sharpened. Clymer offers this service to their customers at a reasonable price.

If you are going to chamber either by hand or by lathe get the best grade of sulphur base cutting oil you can buy.** As you know, oil by itself, is just to wash out chips. The more sulphur in the oil the better, as this makes for easier cutting and a smoother finish.

If you are just going to cut one or two chambers with a reamer, you can get by with just a Finishing Reamer; but a gunsmith who will cut many chambers should use a Rougher so as to save wear on the finisher.

Care in the use of the reamer when cutting the chamber is important. To prevent loading the flutes with chips you should clear the reamer about every 1/32 of an inch in depth. Be sure to brush the reamer with a small brush to clear the chips.

In our own shop when we check a reamer we put the barrel in the head stock of the lathe, making sure the muzzle and breech end run true. If the bore runs out you stand the chance of breaking the reamer and also cutting an oversize chamber.

We insert the reamer in the drill chuck of the lathe. When you start your cut, be sure the lathe is turning at a low speed, then feed the reamer slowly so it will not grab as it starts its cut as it can cause the reamer to chatter. If this happens remove the reamer and take a drill a little larger than the neck of the reamer and drill out the chatter marks - replace the reamer and start chambering the barrel.

When chambering by hand make sure that the reamer is true with the bore. Caution should be used as even though the reamer is heat treated and drawn you can snap off the pilot if you cock the reamer to one side. Press down on the reamer when first starting and turn slowly, so that the reamer will not jump and cause chatter. Most of the chatter in chambering a gun is caused by improper use of the reamer.

Very little polishing is required to finish out a chamber if care is taken with the reamer during the last few thousandths cut. It is a good idea to clean out all the chips in the chamber as you make the last few cuts, to prevent scoring the chamber wall with chips.

Check the reamer often to make sure that it has not loaded up with steel along all edges. We scrape off any small "bugs" with a piece of carbide or smooth piece of steel, making sure not to burr over the cutting edge.

      * Special India stone No. F444 is ideal.

      ** Do-Drill is designed for this operation.

   - Max Clymer, Oak Park, Michigan

HEADSPACE AND WHAT IT MEANS TO YOU

("P.O." or "Parker" as he is called by all who know him, is a columnist, writer, author, manufacturer and a gunsmith in the purest meaning of the word.

Of no other man have I heard it said so many times among leaders in the gun game and practicing gunsmiths: "Does anyone know as much about the subject as Parker Ackley? If you asked me, I'd say 'No'"...Bob B.)

Headspace in rifles has always been of the utmost importance but doubly so since so many shooters have turned to handloading their own ammunition. Shooters who handload their own cartridges must have a thorough understanding of headspace for their own safety.

Headspace is hard to define. Many definitions can be found in many books on arms and ammunition as well as in gunsmithing books and manuals, but none seem to accurately describe it. Some describe it as the DISTANCE or SPACE between the fully locked bolt and the head of a fully chambered cartridge. Some describe it as the distance from the face of the fully locked bolt to a point within the barrel or chamber which stops the cartridge and holds it firmly, preventing it from going further into the chamber. Whatever the definitions say, the best way of clearing up the mysteries of headspace is to describe the methods of measuring it.

Four methods are used to measure headspace in rifles and these four methods are dictated by the design of cartridges. Among modern cartridges we find four general types or classes: rimmed, rimless, belted and the rimless, taperless pistol cartridge.

1. Rimmed cartridges are designed with a rim or flange which is considerably larger in diameter than the major diameter of the body of the cartridge. This is the simplest and most reliable method and the rimmed cartridge will normally withstand higher pressures than other types since the rim actually forms a wider more rigid support around the primer pocket. For example, the .30-40 Krag case is a typical rimmed example of the rimmed design. The wide rim is greater in diameter than the body of the case thus forming a rigid solid disc of metal around the primer pocket. This design is plainly shown in the drawing below for the .30-40 cartridge. This is the reason why the .30-40 is the first choice of many experimenters who work with extremely high pressures. In this rimmed class, headspace is measured or determined by the thickness of the rim.

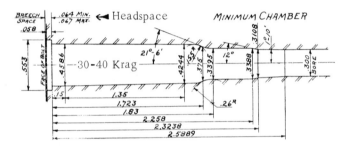

Sometimes the barrel is counterbored so that the rim is completely inclosed within the barrel when the breech block or bolt is closed against the end of the barrel. Such a system is employed in actions such as the Winchester Hi-side single shot. Sometimes the bolt is counterbored or recessed to accept the rim of the cartridge while the rim comes to rest against the flat end of the barrel, an example being the Krag. The following table shows the minimum head space for a few popular rimmed cartridges. Maximum headspace is not shown, but usually is about .003 to .004 over minimum. It will also be noted by studying the table that the headspace for the .219 Zip., .30-30 and .32 Spl. is the same, so that the same gauge can be used for all three:

Caliber	Minimum Head Space		
.22 Hor.	.065	.30-30	.063
.218 Bee.	.065	.30-40	.064
.219 Zip.	.063	.32 Win. Spl.	.063
.25-20	.061	.357 Mag.	.052
.25-35	.063	.44 Mag.	.060

2. Rimless cartridges are designed without a rim or we might say that the diameter of the rim is the same as the body of the case. In this design, some other provision must be made to stop the cartridge at the proper place because of the absence of the rim or flange. The only logical solution is to use the shoulder of the cartridge to serve this function, therefore the headspace measurement for rimless cartridges becomes the distance from the face of the fully locked bolt to some point about midway between the upper and lower corners of the shoulder. This point is designated as the DATUM line and altho the datum line is often shown on data sheets for other types of cartridges, it is only used in connection with rimless cartridges. The drawing for the .30-06 shown below shows the location of the datum line which, for the .30-06 is the point on the shoulder which measures .375. The datum line varies with the size of the cartridge and the following table gives the datum line measurement for a few common and popular cartridges. In connection with rimless cartridge headspace measurement, we must always point out the exception to the rule which is the .30-06.

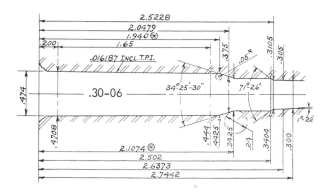

For some reason the old method is retained for the .30-06 and the measurement is made from the bolt face to the top corner of the shoulder and since the headspace measurement for the 06 and .270 Winchester is the same, the old method also extends to the .270. The table shows the headspace measurement for the 06 and .270 as 2.0479 instead of the 1.940 dimensions to the top of the shoulder. All other rimless cartridges are measured to the datum line. The table also shows minimum headspace measurement as well as the datum line and this minimum measurement is the length of the "go" gauge. Rimless headspace gauges usually come in sets of two and three. For example, the "go" gauge for the .30-06 is 1.940 (2.0479) and the "nogo" gauge is 1.946 (2.0539). The field gauge, which is only useful in determining just how bad the headspace condition is, would be 1.950 (2.0579). Gunsmiths fitting barrels can get by with only the "go" gauge by making all chambers so the bolt can be closed on this gauge with a light "feel". This method also insures uniform headspace in all of the rifles made by this method. Of course, the headspace can be anything between the "go" and "nogo" measurements and still be permissible.

The following table shows the minimum headspace measurements and the datum line measurements and it will be noted that one gauge can sometimes be used for more than one cartridge; for example, the same gauge is used for .270 and .30-06 and one gauge also works for the .308.

Caliber	Datum	Minimum Head Space
.222 Rem.	.330	1.2936
.222 Rem. Mag.	.330	1.4925
.22-250	.347	1.5742
.220 Swift	.335	1.806
240 Cobra	.335	1.840
243 R.C.	.347	1.800
.243 Win.	.400	1.6300
.244 Rem.	.375	1.7767
.250 Sav.	.347	1.5792
.257 Robts.	.375	1.7937
.270 Win.	.375	2.0479
7 mm.	.375	1.7937
.280 Rem.	.375	2.100
.30-06	.375	2.0479
.300 Sav.	.3968	1.5967
.308 Win.	.400	1.630
8 mm.	.375	1.896
.358 Win.	.420	1.6027

3. The third method is the belt. Belted cartridges are often thought of as being synonymous with MAGNUM cartridges and altho this is not necessarily true, it is usually the case. Belted cartridges are designed with a belt which replaces the rim in the rimmed class. The belt is wider than the rim, usually measuring .220 from the bolt face to the forward edge of the belt instead of around .063 to .067 for rims. The belt is not nearly so high or pronounced as the rim but is sufficiently high to act as a definite stop as the cartridge is chambered but not high enough to interfere with feeding of the cartridges from the magazine as happens with true rimmed design.

4. The fourth method deals largely with rimless pistol cartridges altho there are a few rifle cartridges which fall into this category. Since this class of cartridges has no rim, no shoulder or anything else which

can be used to stop the cartridge at the right place, the mouth of the case becomes the only remaining possibility so with cartridges like the .45 ACP which has no rim, no shoulder and no body taper, the chamber is cut to the proper depth so that the mouth of the case contacts the end of the chamber solidly.

Nothing is mentioned above for measuring headspace about the so called "IMPROVED" series of cartridges. A multitude of so called Improved cartridges has been designed by gunsmiths all over the world and many of them are so designed as to allow the use of factory ammunition. Headspace for rimmed Improved cartridges, of course, is the same as for the standard versions but as a general rule for Improved rimless cartridges the headspace is .004 thousandths less than the standard minimum. Gauges are available from the various gauge makers suitable for all of these Improved cartridges, for example, the 1.940 minus .004 is used for the Improved .30-06. The gauge for the Improved .257 would be 1.794 minus .004. This method is necessary because of variation in factory ammunition to ensure a crush fit at the conjunction of the shoulder and neck. This allows the fire forming of factory ammunition without loss of brass and with no danger to the shooter.

Handloaders should make themselves thoroughly familiar with the problems of headspace, especially for the type of cartridge they are loading. There is a particular problem with the rimless class of cartridges because the headspace can so easily be altered by improperly adjusting the sizing die in the tool. This adjustment is also important with the seating die. Dies should be set so that the shoulder of the case is just barely touched when the case is forced all the way into the die. It NEVER should be taken for granted that this adjustment will be correct if the die is simply screwed down against the shell holder. More often than not this method results in incorrect headspace.

Sometimes dies are so long that they will not size the cases all the way down to the shoulder. This does not result in a dangerous condition but does often result in the sized cases not allowing the bolt to be closed especially if the cases have been fired in some other gun. When dies are found to be too long, they can be cut off a few thousandths at the bottom so as to allow the die to be set close enough to accomplish true full length sizing. Dies which need shortening should be taken to a qualified gunsmith or sent back to the maker, since this is a job not to be done haphazardly.

- *P. O. Ackley, Salt Lake City, Utah*

ON THE WAY TO THE HOSPITAL
The other day two gunnuts dropped in on Army Sgt. Ken Mac-Naughten of Hapeville. They mentioned casually they were going to

a hospital and Sgt. MacNaughten assumed they were planning a visit to some sick friend. About an hour later while the sergeant was showing them his store of weapons, a young woman waiting in their car blew the horn. They ignored her and kept on looking. Then a few minutes later the horn blew with a loud note of urgency. "Why don't you invite her in?" asked the sergeant. "No, I guess not," said one of his guests. "She's going to have a baby and wants to get to the hospital..."

- *By Hugh Park in the* Atlanta Journal, *but sent to us by Sylvia Redfield, Opheim, Montana*

BREECHING A MUZZLE LOADER BARREL

First, get the barrel at least 4" longer than the finished barrel is to be. Then, cut off the extra 4 inches, and square up the cut end of the barrel in the lathe. This has got to be true, so use 4-jaw chuck and indicator to line up. When square, drill 1/2" deep hole centered in bore and tap with appropriate thread. Take the bolt to fit the threads you just cut, cut off the head of it to the threads. Saw a hacksaw slot in the end and screw it into the bore as tight as you can.

Now, take the 4" piece you cut off, chuck into lathe, indicate, square off and then drill and tap with same thread used before. Screw the extension on the barrel and line up tight with flats even. Now, drill and tap for 8-32 or 10-32 set screw in tang end. Put in, screw as tightly as possible, saw off flush, file smooth and peen with center punch.

On the barrel, drill and tap for 1/4-20 recessed allen head screw to contact the "plug" bolt you installed in the bore. When it's in and tight, you can saw out the tang in the conventional shape. This will give you a tight breech and will stay in forever unless you want to take it off - which you can do.

- *Don Grimble, Eagle Harbor, New York*

BARREL THREAD AND SHANK DIAMETERS

Good friend and Master Gunsmith Ben Newman was in the other day and wanted to know if we had a ready reference of most of the popular barrel shank and thread sizes. Said he had a beauty that he had clipped out of some past *American Rifleman* that he kept in a special file, and when anything new came in that was not on the *Rifleman* sheets, he drew it up and put it in the folder too.

If you're ever in need of such information, the particular *Rifleman* to check are: February 1962, pages 28-30; July 1964, pages 40-41; and October 1965, pages 68-69.

- *Ben Newman, Agency, Iowa*

CHAPTER 4

SCOPES & SIGHTING

LATHE JIG FOR SIGHT MOUNTING

For mounting sights on Springfield and Mauser receivers, I no longer fool around with the old drill press routine. I just use my lathe and milling attachment on the lathe carriage. If you mount the action in the vise and make sure it is perpendicular to the head stock, it's almost impossible to get a sight mounted out of line. And if you're going to be doing a lot of these jobs, it pays to face off the bottom of the milling vise jaw so that it's parallel with the drill bit. Then when the base of the receiver is mounted on this surface, you know durned well that the action is set up correctly.

To drill the holes, first temporarily mount the rear sight on the action in its proper position. A drill that will just fit the hole in the sight mount is chucked up and the action is moved vertically and horizontally until the drill lines up perfectly. At this point a #31 drill is used and the carriage feeds the action into the drill bit. The beauty of this is that there are no squares, levels, luck or even swearing involved - well, hardly any swearing!

I haven't had one job fail with this set-up. The worst that can happen is that a minor correction on the inside of the sight mount must be made to true the sight exactly. And this correction is usually much less than the amount I've seen sights off that were put on by other jig arrangements.

- *Ken Stannard, Weehaken, New Jersey*

QUICK SIGHT JIG

Here's a kink I haven't seen written up anywhere that works fine for mounting scope blocks and receiver sights when one has no jig. Clamp them on with Twin-Weld. When set, remove clamps, check to be sure the position is correct and then use the mount itself as a drill jig. If desired to remove for one reason or another, heat lightly with a propane torch and the Twin-Weld will let go and will pull off easily while still warm. (Note by Bob B.: If surplus shows around the edges of the bases, you can wipe off and leave a smooth finish to the Twin-Weld by using vinegar on a cloth.)

- *W. E. Beckstrom, Eureka, Montana*

SCOPE BASE MOUNTING DOPE

Nothing looks worse than a mount base canted on a receiver! A good job can be assured by squaring the base with the bottom of the receiver. By using two machinist's squares as shown in Fig. 1 and carefully aligning the blades as shown at the arrow, that base is square! Use of two parallel clamps gives you the "tipping" adjustment to do this precisely. BE SURE THAT THE RECOIL SHOULDER IS BUTTED SOLIDLY to the clamp first before proceeding.

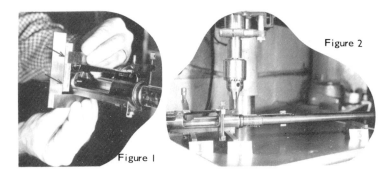

Figure 2

Figure 1

After clamping, rest the receiver on two parallel pieces of steel - or "V" blocks turned at right angles to the receiver - on the drill press table (Nos. 1 and 2) in Fig. 2. An adjustable parallel at No. 3, Fig. 2, is a big help. A fairly large production type table on the drill press table is a fine thing. It will pay for itself in scope mounting alone and beats rigging up some sort of outboard stand or clamping a 2 x 6 board to a small table. The best, of course, is the scope mounting JIG.

Now spot drill the holes with a #28 drill and then tap drill with a #31 drill. Now TAP right through the holes in the base (a ratchet 'T' handle beats all others) for INSURED alignment. If you were careful and located these clamps properly, all holes can be completed before the clamps are removed.

- *Maynard Buehler, Orenda, California*

SCOPE MOUNTING ON CASE HARDENED RECEIVERS

A tip worth remembering when mounting scopes on guns with case-hardened receivers: use your hand grinder and a pointed mounted wheel to cut thru the case hardened skin before starting to drill. RE-MEMBER: there is also a case hardened skin on the inside of the receiver ring. When your drill reaches this skin set your drill press to top spindle speed and the drill point will break thru the skin -- if you leave the spindle at normal speed the chances are that the drill will grab.

- *Bob B.*

SHUT MY MOUTH

Sort of makes me feel like the guy - little, short and bandy-legged - who walked into the bar, downed three real quick fingers, banged his glass on the bar, looked around and snarled: "I can lick any son-of-a-bitch in the house." A real big bruiser proceeded to slap the ever-livin-peewaddin' out of the little fellow. When he could finally talk, the little guy looked around and said, "Hell, if I'd known there were any sons-of-bitches around I'd of kept my mouth shut."

- *Bob B.*

BREAKING THROUGH THE HARDENING ON AN ACTION

When using the B-Square Scope Jig, set it up as per usual on the gun. Then take a Drill-Countersink (like you show in the catalog) with a body diameter of 5/16" and break the edges of the cutting flutes on the body off - but not the ones on the drill. Insert this in your drill press and you will find that it just fits the hole in the B-Square Jig without the bushing. You might have to polish the sides of the countersink body just slightly. Now, you have a fine drill to break the hard skin of a receiver.

Do Not use power to the drill press. Turn the belt by hand while exerting pressure on the drill press handle. It will cut right through in exact position. Works especially well when used prior to the special carbide drill as it gets the hole started and eliminates drill breakage. In a pinch, the 1/8" drill point can be used for the #31 drill if a special carbide drill is not available. The main thing is that the small start through the skin keeps the drill straight and prevents any wandering of the drill tip as often occurs even with a bushing.

- *Ralph Walker, Selma, Alabama*

MIKE FOR SCOPE JIGS

Noticed that some of the boys have mentioned a need for different hole spacing for their Forster Scope Mounting Jigs. I ran across the same problem. Solved it by taking a depth mike that I had around the shop and fitting it with a T-segment to fit into the slot on the Forster Jig. This can be slid in the base with the drill bushing holder. Thus, I have any hole spacing measurements I need up to an inch, and in thousandths, yet!

- *Jerry Stevens, St. Louis, Missouri*

DEPTH GAUGE FOR SCOPE MOUNT HOLES

Drilling through the barrel into the bore or through the receiver into a chamber is a dread we all have. Several methods of providing a stop of some kind are usually given by the "experts", but everybody is in too much of a hurry to use them except when working on a really expensive job.

I do the job simply and quickly with a little "Depth Gauge" set I made up. Take a piece of iron - anything will do - and drill a hole through it with the drill you will be using on the scope base screws - usually a #31. Now, turn it down on the lathe to about 3/8" O.D. and about 1" long.

Set up your rifle and jig with the drill bushing in place. Insert the drill through the collar you just made, and insert the drill in the drill bushing of the jig. Take a common thickness gauge and put it between the bushing and the collar with the number of leaves of the gauge the same as the drill depth desired. Tighten the chuck by hand slightly over the end of the drill. Now press down with the handle of the drill press and the chuck will slide down the drill until it touches the collar with the drill pressed against the receiver through the drill bushing of the jig. Tighten the chuck with the key. Remove the gauge. Turn on the drill press and drill the holes. The collar will ride with the drill. When it bottoms on the drill jig bushing, you have drilled to the exact depth you set with the gauge. (Actually is a whole lot simpler and faster than all these words it takes to explain it!!)

The system is foolproof, and works just as well without a jig, as the collar controls the "usable" drill length to the exact depth you want to drill, and no more. To even make it easier and faster, square off the leaves of the commercial thickness gauge and notch the end for clearance around the drill. Or make up a set of thickness gauges of scrap steel to the exact thickness you want to use for guns you frequently get into the shop. Then, no more shuffling leaves - just pull out the right gauge and set up the drill depth in a minute.

- *Ralph Walker, Selma, Alabama*

SIGHT MOUNTING LEVEL

Want to mention a shop gadget that has proven very handy for sight and mount jobs. It is the Magnetic Level. It is the only one I've found that is thin enough to fit inside a standard dovetail. Being magnetic, it holds right on the dovetail bottom and with the adjustable level feature, it is real handy for leveling the barrel and action, no matter whether in a jig or vise.

- *D. E. Schell, Lynwood, California*

LEVELING GUN BORE

Have found another use for the Site-A-Line besides bore sighting when using the Forster Drill Jig. Stick the right caliber spud into the barrel to level up by using a level on the spud. Of course, the drill press table must be level also. (Note: This idea of Walter's could be used even when the Forster jig is not being used. How many times have you sweat trying to find a spot on a gun you could use as a leveling spot!!!)

- *Walter B. Crow, Uvalde, Texas*

SCOPE MOUNTING

Incidentally for those without a Forster Jig, a square (truly square) block about 2"x2"x4" bolted to a drill press table and the action held to it by a clamp works almost as well. You can tap & drill one hole at a time by using the drill chuck for a tap holder. True as a die but drill press table must be level.

- *Horace M. Frantz, New Egypt, New Jersey*

INSTALLING WEAVER K8 SCOPES

For Pete's Sake DO NOT use your full strength to tighten the Pivot Tension Screw, located on the side of the front mount ring opposite the thumb nut...it has a spring washer under its head. Just tighten it enough to eliminate all looseness - and that is ALL. Otherwise, SIR, you will bust it!! At "just tight" it has been tested, along with a scope, mounted on a big air-driven jackhammer and never did

loosen...
- Bob B.

MOUNTING SCOPE ON S & W MOD. 53

The M53 is exactly the same as the K & N frames but S & W Co. put that front sight screw (on the M53) exactly in between the ones on the K & N frames. There is no room to drill another hole in our base and, anyway, it is not needed. I definitely recommend the use of 6x48 screw in the forward hole as described for magnums and eliminate use of the original sight screw. This little Jet doesn't appear to have much recoil, but it is sharp and a scope is too heavy for that little screw, I feel.

- Maynard Buehler, Buehler Mounts, Orinda, California

SCOPE MOUNT SHIMS

Was having troubles mounting a scope on a certain gun because of irregularity of the receiver. Many of us have used the same method in solving the problem - but maybe many more haven't thought of it. Here it is, and I quote: "I came up with this if you are interested. For elevation I used rear main bearing shims for a Chevy which mike .002". They can be procured at any Chevy garage. I drilled the holes then cut the outside dimensions (they come in group - about 10 to 15 struck together, real handy). I found one shim moved elevation approximately one inch so I had little trouble getting gun right where I wanted it." After getting the scope mounted Jim sighted it in and got four shots touching at 100 yards - and then like the rest of us so often do, threw one out so the final group was 1-1/2"...

- James C. Crabb, Dumas, Texas

SCOPE DRILLING 99 SAVAGE

When drilling the screw hole next to where the breech block locks up on the 99 Savage, have found it best to use your #28 solid carbide drill and drill through the case. It may be as much as 1/8". Then follow with #31 cobalt or hi-speed drill. Have used this on last three guns. Of course, a longer screw has to be used.

On the Forster Drill Jig bottom I place 1" square cold rolled steel to raise the jig up to clear the Savage finger lever bracket....

- Walter B. Crow, Uvalde, Texas

A DRY FRENCHMAN

With all the happenings in France these days our local doctor wants to know the name of the Frenchman who had been too long in Algeria and became completely dehydrated? Pierre...

- Dr. K.W. Caldwell, Montezuma, Iowa

1X SCOPES ON SHOTGUNS

You fellows who live in rifle shooting country are not going to be much interested in this - but the other guys have put up with years of talk about big game rifles, so bear with us while we do a bit of talking about slug shooting shotguns...

A while ago we ran a letter from F. L. Grimes about his experiences with 1X scopes on shotguns for eastern (and south-eastern) deer hunting. Here's more information from him:

We equipped 3 different guns with 1X Weaver scopes we got from you, and all of them with #56 Weaver top mounts and split rings. We have installed the side mounts but frankly don't like them at all, either from an installation point of view or from general appearances.

Guns with chokes are about right for sight plane with #56 left on the gun, i.e., the bird can be left on top of the barrel, just under it, rather than cover it up. (With scope off for open hunting).

We use only two mounting screws with the #56, and these have proven adequate. So far, no trouble. This way the owner of the gun can remove the mount easily, and re-install, if he wishes. On the #56 mounts we file another slot 3/4" forward and back for eye relief. The #56 as now furnished, permits no movement, or very little, with the 1X scope....With scopes on the guns, we like lace-on leather cheekpieces 1/2" high in most cases. Personally, I prefer 5/8" height on one or two guns I've shot.

Sighting: For shotshells, the dot in the scope seems OK. For slugs I would prefer a dot about 1/3 size of the present one, for the present dot covers too much area at 60 yards and especially is this so at 100 yards. For slug shooting we use the top of the dot as the sighting point, and sight them in to be 3" high at the 60 yard mark.

- *F. L. Grimes, Almond, New York*

WEAVER N MOUNTS & CUSSING

Many of the boys sweat and swear putting on those N mounts. Tell them to locate the Marlin 56 adapter plates and then use the Weaver Tip-off Mounts. I have used this idea several hundred times in the last few years. Stronger than the N, gives a quick detachable mount - and easier than milling too!

- *Fred Davis, Falls Church, Virginia*

MODEL 43 WINCHESTER SCOPE MOUNTING

To keep from losing all the hair on your head fighting those hard receiver rings, mount the front base on the barrel.

- *Wayne Fleming of right here in our institution, by cracky...*

DOUBLE BARREL SCOPE MOUNT

Don't know if any of the other boys have mentioned this, but I may have found another use for the lowly adapter plate (scope) for Marlin rifles. It works nice on solid (Not Model 24 Win.) rib double barrels for slugs or birds (with dot). Looks fairly neat and low. And at least one barrel can be zeroed where you're looking - for slugs - and Kentucky windage used for the other barrel...

- *Kroll Repair Service, Lanark, Illinois*

TIP-OFF MOUNTS

I've found the easiest way to mount those tip-off mounts is to cut the grooves when there aren't any present in the gun and customer doesn't want the loading port bridged. I badger the local dentists for OLD DENTAL BURRS (!!) which have a 3/32" shaft and fit nicely in those high-speed hand tools. After scribing lines where I want the grooves I cut a shallow groove with the burr, and brother I believe they'll cut anything. Once the ice is broken it is a very simple matter to cut a straight groove with a triangle needle file....Actually, these high speed hand grinders are the greatest thing since the bomb and any of the fellows that don't have them are wasting time and energy!

- *Al Geyer, Lafayette, Louisiana*

SCOPE SCREWS

Having troubles, once in a while, with scope screws staying put in barrels or receivers? Clean the holes out well with alcohol and apply a few drops of mixed Acraglas.

- *Bob B.*

ACRAGLAS SCOPE BUSHINGS

Without being ubiquitous (a two-bit word I learned from my Missus meaning yakking too "D" much on the same subject) here is a cute gimmick sent in by Jerry Shannon:

Customer purchased a heavy scope with a 1" tube from me and I mounted it on his 70-300 Kodiak which I had previously chambered for this cartridge. I put bases on his 70 and then he brought in an Alaskan 2-1/2x to see if it could be adapted. This is where Acraglas came in.

I made a ring (2 of 'em) of mild stock and split it to serve as bushings to bring the 7/8" to 1" ring size. I then took a third ring and split it, using half rings on under side of scope to ride on mount bases. This was necessary because of the 7/8"-1" dimensions. Normally, two small screws would have been used to secure the half rings, but I scribed ring positions and carefully roughed up the tube inside the scribe marks, mixed a small amount of Acraglas, coated the tube with release agent except inside the scribes, put the half rings in place and clamped them very tightly to prevent any shifting. This job was done two years ago and both rifles have been used continuously since, shifting scopes from one to the other and no trouble. The half rings are as secure today as ever....

- *Jerry Shannon, Spanaway, Washington*

USING A COLLIMATOR

A Collimator will sight in a rifle for almost all hunting situations and will save time and ammunition in the process. If extreme precision is required and if the sights and weapon are adequately accurate, it may be a good idea to shoot-in the rifle to confirm the zero and make final adjustments, but in most cases this is not necessary.

In almost all cases, by following the procedure outlined below, it is possible to get a scope-sighted rifle zeroed to within one or, at the most, two inches of the required 100 yards zero. I have found only one type weapon on which it won't work - handguns. This is apparently due to the barrel rising in recoil prior to exit of bullet. As a result, the collimator will consistently zero a handgun high, but can still be used to correct the windage.

The principle of this tool is quite simple. It projects an image of a pair of crossed wires an infinite distance along a line parallel to the center-line of the last two inches of the bore, providing a point at which to start to zero a rifle (same principle would apply to a shotgun). Think of this point as what would be seen if it were possible to look precisely along the center line of the bore while looking thru the sights.

Therefore, if the sights are aligned on this spot (the intersection of the crossed wires in the collimator), the line of sight is established precisely parallel to the axis of the bore. If the rifle were fired with this sight setting, the bullet would be launched parallel to the line of sight and would immediately start to drop further away from it.

Of course, this won't do, so computations must be made to ascertain the required convergence of the lines of sight and bore to arrive at the required zero. This convergence must take into account the bore-to-sight distance as well as the drop of the projectile below its line of departure.

The bore-to-sight distance can be measured with a scale - but the drop due to gravity is a different story. When dealing with a factory load for which data is available the information wanted is usually the mid-range trajectory. This is given in inches and is the highest point of the trajectory curve above a line joining the muzzle and the point of impact. This is assuming a parabolic trajectory curve which is not too big an assumption over most hunting distances. It is also assuming that the line of fire is more or less horizontal, which is usually done anyway.

This mid-range trajectory can be proved to be one fourth of the drop below the line of departure at the impact range. So the drop for factory ammunition is available, which will take care of most situations. When using hand loads the Powley Computer and the Speer Ballistic Calculator are the obvious answers.

Knowing how to obtain the data to zero the rifle now, we'll select a particular set-up and follow it thru. A 30-06 to be zeroed with 150 grain factory loads at 300 yards. The center line of the scope is 1-1/2" above the center of the bore.

Now looking in the table of factory ballistics, note the mid-range trajectory for the 150 grain 30-06 at 300 yards is 6.1", so multiply this by four and get 24.4". This is the amount the bullet drops below the line of departure at 300 yards. Now add the 1-1/2" to this drop to find how much the point of impact is below the aiming point. This gives 25.9".

Now we want to know thru what angle the line of sight must swing to intersect the path of the bullet at 300 yards. We know that at 100 yards, one inch subtends an angle of approximately one minute; at 200 yards, 1/2 minute; and at 300 yards, 1/3 minute; etc. We are dividing the inch by the number of 100 yard increments and getting the angle it subtends at that range in minutes. To get the required angle divide 25.9" by 3 and get 8.6 minutes. If the scope has 1/4 minute clicks, multiply this 8.6 by 4 and get 34 (rounding off), the number of clicks to depress the line of sight (this will be "up" on the elevation adjusting knob).

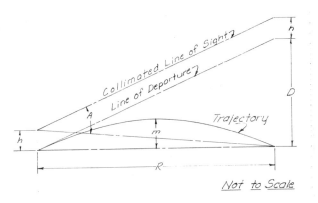

Not to Scale

Let h = Distance in inches from bore to scope center line.
Let m = mid-range trajectory in inches at "R".
Let R = range in yards.

Let D = drop of bullet in inches below line of departure.

Let A = angle in minutes between collimator and line of sight when zeroed at "R".

From the above discussion:

$$A = \frac{4m + h}{\frac{R}{100}} = 100\,\frac{(4m + h)}{R}$$

If the drop has been found from some source other than mid-range trajectory tables the equation becomes:

$$A = \frac{100\,(D + h)}{R}$$

This may look like too much work but after you get on to it the whole works won't take five minutes. That's a good deal faster than driving out to the range unless you are one of the fortunate few who has a firing point where he sits at his bench.

To zero iron sights use proportions to find the amount to raise the rear sight from the collimator "zero" to zero the rifle for the desired range.

First, as before, find how much the bullet drops, and measure the distance from the axis of bore to the aiming point on the non-movable sight (usually the front sight). This sounds like splitting hairs but it is best to make the calculations as accurately as possible and then make "the big guess" after having the best information available on which to base it.

Now measure the sight radius with a steel tape (measure it as accurately as possible) and "zero" the sights on the collimator.

We can set up the proportion now.

Let S = sight radius (in yards).

Let x = distance (in inches) the rear sight must be raised to arrive at the desired zero.

D, h, and R are the same as before.

$$\frac{x}{S} = \frac{D + h}{R}$$

Multiply both sides of the equation by S,

$$x = \frac{S\,(D + h)}{R}$$

Note: It is necessary to use a center hold when setting up the collimator so if a 6 o'clock hold is required, add the amount of 6 o'clock to the expression (D - h) before multiplying by S.

Using a depth micrometer (precision is important here as a little bit makes a big difference), measure from some point to the rear sight (a flat surface if possible which moves with the aiming point) down to a fixed surface on the barrel or receiver. Record this dimension and add on the "x" found above. If the sight is of the type that doesn't have known predictable adjusting increments, use the "move-and-try" method until you have raised it the required "x" as measured with the micrometer.

Another time saver is in selecting the proper iron sight, front or back. Looking thru the other sight at the collimator hold a scale in the bottom of the dovetail (or whatever reference point suggests itself) and read on the scale the proper height for the replacement. This will save time over the old method of measuring two or three places and referring everything back to the bore axis and then after it is all done finding that something has been overlooked and the weapon doesn't shoot where you point it.

Forend pressure can be set or corrected very easily by zeroing on the collimator with the stock off and then checking for change in the relative positions of the scope and collimator reticles when the stock is on. When fitting a new stock with which forend pressure is required it is easy to get an even pressure of predetermined amount.

With the stock off, zero the scope windage on the collimator, clamp the action in the vise and, with a spring scale, pull up on the barrel at the pressure point with the desired amount of force. While this force is being applied, adjust the scope's elevation to zero on the collimator.

Now it is simply a matter of inletting the stock to reproduce this scope-collimator relationship and you have your forend pressure. This is the only way to do the job properly unless you have an electric bedding device installed in the stock, which is certainly not a very aesthetic addition to a nice sporter.

Now some words of caution. Like any tool the collimator can't correct for improper use or un-predictable situations. It is dependent on two things. (1) The axis of the spud must be parallel to the axis of the last two inches of bore, and (2) the line of departure of the bullet must be coincident with the axis of the last two inches of bore. Any deviation which occurs in either of these can throw off the end result.

In the first case, an improperly chosen or bent spud will cause an un-parallel situation to exist. Also, metal fouling in the bore will cause it as the collimator spud will locate on the metal fouling rather than the bore.

In the second case, the condition of the crown can cause problems. It must be square and un-injured. It not, the rifle may group good but not in the proper place which would make it necessary to zero it on a range. A severe mutilation, one substantial enough to resist change from shot to shot, would change the impact point but the rifle still might group good. Also, metal fouling could unbalance the bullet and cause it to take a course other than the desired one.

The point is this, if something goes wrong and the rifle doesn't shoot where it should after being zeroed in with the collimator, don't blame the collimator. First, check for bore fouling and crown damage if you know you have chosen the proper spud (you wouldn't be so stupid as to pick the wrong spud, but I have been) and the optical equipment is in good shape. This checking is after the fact, of course, for by the time you have trouble, the "fat is in the fire". It is a good idea to do this checking before trying to zero the rifle in the first place.

One last remark and we'll wind this up. When looking thru a scope at the collimator it is easy to check for parallax in the scope. Most hunting scopes are set with zero parallax at some reasonable hunting distance and at any range beyond that there will be so little that is hard to see. The collimator or reticle is beyond this (infinity) so there should be very little if any parallax. If there is an appreciable amount, the time to correct it is BEFORE trying to zero the rifle, not after you have made an idiot of yourself and the disgruntled owner has missed his buck and is in the process of maligning your ancestry in short 14th Century English words.

- *Bob Sconce, Deming, New Mexico*

COLT FRONT SIGHT

I knocked the sight off my Colt Officer Model Target revolver and had silver-soldered it three times. I knocked it off the fourth time about the time I bought my first Twin-Weld about a year ago. I put it on with that and there it is today!...

- *Raymond H. Greene, Mountville, Pennsylvania*

REAR SIGHT FOR M1 CARBINES

I am using the Williams W.O.G. on G.I. Carbines - I open a hole in the hand guard .10" to .15" larger than the base of the sight and mount it just forward of the shell chamber. Braze on a bead on the original front sight or use a new ramp. The Medium base is right on most. If not, a bit of your Acraglas will do the trick. The V or U notch seems to be liked the best. The sight radius is a bit short but all customers so far have reported the jobs entirely satisfactory.

- *J. A. Julian, Corning, Arkansas*

MOUNTING SIGHTS ON REMINGTON RIFLES

With those Remington Jigs, by using the proper set of holes, almost any peep sight made for the gun can be fitted to all other Remington rifles of the same general type - not just the three models stamped on the jigs.

  - Jim Winton, Cherry Grove, Oregon

ACRAGLAS SIGHT BASE

I picked up a .22 Greener Martini a year or so ago without a rear sight. Someone had milled away part of the receiver for an odd-ball peep and then removed it. Just to see what I had, without much expense, I mixed up a gob of Acraglas and put it on the hump. Just before it set, I stuck on an adjustable M1 Carbine peep. It is definitely not a target sight, but it works fine for plinking and is adjustable for windage and elevation. After a year it still is solid!

  - Larry S. Sterett, Biggsville, Illinois

.45 AUTO SIGHTS

Order a rear sight for a Model 52 S&W direct from S&W. Open up the rear sight slot on the .45 auto, make new front sight to match the S&W style and install on the .45. The result can be a matched set of auto target weapons - the S&W Models 41 & 52 and the modified .45. The Model 41 is a natural companion to the 52 if the 41 is the Bull Barrel. The .45 can be further improved to feel and balance like the other two guns by adding weight.

  - Richard W. Benjamin, Anaheim, California

SHOTGUN REAR SIGHTS

Have just had a rash of installing Lyman No. 11 rear sights on shotguns that loosened up and popped out. But no more- I Acraglas them! After drilling and reaming the hole for sight to proper depth, I twist a piece of cotton on a toothpick, dip it in Carbon Tet and clean the hole in the rib and the sight shank. A drop of hardener and four drops of resin does the trick. I use a pipe cleaner to put the Acraglas in the hole and on the sight shank. Tap the sight into position and let it harden, and I have never had one come out. In fact, if the sight is broken off you have to drill the sight shank off to replace!

  - Fair's Gun Shop, Grand Forks, N. Dakota

MAIL DELIVERY

Speaking of the snow! It was that snow pile-up and a comment by Mrs. Jason Lucas (wife of the very straight speaking fishing editor of Sports Afield) that suddenly made me realize you had never been brought up to date on a matter that concerns all of us. Namely, mail delivery. She told Jason that the reason they have better mail delivery in Canada, where she hails from, is that they use dog teams up there.

Well now - and this I fully meant to pass on to you a long time ago - our government did take a lesson from the Canadians on this dog team business, but in the process of getting the lesson, the Canadians also slipped in another lesson. This is what happened: The United States Post Office Department discovered that the Canadians did have about ten times better parcel post and mail delivery. Our men went up there and thoroughly investigated the situation and discovered it was due to the dog team service. So, shrewd Yankees that they are, they made a deal to buy sufficient dog teams to service all parts of our country where snow is prevalent. However, the Canadians are a very determined people and fiercely proud of their service and most anxious to stay on top of the heap.

This I am sure you didn't know: The dog teams were purchased from the Canadian people and immediately put into service. So, why aren't you getting better service? The answer is very simple. Those wily Scots up there put one lefthanded dog in every team and when you stop and consider how many fire hydrants there are in every town and telephone poles between each village, you can well understand the frustrating delays that are encountered. Between the righthanders, the lefthanders and the squatters, the situation is damn near intolerable and my sympathies are entirely with the United States Post Office Department! (Wrote this to Jason a couple of days ago - no time for answer yet.)

- *Jason & Mrs. Lucas*

MUZZLE LOADER PEEP SIGHTS

For a good set of receiver peep sights that require no alterations and are good and sturdy, try the Lyman #57SA rear and #17AHB up front...

- *Monessen Sport Shop, Monessen, Pennsylvania*

PEEP SIGHT BROACHES

George Whittington, past President of the N.R.A., Amarillo, Texas, and Bill Carter of Carter's Gun Works, Charlottesville, Virginia, were in the booth at the same time and all of us yakking. One of them came up with the fact they use those Peep Sight Broaches we list to make their own plastic front peep sight discs. Can get the hole just exactly the right size.

- *Bob B*

SIGHT SCREW KIT

Noticed an ad in a *Rifleman* for a sight screw kit, so immediately dug out one of our catalogs to check and we are still all right - we're about 50% cheaper and ours have rolled threads which, being heat-treated as they are, makes them much stronger than a screw machine

thread. Rolled threads are like forging and the grain structure of the steel follows the thread. On a cut thread the grain is also cut.
- *Bob B.*

HOW TO KEEP FROM LOSING THE SHOTGUN SIGHT TAP AND DRILL

I'm the sort of guy who keeps putting things back into the wrong drawer so that I never find them when I have to have them in a hurry. So, to keep track of the tap and drill for installing shotgun front sights, I put the proper size tap and drill into the hollow handle of my shotgun sight installer. To keep these expensive little gems from falling out and getting lost again, I slip a .38 cal. rimmed case into the end of the large installer, and a .25 cal. rimmed case into the small installer.

The cases act as caps, the rims let you pull them out easily...and the whole works stays together so you know where it is when you need it. Works well for taking the replacements to the field too, if you're a front sight breaker!
- *John Haasberger, Granger, Washington*

BALL BEARING FOR PEEPSIGHT ADJUSTMENT

Grind the bottom of a "Zerk" grease fitting. In most cases, the little ball bearing in these fits the sight just right!
- *Willy's Gun Shop, Wadena, Iowa*

SIGHT/RAMP MEASURING

One of the "sticky" jobs in the gun shop is determining the proper ramp/sight combination to order in order to be reasonably close to "on" when sighting in. The method below is simple to follow and comes close to bore alignment. It is much better than writing your supplier that you have such and such an action with an unknown barrel diameter - and expecting him to know the answer. He doesn't!

1. Measure Outside Diameter of barrel at location of REAR sight. Divide this figure by 2.

2. Determine Minimum Height of rear sight to be used. Add this figure to your answer above. (Both Marble and Williams show this information) If a Peep sight is to be used, add 1/8" (.125") to your answer.

Regular Ramps

3. Measure Outside Diameter of barrel at Muzzle. Divide this figure by 2.

4. Subtract this figure from your answer in "2" above. This gives you the Overall Height needed for ramp & sight.

5. Look in the columns below headed "Total Height" or "Total

FRONT SIGHT ELEVATION CORRECTION CHART
for Iron Sights

Distance Between Front & Rear Sights	14"	15"	16"	17"	18"	19"	20"	21"	22"	23"	24"	25"	26"	27"	28"	29"	30"	31"	32"	33"	34"
							AMOUNT OF ADJUSTMENT NECESSARY TO CORRECT ERROR														
Amount of Error at 100 Yards Given in Inches 1"	.0038	.0041	.0044	.0047	.0050	.0053	.0055	.0058	.0061	.0064	.0066	.0069	.0072	.0074	.0077	.0080	.0082	.0085	.0088	.0091	.0093
2"	.0078	.0083	.0089	.0094	.0100	.0105	.0111	.0116	.0122	.0127	.0133	.0138	.0144	.0149	.0155	.0160	.0166	.0171	.0177	.0182	.0188
3"	.0117	.0125	.0133	.0142	.0150	.0159	.0167	.0175	.0184	.0192	.0201	.0209	.0217	.0226	.0234	.0243	.0251	.0259	.0268	.0276	.0285
4"	.0155	.0167	.0178	.0189	.0200	.0211	.0222	.0234	.0244	.0255	.0266	.0278	.0289	.0300	.0311	.0322	.0333	.0344	.0355	.0366	.0377
5"	.0194	.0208	.0222	.0236	.0250	.0264	.0278	.0292	.0306	.0319	.0333	.0347	.0361	.0375	.0389	.0403	.0417	.0431	.0445	.0458	.0472
6"	.0233	.0250	.0267	.0283	.0300	.0317	.0333	.0350	.0367	.0384	.0400	.0417	.0434	.0450	.0467	.0484	.0500	.0517	.0534	.0551	.0567

Chart Courtesy Marble Arms Co, Gladstone, Michigan

How To Use Above Table — Suppose a rifle, having a sighting radius of 24 inches between front sight and receiver sight, shoots 6 inches high at 100 yards even with the rear sight adjusted as low as possible. Remove front sight and measure **overall** height, preferably with a micrometer. This might be .410 inches, such as a Marble No. 41N. Reference to columns for 24 inches and 6 inches on above chart will show a necessary correction of .0400 inches. This would mean a new higher front sight, with an overall height of .410 plus .040 for a corrected height of .450 inches, such as a Marble No. 45N, should be installed.

When sighting in, shooting should be done with a bench rest or prone with a sand bag or other rest for the rifle. Do not put rifle barrel or forearm directly on solid surface; but put the back of your hand or wrist on the rest and hold the forearm of the rifle securely in your hand with approximately the same tightness of grip you would use when shooting at running game. If the forearm or barrel is rested directly on the sand bag or rest, the rifle will shoot higher than when held firmly while shooting at game as more "muzzle flip" will occur.

Sight Height" for the measurement coming closest to your final figures. This will give you sight and ramp heights.

Lyman Slip-on Ramps

Follow Steps #1 and #2 above.

3. Divide inside Diam. of Lyman ramp band being used by 2.

4. Subtract this figure from .668". (This gives you height from barrel top to bottom of dovetail.)

5. Subtract this figure from your answer in "#2" above. This gives you Sight Height needed for the sight/ramp combination.

Suggestions on ordering sights for Lyman Ramps:

Look in Marble sight specification chart for nearest height. If exact height is not listed, use next highest. Rear sight adjustment when sighting in will bring point of impact up to where you want.

MARBLE Chart To Determine Overall Sight/Ramp Heights

Sight No.	Ramp	Total Height	Sight No.	Ramp	Total Height	Sight No.	Ramp	Total Height	Sight No.	Ramp	Total Height
26NR	3/16"	.3545	29NR	3/8"	.572	34NR	7/16"	.6875	34NR	9/16"	.8125
29NR	3/16"	.3845	31NR	3/8"	.594	41NR	3/8"	.692	53NR	3/8"	.820
31NR	3/16"	.4065	50NR	3/16"	.5945	50NR	5/16"	.7195	50NR	7/16"	.8445
34NR	3/16"	.4375	37NR	5/16"	.5945	37NR	7/16"	.7195	37NR	9/16"	.8445
37NR	3/16"	.4695	26NR	7/16"	.6045	26NR	9/16"	.7295	41NR	9/16"	.8795
26NR	5/16"	.4795	34NR	3/8"	.625	45NR	3/8"	.732	53NR	7/16"	.8825
41NR	3/16"	.5045	41NR	5/16"	.6295	41NR	7/16"	.7545	45NR	9/16"	.9195
29NR	5/16"	.5095	53NR	3/16"	.6325	53NR	5/16"	.7575	50NR	9/16"	.9695
31NR	5/16"	.5315	29NR	7/16"	.6345	29NR	9/16"	.7595	53NR	9/16"	1.0075
26NR	3/8"	.542	31NR	7/16"	.6565	31NR	9/16"	.7815			
45NR	3/16"	.5445	37NR	3/8"	.657	50NR	3/8"	.782			
34NR	5/16"	.5625	45NR	5/16"	.6695	45NR	7/16"	.7945			

WILLIAMS Chart To Determine Overall Sight/Ramp Heights

Sight Height & No. *	Ramp Height	Total Sight Height	Sight Height & No. *	Ramp Height	Total Sight Height	Sight Height & No. *	Ramp Height	Total Sight Height	Sight Height & No. *	Ramp Height	Total Sight Height
									.406	3/8"	.688
.260	1/8"	.292	.281	9/32"	.469	.345	5/16"	.5645	.345	7/16"	.6895
.281	1/8"	.313	.375	3/16"	.4695	.406	9/32"	.594	.437	3/8"	.719
.312	1/8"	.344	.260	5/16"	.4795	.312	3/8"	.594	.375	7/16"	.7195
.260	3/16"	.3545	.312	9/32"	.500	.375	5/16"	.5945	.260	9/16"	.7295
.345	1/8"	.377	.281	3/16"	.5005	.260	7/16"	.6045	.406	7/16"	.7505
.281	3/16"	.3755	.437	3/16"	.5005	.437	9/32"	.625	.281	9/16"	.7505
.312	3/16"	.4065	.312	5/16"	.5315	.406	5/16"	.6255	.437	7/16"	.7815
.375	1/8"	.407	.345	9/32"	.533	.281	7/16"	.6255	.312	9/16"	.7815
.406	1/8"	.438	.260	3/8"	.542	.345	3/8"	.627	.345	9/16"	.8145
.345	3/16"	.4395	.375	9/32"	.563	.437	5/16"	.6565	.375	9/16"	.8445
.260	9/32"	.448	.281	3/8"	.563	.312	7/16"	.6565	.406	9/16"	.8755
.437	1/8"	.469				.375	3/8"	.657	.437	9/16"	.9065

- Brownell's Inc.

INSTALLING FRONT RAMPS

While resting up from a bout with my doctors, I decided to run some tests on the strength of different kinds of front ramp installations. First one was put on with 50-50 silver solder, no screw of course. Turned the barrel upside down, clamped the ramp in the vise, came out 20" from the ramp for leverage and using a fish scales broke the ramp off at 41-pounds of pull.

Next one was put on with Twin-Weld which I let set for 8 hours after installation. Set up the same test, and at 60 pounds the ramp had not broken loose yet and that is all the higher my fish scale goes!

The third one I put on with Acraglas and under the same conditions, it broke away at 55 pounds - though I think I got the proportions wrong when I mixed it, so it should have held all the way if I did the mix right.

But, Bob, think what the pressure must be at 20 inches out from the ramp. I won't say that you couldn't knock it off with a hammer, but then how many times do you do that in the field? Besides, the most important thing is the time you have to work using Twin-Weld or Acraglas. As you know, with solder there is not much time to get the ramp on straight. With Twin-Weld or Acraglas, set it straight and if it looks straight, it is straight.

Then, for my own information, I installed several ramps with Acraglas and then ran them through the hot bluing tanks, leaving them in the tank for an hour at 275 degrees. When I removed the barrel and applied a little side pressure to the ramp, it just fell off. So, it seems that the combination of the high temperature plus the action of the salts knocks out installing the ramps before bluing.

But have decided not to worry about it. Just go ahead and blue the guns first as I have been doing anyway. Then undercut the ramp just a little with a round file or small wheel, put on the Acraglas, set it straight on the barrel, and wipe off the excess on the edges after putting on a small clamp to hold it in place to dry. I have lots of time to work slowly and carefully to get it straight. Just be sure to blue the rifle first, and if you do not use a vice-type sight installer, drive the sight into the ramp before Acraglassing it to the barrel.

- *Dee Davis, Chicago, Illinois*

CHAPTER 5

METAL POLISHING

POLISHING G. I. BARRELS

Here's one that helps keep the color of the pencil favorable in our shop. When we need to clean up a G. I. barrel we catch it in the chuck and rest it (action and all) at the chamber in the steady rest. We turn it slowly and against our portable belt sander. Use a coarse belt on the bad ones and follow with a worn out belt. Going against the rotation of the lathe leaves a nice finish. I get in the space just ahead of the roller where the belt flexes before it gets on the backing plate. This does a nicer job on those G. I. steady rest marks than anything I've come up with. The very deep ones should be draw filed first to save time and belt wear. (Note from Bob B.: About 20 years ago, P. O. Ackley told me he was setting up a deal like this but that he was using an old, geared-down wood lathe for the job. Several have told us about it since, but I never did get it in the Newsletter...)

- *Clint Thomas, Grand Junction, Colorado*

TRIGGER GUARD POLISHING

I put a felt bob in my drill press, load with polish and rev it to top speed. It cuts the time way down on polishing inside trigger guards and other small parts that have to be polished prior to bluing.

- *E. Neeley, Blue Springs, Missouri*

POLISHING SHOTGUN BORES

Wind a long wad of 0000 steel wool around a 3/8" wood dowel at least 36" long. The wad of steel wool should be approximately 3 to 4" long, and if it has a tendency to slip, cut some notches in the tip of dowel with a pocket knife, leaving the chips in place.

Coat the outside of the wad of steel wool with J-B Compound, and run it up and down the bore of the shotgun powered with an electric hand drill. Remove and wipe the bore clean with a patch. Cleans the bore out perfectly of all lead and scruf in a jiffy, and is perfectly safe for you and the gun!

- *Ralph Walker, Selma, Alabama*

FOR POLISHING TRIGGER GUARDS AND OTHER THINGS

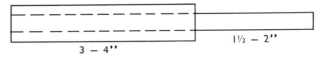

The sketch above is made from a piece of 1/4" drill rod with a soft piece of gum rubber hose slipped tight onto it. Just wrap 4 or 5 turns of sandpaper or emery cloth around it and tie the top tight with a couple of twists of wire and a couple of turns of tape over the wire and part of the rod. Just make sure the lap on the paper is going in the right direction.

Chuck the whole works into the drill press at a pretty good speed, and you can polish out a trigger guard in no time flat! When you wear out the top layer, just tear it off, and you're ready to go again until you've torn off all five layers. I make them up in several grits for all purposes.

- *W. A. Smith, Huntington, West Virginia*

"MA OUTHOUSE"

"A gunsmith of questionable abilities but bragging inclinations was visiting a friend in New York," writes Fred Moulton of *The Rifleman*. "His city friend showed him all the sights including the United Nations Building. 'Isn't that a magnificent structure?' asked his friend. 'Nothin' to it,' said the jack-laig gunsmith. 'I got an outhouse bigger than that!' The New Yorker looked him over and replied: 'Yeah, Man, and YOU need it.'"

- *Fred Moulton,* The American Rifleman

INSIDE POLISHING

For inside polishing of parts - chambering, polishing holes, deburring or the like - instead of splitting a rod with a saw merely wrap around the rod with masking tape - let a little hang over, tuck the emery cloth under it and start to work. It will work on a rod as small as 1/16" or as big as you like. And if you wish to build up a larger drum, just keep on wrapping the masking tape on until desired size is reached. (Note from Bob B.: Amazing, isn't it, how exceptionally good ideas can be so simple yet I never heard of it before...should work like a darn with Grit Cloth.)

- *L. A. "Slim" Spears, Hutchinson, Kansas*

LEATHER POLISHING STEEL

For years I have used powdered Bon-Ami on leather following 555 Polish-O-Ray. It seems to cut a little faster and gives a final polish that looks about as good as talc. For hand polishing, the leather in a gray Welder's Glove works just fine. If a leather belt is used on your band-sander, the aerosol spray can of Bon-Ami works good, too.

- *James F. Smith, Paducah, Kentucky*

SUPER FINE POLISHING

A kink I learned from a machinist years ago may be well known to most gunsmiths, but I have heard many express surprise at the idea. For the finest polish you can imagine on a piece of steel after ordinary fine polishing has been done, use talcum powder on leather. A leather lap can be prepared for polishing chambers, barrels, etc., and run with power...

- *Glenn W. Cosby, Miami, Oklahoma*

BORE POLISHING SHOTGUNS

I have found a tool referred to by automobile mechanics as a Wheel Cylinder Hone to be ideal for polishing shotgun barrels full length and for opening up the choke where needed. The better hones come with two or three polishing stones mounted on spring fingers and the hones are replaceable. By using a thin oil first, the hones cut fast enough to take part of the labor out of the shotgun barrel polishing job, and with a sulfur base thread cutting oil they really put a nice finishing polish. The hones when obtained are about eight inches long with a 1/4" shank but it is no problem to make a shank extension. The power source I have found best is a regular 1/4" electric hand drill.

- *Collins Custom Bullets, Roswell, New Mexico*

LIKE-NEW ARMOR

Cartoon showing a medieval salesman showing a suit of armor to a customer, saying "This one is in perfect condition - it belonged to a coward."

- *"Bix" Bixby, Mt. Pleasant, Michigan*

CLEANING GUNS

When cleaning and oiling guns for customers a guy can have lots of troubles. I used to scrape and cuss and wash in solvent. Now I dump the works in one of my little bluing baskets - put some of your gunsmith cleaner in a pail of hot water and cook 10 or 15 minutes. Rinse in hot water and then blow off with an air gun and they are cleaner by far than I ever got them before...

- *Paul G. Westphal, Austin, Minnesota*

INSTANT TARNISH

I built a brass blunderbuss and the bright, shiny brass was offensive. After trying several things I found that the cleaning patches from my dirty black powder muzzle loading guns rubbed over the shiny brass gives a nice tarnished look to the fittings.

- *Paul Adams, Guantanamo Naval Base, Cuba*

CLEANING ALUMINUM

Paul Westphal, whose aluminum boat had turned somewhat black (they do in these parts) said..."I just opened the package from you with the Simichrome Polish in it. I took it out and tried on those spray rails. It's almost unbelievable how quick it put a brighter-than-new-polish on those aluminum rails..."

- *Paul Westphal, Austin, Minnesota*

TAKE BLACK OFF ALUMINUM

--how to take the black finish off aluminum gun frames - something that is pretty hard to do. Frank de Haas put two spoonfuls of drain cleaner in a shallow pan of water and dumped in the grip frame. "About 10 seconds later," he said, "I fished it out mighty fast, dunked it into some clean hot water I had ready, and the grip was as shiny as a new dime! Now I'd like to know how to put a yeller finish on it." He got the idea from once having dropped an aluminum part into his bluing bath by mistake (as haven't we all!!!) and seeing it fizzle, crackle and pop...A few have even lost complete choke attachments that way, huh?

- *Frank de Haas, Orange City, Iowa*

CLEANING UP DIRTY NICKEL PLATE

Got in some Smith pistols the other day that I got all blued up for the customer, only to discover that the nickel plated monogram on the grips looked bad. So, took a cotton ball, dampened it with T-4 and scrubbed up the plating. Wiped it off before it had a chance to do any coloring, and it really cleaned up that nickel plating! Don't know why it works, but used as a cleaner it really works great.

- *John Haasberger, Granger, Washington*

BUFFERS

The Baldor buffer I bought from you sure put a dent in my wallet. It also puts the finest finish on a gun I ever saw. If more of us even had a chance to try one - just once! - the contraptions most of us use would sure disappear.

- *The Foothills Gun Shop, Layton, Utah*

APPLYING POLISH TO WHEEL

Here is a wrinkle on putting Polish-O-Ray on felt wheels. I have a 1/3 horse double shaft polishing motor. For years I used the recommended way of putting on the compound and was never satisfied with the ragged look when the compound was put on at high speed.

Hold the stick of Polish-O-Ray against the felt wheel tightly enough that the motor 'lugs' to slow speed. There is not enough speed to sling off the soft compound. When the coating is very smooth, cut the switch. I have done this for a long time and the motor has never heated enough to throw the thermal switch...Spread this around if you like...

- *Bruce M. Jennings, Jr., Casper, Wyoming*

DRYING POLISH-O-RAY ON WHEEL

It seems that on some occasions Polish-O-Ray doesn't dry quite fast enough on the wheels and a fellow has to set and wait a spell. I have found that if a small torch or one of those Presto units is held across the face of the wheel for a few minutes while it is running, it speeds drying by over half the time...

- *Bill Boyd, Sioux Falls, South Dakota*

KEEPING OPENED POLISH-O-RAY

Am enclosing a plastic bag (like you use for deep freezing vegetables or get carrots in at the market), that is the slickest thing to keep opened Polish-O-Ray containers in - just put the polish in the bag, work most of the air out by hand (balance can be sucked out) and twist the top several times. Double the twist over itself, wrap a rubber band around the twist and put it away where it won't get a hole poked in it.

I kept a small piece this way for over six months. The paper got moldy and loosened. But a little tape wrapped around it held it together.

- *Paul Westphal, Austin, Minnesota*

POLISH-O-RAY BAGS

Putting rubber bands on and off those Polish-O-Ray bags is strictly for the birds. Use those little metal paper clips or wooden clothespins...on and off without all that finger fumbling. Give the open end of the bag several tight twists, bend over, stick on the clip and it stays fresh. That clothespin gimmick is also good for the polyethylene bags you store tobacco and food and stuff in, too!!

- *John Amber, Ye Excellent Editor of "Gun Digest"*

POLISH-O-RAY STORAGE CANS

I take one of those airtight cans that the Government ships ammo in (we used to call them fifty-caliber cans), put a little water in the bottom, then a grill made of bent hardware cloth or the like and lay the opened tube of polish on the grill. Since I started using this method, I haven't lost a bit of polish!

- *Hank Tillinghast Jr., Colorado Springs, Colorado*
- *R. G. Bealieu, Chestnut Hill, Connecticut*

POLISH-O-RAY PROTECTIVE CUP

Get yourself some No. 109 Tupperware cups. They fit perfectly over the ends of open Polish-O-Ray tubes and will keep them from drying out, especially if you put in a small piece of dampened cloth.

- *Fred Davis, Falls Church, Virginia*

CONVENIENT POLISH CAP

John Frazier was in the other day and after fixing himself up with a wee bit of Key snuff advised that those "snoose" cans were the best possible caps for Polish-O-Ray! And Jerry Shannon wrote that those old glass jars with ground to fit caps like you used to find in drug stores were excellent for storing Polish in. I wrote and told him that back in this country the antique dealers were paying right fancy prices for those things and he should buy them for investment and not polish...the modern ones you find in dime stores have glass lids that are too sloppy to use.

- *John Frazier, Chariton, Iowa*
- *Jerry Shannon, Spanaway, Washington*

POLISH-O-RAY IN JARS

I keep my compounds in gallon jars - have 4" lids - used for mayonnaise...get them from most cafes.

- *Sprague Gun Shop, Monticello, Illinois*
- *Dave McCleery, Sodus, New York*

POLISH-O-RAY IN THE "FRIG"

Herrick's Gun Shop, Glendale, Arizona, where it is mighty hot and dry most of the year, brings his Polish-O-Ray back to proper softness by sticking the tube and a piece of damp cloth in the pastic bag that comes with each tube into his wife's refrigerator. In a couple of days it's ready to use again.

- *Herrick's Gun Shop, Glendale, Arizona*

SOFTENING POLISH-O-RAY IN THE PRESSURE COOKER

You can reduce your hardened Polish-O-Ray clear down to the consistency of bouillon soup in your wife's pressure cooker with the right amount of water. I didn't have enough hard on hand to experiment as to exact amount of water but, BELIEVE ME, IT WORKS! My hard polish had been that way for over two years. I might suggest a dash of clear gelatin to slow down drying action after reducing (I mean cook the gelatin into it).

- *Francis A. Green, Cheyenne, Wyoming*

SOFTENING HARDENED POLISH-O-RAY IN THE FREEZER

--as all of us know who use this wonderful little item for gun polishing, there are times when we forget, leave it out in the hot, dry world and the polish gets so hard you could use it to drive tent pegs into cement. M. Adams was in the other day and said that Polish-O-Ray that is hard and can no longer be used can be brought back to useable condition by sticking it into the deep freeze for a few days and then taking it out on a real damp day and letting it thaw. Draws moisture clean to the center and tho not quite as good as when new, is a lot better than throwing away.

- *M. T. Adams, Liberty, Missouri*

BRUSHING ON HARDENED POLISH-O-RAY

I find it unnecessary to discard Polish-O-Ray in case it dries hard accidentally. In such cases I merely soak off the end of the stick in a can of water - making a thick paste and apply to wheels with a brush...

- *George S. Bunch, Hyattsville, Maryland*

SOAKING HARDENED POLISH-O-RAY

At last I have found a way to soften your Polish-O-Ray after it is hard as a brick. I have been keeping it in a fruit jar after opening it. So, if one gets hard, I put it in the jar with about 1/2 inch of water and seal it. Two weeks later it is soft throughout.

- *Larry Wisehart, Hobbs, New Mexico*

EVERYTHING'S BIGGER IN TEXAS

An Easterner went to Texas. After the trip he was pretty dry, so he stopped at the bar of a country club to wet his whistle. He ordered a "shot" and the bartender poured about a pint of corn into a mug that he was used to drinking beer out of. "Is that a shot?" he asked the bartender in amazement. "In Texas," said the bartender, "That is a shot." The easterner at least knew his capacity so he gave the "Texas" shot back and ordered, instead, a short beer. The bartender then placed a pitcher of beer on the bar. The easterner looked at it and asked: "Is THAT a short beer?" "That," said the bartender, "is a short beer in Texas." Since the easterner was very thirsty he drank the 'short' beer and so it wasn't very long until he felt nature's results. He asked the bartender to direct him to the Men. The bartender told him to "go down that corridor to the end, turn left and it is straight ahead." He got to the end of the corridor O.K. but, being somewhat woozy, he turned right instead of left, which took him to the swimming pool. And, being somewhat rubber-legged, he tumbled head-first into the pool and started screaming for help. The bartender, hearing all this commotion, ran down to see what had happened and called out..."Are you all right?" "Yes," answered the easterner, "but for God's sake don't flush it..."

- *A. D. Abramow, Lima, New York*

POLISH-O-RAY FOR PLEXIGLAS

I've found that Polish-O-Ray works wonders on polishing up Plexiglas. Doesn't scratch the surface, and takes out any scratches that might already be in it from handling or use.

- *Louis Baker, Zachary, Louisiana*

TYCRO POLISHING WHEELS

Been using the Tycro wheels I got for about 3 years, and am very satisfied with them. Last a long time and give a good finish.

- *Burgin's Gun Shop, Unadilla, New York*

METAL POLISHING

It is my belief that the best possible sets of instructions on how-to-do-it are those written by people who have just mastered the art themselves and still have all the problems they conquered firmly in mind. If they wait a few years the tricks they discovered have become such a habit with them that they are prone to forget, when writing about it, to throw them in. The result is a very learned dissertation which is of value to no one but another "expert". This is true in any trade you wish to name - gunsmithing, engraving, car repair, rock-hounding - you name it!

I wrote the following instructions on gun polishing back in the 1940's as part of a book I never got finished. The techniques had been worked out and proven successful. They are those used by Master Metal Polishers in all phases of industry. The illustrations by M. C. Ray (now retired) are from photographs taken by Major Don Tyler USAF (now retired) of actual polishing operations in our specialized gun bluing shop (long since closed). By following these instructions you just cannot go wrong.

Twenty-five years after writing the following, there is just one thing to add: Once you have mastered the technique you will find yourself very critical of other blue jobs - I know I certainly am. The first thing you will do is examine the other fellow's work under a strong, angling light for ripples, gouges, funnelled screw holes and rounded corners. "Hah!" you will say. "That, sure as the devil, isn't my work!" In other words, you are on your way to becoming a craftsman - which is the purpose of the article in the first place...

- Bob Brownell, April, 1969

It is my sincere hope that those who read this do not get the idea that the simple act of reading the material and studying the illustrations will, by some dark magic, transform the reader into a master craftsman. Would that this were true. If it were, anyone who read a book on engineering could henceforth build the Oakland bridge without further ado!

As David Murray of Smith and Wesson so aptly phrased it in one of his letters to me during our discussions about the article: "Here in the factory we estimate it takes about fifteen years to make a really good polisher, and until he is good, he is incapable of handling the more difficult operations no matter how hard he tries or how long he takes..."

Fifteen years is a mighty long time and it is doubtful if many individual gunsmiths ever reach that stage of achievement. However, it is my belief that what I have written and what others have written for me will be of great assistance in getting the reader started off in the right direction - a good enough start that his finished polishing job will be, in many ways, equal to - or better than - most factory jobs. Indeed nothing to be ashamed of.

The true idea of this article, then, is to fill in a glaring omission on processes in every gunsmithing book I have ever read. The actual act of bluing a gun by the modern heat immersion process is described, of course, but all the pitfalls, dangers, etc., are nowhere brought out. This can be said, too, of polishing. These two separate acts are closely related. So closely related that one cannot be discussed without automatically bringing in the other.

Every gunsmith I have ever known frankly admits that the older rust and rub method of bluing and the correspondingly slow elbow grease method of polishing is a mighty hard way to make money. And as all gunsmiths like to make enough money to keep a few beans in the pot, I will leave "Browning" up to Angier's excellent book on the subject, *Firearm Bluing and Browning*, and content myself with the faster, and I believe, superior modern methods.

In gathering the information I contacted several arms manufacturers as well as some leading gunsmiths and, with but few exceptions, those contacted let it be known in one way or another that I was "off the beam" for divulging the secrets of polishing to the general public. The real commentary on the above is the converse, though - the superior craftsmen did not hesitate to make their entire fund of knowledge available!

Which all adds up to the fact that anyone who has something special or has done something special owes his start - his kick in the pants, as it were - to someone else's good will and kind assistance. In my own case I owe a great many, but chiefly am in the debt of the technical division of the National Rifle Association, whose combined knowledge of things even remotely connected with firearms would fill many a big book. And then, too, there is M. C. Ray, Cleveland, whom I met via letters, doing some gun swapping, and who was always in there plugging with knowledge I would never have gotten without his assistance.

Another source of information has been the many thousands of letters I have received during the last many years from gun nuts and gunsmiths explaining their troubles with the modern bluing methods. The answering of these letters has put me into the everlasting debt of their writers; for in so doing, practically every problem the gun bluer could stumble onto will be incorporated in the article on bluing. Many of them are problems the individual might never stub his toe on and then again the most freakish one may be the very first snag you will hit.

A good gunsmith is like a good cook in that he takes a recipe and follows it to the letter, then, as my wife says (and she is a good cook) "departs therefrom." So may I suggest you follow my instructions as closely as possible, and then if you find a better way of doing it, please let me know. However, don't blame me if you really mess up someone's pet shooting iron with your own recipe!

As this is being written for those who have never polished as well as those who have polished, a little history of my own experiences may come in handy.

When I first decided I was the answer to a maiden's prayer and would set me down and blue a gun, I procured a slug of books with the idea of finding out how it was done. We've all seen Smith & Wesson's blue and to me it is the acme of super finishes. So that was the finish I decided to develop. Just one thing was wrong. I didn't know how and none of the books I had bought gave me the slightest hint.

I followed their instructions. I got felt wheels, leather wheels, muslin wheels, wire wheels, rubber wheels, wood wheels. My shop gradually started to take on the aspect of a wagon factory. I bought reams of emery paper, crocus cloth, and many cakes of rouge, white clay, and a couple kegs of emery.

No matter how I built up the wheels, broke them in, babied them, the net result was a damned good sample of a polished plow share when done. I raised particular cain with messes and abrasives over the shop, in my hair, in my dipping oils, and Lord knows how many guns I had to clean in gasoline to remove the powdered emery and other traces of my jack-leg enterprises. All this leads to what? Sandpaper, elbow grease, sweat and profanity. And that will not produce a S&W finish.

In one of my letters to the before mentioned M. C. Ray, I told of my polishing troubles. He, bless his heart, sent me a tube of one of the new, modern abrasives which can be applied to a moving polishing wheel without a lot of mess and trouble. It was sunlight in the storm, a one way ticket to heaven. From then on it did not take too long nor too much trouble to develop a system of polishing which, when compared to mass production methods later, was found to be identical with what is commonly known as "Master" polishing. This type of polishing compound can be secured from many sources and in various forms. Advertisers in *The American Rifleman* can supply you with what you want.

I have found that there are three breaking points during the polishing process where you can stop and blue the gun and get three different types of finish. You can call them what you please, but personally, I term "Standard" for the first break; "Pittsburgh" for the second break, and "Master" for the last and best.

The Polishing

Now to get on with the business, which consists of first taking the gun completely down. If you are so busy or so lazy you cannot do this, send the gun to a commercial bluer. There is no other way to do it correctly. With all the parts spread out before you on your work bench, determine which parts are to be blued. In other words: blue or re-finish every darned part which shows...every screw, pin, or what have you. Put these, along with other parts to be polished, in a small box and transfer them to your polishing bench or table beside your polishing head.

You who have never polished probably wonder what a polishing head is. It is a hunk of something stuck to the end of the shaft which protrudes from the end of an electric motor. This hunk of stuff is generally flat one way and round the other. The face or outside diameter of it will henceforth - just between us girls - be called the periphery so as when you someday walk into a factory and ask them what they use on the periphery of their polishing buffs you will immediately be taken as one who knows his onions.

Most polishing wheels, for practical purposes, are composed of muslin or felt, and with the proper use of these two substances one can accomplish marvelous results. A loose buff is a muslin wheel composed of many layers of muslin cloth which have not been stitched together except at the hole in the middle which goes over the shaft of your motor. A stitched buff is one composed of the same sort of material but the whole bunch have been stitched together in a spiral sort of way so that it makes a good dense wheel for polishing, running a poor second, though, to felt wheels for the production of Master finishes, but very satisfactory for average work.

Anyhow, you have your parts over beside your polishing head. In your mind you have decided what kind of a finish you want to develop on the surface of the steel so you go to work. In case you haven't decided what kind of a finish you want perhaps it would be best to start from scratch with each individual type of finish, how it gets that way, why, and what happens.

The following must be followed closely, for any deviation is...well ...a deviation and the results are yours and no one else is responsible for them.

Some guy brings a gun into your shop. Suppose it is a .45 Automatic. There are lots of them to be blued and it is a good gun to take as a sample. It has the flat spaces of a shotgun, the round surfaces of a rifle. This guy who just walked in your shop has so many dollars to spend getting it refinished. You can tell him for that amount you will completely reblue the gun, remove the pits in the process, and hand him back a shootin' iron as well finished as when new.

As I said before: completely strip the gun. There are mighty few parts on the .45 ACP which don't show, and because of their nature, bluing of these few parts is unnecessary. In the higher priced jobs you can do things to them which will make their owners mighty darned proud to have done business with you.

The first thing to do is remove all the old blue and pits. Now, this is the first gun you have ever polished in your life so you have some pretty important questions to be asking yourself about now: shall I get good polishing heads or should I get by as cheaply as I can and let the quality of my work suffer? Those are the questions only you can answer so we will describe the polishing of the .45 ACP you just acquired as though you had decided to get by *as cheaply as possible* and later on will approach from a different angle.

The critical thing in polishing, whether you are doing it as cheaply as possible or are using the best material available, is the amount of power possessed by your motor in relation to the diameter of your buffing wheels. The faster surface speed you can deliver and still retain the polishing compound on the wheel's periphery, the better your job will be and also the sooner you will get done. You will find as you become more acquainted with polishing that nothing, so far in your experience, drags the motor down as easily as a large buffing wheel. So if all you have is a quarter-horse motor, don't immediately step out and buy twelve inch or fourteen inch wheels. The largest wheel you can possibly use on such a source of power is six inch and with a one horse motor a wheel of eight inches is practically maximum, especially if the spindle speed is 1750 rpm. On a larger motor though, you can use larger wheels but the spindle speed must be reduced proportionately. I will take it for granted that you have the usual quarter or half horse motor with a spindle speed of 1750 rpm during this dissertation on this, the cheapest of the three polishing processes.

Right now is a good time to do it, so let's make a rule of nothing larger than a six inch on a motor about half horse or less. Nothing larger than an eight inch on a one horse motor or less when using grit abrasives. Four inches can be added to the wheel's size when the fine "stainless" polishes are used.

Which all leads up to your buying three or four 6" x 3/8" x 1/2" stitched muslin buffs and eight 6" x 3/8" x 1/2" loose muslin buffs. Take three of the stitched muslin buffs, and fasten them on your polishing arbor (the shaft which comes out the end of your motor). Then take a hunk of red crayon and on the side of the outside wheel, write the figure "140" and with the same crayon draw an arrow above the center pointing towards you. Then turn on the motor. If the wheel doesn't turn the direction the arrow points, change the direction of rotation of the motor. I explain it thus for it took me three years to discover what the heck was meant by clock-wise...which is the direction your motor must be turning.

As you have written the figure "140" on this wheel, avail yourself of a tube of No. 140 polishing compound and with the motor running, press the end of the tube to the wheel's periphery with a reasonable amount of pressure. Hold it there until the wheel shows signs of taking on abrasive and then stand back for a few moments and let what abrasive has adhered harden. Again hold the tube to the wheel with the same pressure and with circular motion of the tube let the polishing face take on enough abrasive to show an even color. There are times at this point when even an experienced polishing hand can slip: don't get in a hurry about starting to polish. Give the "green" (not dried) polish ample time to set up before applying the work to be cleaned.

Holding the slide firmly with each hand - and be damned sure to always wear gloves when polishing - hold it at right angles to the periphery and polish the "V's" or serrations on each side which have been milled there for the purpose of making it easier to cock the gun. Then turn the slide so that you are holding it perpendicular to the axis of the wheel and move it downward against the wheel. (Figure 1)

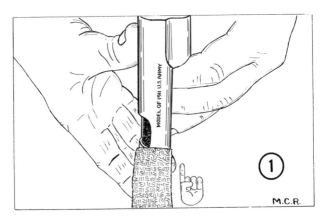

As you move it downward also move it in a circular motion, maintaining an even pressure against your polishing surface. Stand with your feet well braced and your elbows close to your hips...gives you more strength and poise. Take your time with this first pass and after its completion examine the piece under a good light, which should always be present where it will do the most good. You will note that all the old blue, part of the pits and some of your right angle buffing marks are already gone...so take another pass and examine, remembering to maintain perpendicular-to-the-axis, downward motion, circular motion. The second or third pass will leave that side of the slide in the "white", so do the other side in exactly the same manner. You are then ready to do the top.

Grasping the slide fore and aft, give it the works up to within about 1/2" of front sight (you have removed the back sight!!!!!) Work around the sight as well as you can, remembering that most guys are a little touchy about having their sights buffed off! When you have that done you are ready for the back, front, and spring retaining housing. By this time you will see you have enough ability to move the housing down over the wheel and get the rear and front easily. (Figures 2 & 3) The spring housing presents another problem. Do what

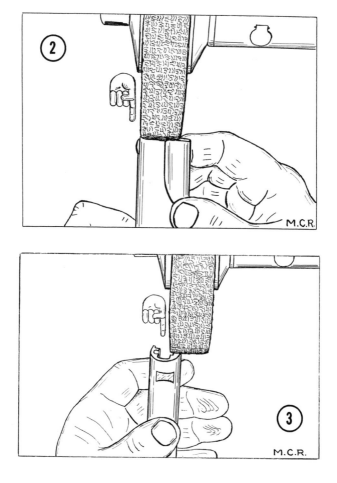

you can at right angles to the wheel and the balance by riding the very edge of the wheel. Then examine closely.

To your disgust, you will find you have rounded all the edges, front and rear and around the cartridge extraction port. Why? You did not come straight into the wheel with your work, and did not have the slide in actual polishing movement when you went to work on it. So doing it a little easier, remove your damage and do not, under any circumstances, make a full length pass over the cartridge port or go on past the ends of the piece...rather come up to within about an inch of the end and then reverse your piece and polish what you missed. You are not done with the slide by a long shot, but lay it away and get the frame. Look it over. See those screw studs sticking out? Avail yourself of a big heavy screwdriver and remove them. If you examine the factory's polishing marks you will see that they did not polish the gun with those studs there, so neither should you. In many cases these studs are in so tight it is impossible to remove them without ruining them, so if you find they can't be taken out, the only thing you can do is to polish around them as best you can.

During all the work on the slide you probably discovered without my saying so that you had to add abrasive to your wheel from time to time. If you didn't, you should have, for it goes without saying you cannot polish without it.

So, being sure you have ample polish on your buff, you proceed with the frame. Let's start on the left side as it presents more problems than the right. Hold the frame at about a thirty or forty degree angle to the wheel and start on the front end, bringing the frame down on the wheel as far as the plunger tube. At this particular point you can raise particular mischief with the slide stop latch hole, so take it easy. The sides of the tube are very thin and a wee bit too much pressure on it with your polishing wheel will grind it down to nothing. So beware! Now, if you've held the grip to the right of the wheel when you started this buffing pass, you can continue on past the plunger tube and continue onto the magazine housing. If you haven't, you can change your angle and proceed.

At this point it will be well to make the following suggestion: Do not ride the metal in one continuous push in going past the plunger tube. Rather, continue your circular motion and downward motion, coming up to the tube and swinging past, letting each cycle take care of the full area adjoining the projection.

Note well—ALWAYS USE THIS METHOD IN GOING AROUND PROJECTIONS...AND I'LL REPEAT: UP TO, AROUND AND DOWN; UP TO, AROUND AND DOWN until you have completed that particular area. Okay, get in a hurry and ride around it and the resulting gouge in the steel is all yours and no one else's!

When you get back to that part which rests on the thumb and index finger web, continue with your polishing but swing the gun on around so that when you have completed the pass you take the gun from the wheel at a right angle to slide channels.

The milled out housing is best done at right angles. Start on one side and continue on around to the hole on the other side, attempting (and you can) to cover the entire length of the grip with each swing. If you don't do this the lap of each cross swing will show in your finished product as waves and ridges. (I'll go into more detail on this flaw later but thought it best to mention it here, too.) Well, you've gained enough experience by now that the top and bottom of the grip safety housing should seem easy - but pause a moment before blundering into something which might cause you one or two headaches. The underneath part should cause no trouble but beware of the top. If you slam it into the wheel and clean it up, what are the rounded edges going to look like?!

So, before doing them, buff the other side of the frame. This is a snap, for it is possible to clean that large flat surface easily, covering everything in wide sweeps as you move from front to rear. Clean up the underside of the forward end and the outside of the trigger guard.

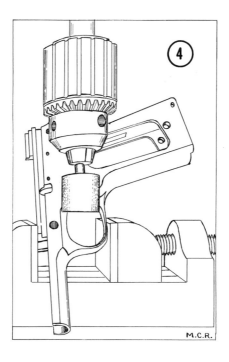

While you're doing that, notice the clever little sharp angles where the guard goes into the frame, and the compound angle and curve where it goes into the magazine housing.

Without some special implements you will find it impossible to do this or any trigger guard in a manner worth a spent slug. And again we've run into that first question: equipment. For a total outlay of 75 cents to a buck you can get yourself a little jigger which will save you more time than Woolworth has dime diamonds. Maybe you haven't noticed but there are some pictures accompanying these rantings of mine. Now is the time to study them. (Figures 4 and 5) The jigger I

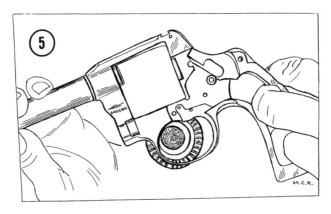

mention and the various methods of using it are doggone well brought out. If you can't buy something like that, go to your machinist and have a couple or three made, and if you can't do that, split a dowel pin, or hunt up a large cotter pin, chuck it in your drill press, fasten some sandpaper in that and proceed as best you can. And the next time you

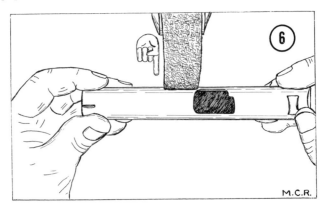

are in the city get some of them.

Now buff up the heads and ends of the small parts and go back to the slide and have your heart broken. Turn it at right angles to the face of your buffing wheel and buff out all former polishing marks with the same weight grit. (Figure 6) Brother! But that's what it takes, for while doing this you will discover all the blemishes you missed, pits, etc. Also it contributes greatly to the final smoothness of the metal. Do this on the frame, also, and on all the small parts; go over them twice at exact right angles with the same grit before proceeding onto the next grade of finer abrasive.

As this is the "Cheap" job of polishing, the thing for you to do now is bring the slide, and the other parts to a condition suitable for bluing.

Take four of the eight 6" loose buffs and put on the arbor, marking them with the arrow as before but writing "240" instead of "140" for the grit number.

These new loose buffs are messier and lintier than the chaff blower on a threshing machine when first being used. Turn on your motor, take an old file and ride the edge of the wheel (its periphery) until you are about to choke and then rest for awhile before putting on the 240 grit polish. Here, too, you will experience some difficulty in getting the polish to stick the first few times but persevere, and success will be yours.

Go over the slide with the 240 grit in exactly the same manner as you did with the 140 but travel lengthwise over the whole business and keep polishing being sure to turn at the right angles until all previous polishing marks are buffed off. (Figures 7 and 8)

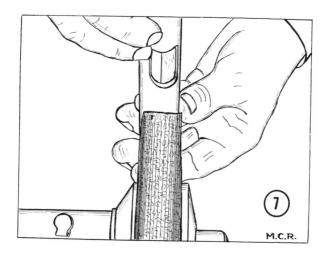

M.C.R.

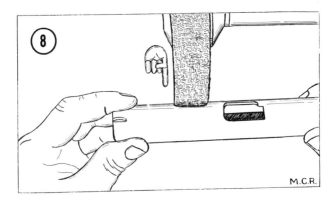

Did you note that "buffed off" statement in all its implications? Heretofore, you have, in all probability and unless taught by an apt teacher - been told to always buff with the grain. That is wrong. If you want to level off anything rough, cut off the rough parts rather than trying to level them down. Just how long would it take a man to level a plowed field with a board if he traveled parallel to the ridges as compared to the man who traveled at, say a ninety degree angle, to the ridges with his board? The latter man would be done days before the former...So be it with you, good reader: *ALWAYS polish at an angle to your former polishing pass.* This cannot be repeated too many times for it is of utmost importance in obtaining a smooth finish on steel.

In putting this final polish on the slide prior to bluing, hold the slide mighty, mighty firmly and rapidly force it down the cutting face. (Figure 9) Ride hard at first and gradually taper off to a very light pass, giving enough pressure, though, to insure complete lack of slap marks.

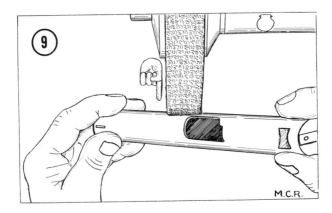

A suggestion here, rather a trade secret. When bluing a shotgun it will develop a beautiful frosted black if you will do this final polishing business with the loose buffs using 140 grit instead of 240 grit. Hold the barrel firmly at each end and move it completely across the wheel and then move it a bit towards you and repeat. Continue this until the whole of the barrel is covered. Catch on to what is being done? You are allowing the slap of the loose polishing wheel to remain on the steel's surface, giving a sandblast effect. It takes a little practice to get a smooth frost, but once mastered it comes easily and the resulting saving in time is more than worth the time you will spend learning it. (This same maneuver is tops on guns so badly pitted that removing the pits would be asking too much. It is the cover-upper in the polishing business and comes in handy on any rough gun.)(Figure 10)

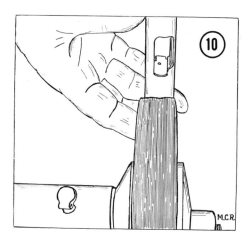

The gun is now ready to be blued. But here are some things which have happened to the gun you have just polished - the pin and screw holes are funneled. This is unavoidable when muslin wheels have been used exclusively, though bluing will, to a certain extent, cover over the damage. You can, by taking plenty of time and by letting the polish harden on the buffing wheel, eliminate most of this funneling of holes. Just take it easy - plenty easy when the wheel passes over each hole - leaving the metal a little rough rather than bringing it smooth and damaging the fine lines of the gun.

Furthermore, you still have some rounded edges...Again unavoidable with muslin, but by judicious pressure on the corners and always attempting to start on the edges and working towards centers, the rounding of edges can also be completely eliminated.

Wherever there are side plates, inspection plates, yokes, or any two separate pieces of metal closely fitted together to present a continuous outer surface, put those pieces together before starting to polish and hold them there with screw blanks or the original screws if need be. You can round off the flattened screw head and it will look not so bad, but if you round off the edges of side plates, take-down rifle couplings, etc., etc., there is but one word for it and that is "Jack-leg".

This all reads as though you have taken up a lot of valuable time. Maybe you do the first gun or two but after some experience you will find that the real time spent is not in polishing but in assembling and disassembling. Further, you might discover you can use still another step of polishing for the same price and deliver a smoother gun to your customer. If so, follow the 240 polishing step with a 400 grit abrasive on loose muslin wheels.

As a whole I've mentioned nothing but the 45 ACP so far and have made no mention at all of various chemical ways of removing rust or case hardened surfaces which must be removed for best results.

I've found that a 10% solution of sulphuric acid and water in a pyrex dish brought to a boil cannot be beaten. All small parts go into this easily and as the stuff acts fast, they need not be left there long. Such large pieces as the housing on a Krag, which you might not be equipped to remove from the barrel, can be held over the dish and swabbed with a wool cloth dipped into the solution.

You will find that case hardened surfaces such as on some shotgun actions, the Colt Single Actions, etc., need not be acid treated, for the simple feat of polishing generally gets below the thin hardened skin and permits a deep penetration of color.

The magazine plate on the Krag, floor plate on the Springfield, and the entire frame of the Luger will give you a hundred percent less trouble if you will first pickle before polishing. In the bluing article I will go into more detail on some of the experiences you will encounter with various grades of steel and cast iron but as that does not enter into the polishing process, it need not worry you now.

In case you do use this acid treatment, immediately flush the parts in cold running water after removing from the bath, then immerse in boiling water. Leave them there long enough to insure thorough heating, remove and dip in some of the water displacing oils or let dry and dip in any good oil. If you don't do that, they'll rust, so help you.

In attempting to polish and blue the Luger and some other foreign make guns you will find that all the old blue, inside and out, on the frame, tends to turn a high "mukkle-dunn" color when blued in a manner to be described later. So completely strip the frame (which you are supposed to do anyhow) and leave in the pickle until the whole business turns a light gray. Determine this by removing from the bath often, and plunging into cold water, scrub with a brush and examine.

I have seen several newer Lugers, Walthers, Mausers, Brownings, etc. which as near as I can determine by experimenting, are blued in identically the same manner as a process described later on with the exception of some of the Lugers, whose Schnobbles had best be treated with the pickling bath to derive the best effect.

By the way, you can pickle any gun and blue without polishing and get a finish similar to these damned war finishes you see around. Will make you wake up during the night screaming, but it can be done.

You will find that to really clean up a rifle or shotgun barrel in a hurry it will be expedient to polish it for the first time through, parallel to the axis of the bore; and then with the same wheel and the same grit, polish it at right angles to the axis of the bore. In doing this, though, you MUST take as wide sweeps as you can to prevent lap marks. Then if you wish a duller finish, turn the barrel parallel with the wheel's periphery and with the 140 grit on the loose muslin wheel polish downward, but just let the face of the wheel graze the barrel and proceed very, very slowly. The only thing which will tell you when you've enough is by looking at it.

Well, you blue this guy's 45 and he's pretty danged well pleased and, as all gun bugs are great talkers amongst themselves, he tells his shootin' pals about it and the first thing you know you snag another sucker in the form of a young squirt who has a Marlin 39A on which he thinks maybe he'd like to spend a little more than the owner of the 45. You can see the handwriting on the wall: you're going to do some bluing business, so you tell him: "Okay, bub, come back in a few days and I'll have her for you."

You look the gun over - case hardened receiver, nicely polished barrel, etc. How are you going to equal or better the original finish? Do it this way:

Buy yourself two soft, one medium and one hard felt wheels, all eight inches in diameter, and then you'll discover your purse is empty but with care and the like, those wheels will last you many, many, years. Somewhere later on I've some dope on felts - nuts, as long as we are going into felt wheels, now is as good a time as the next:

Always, for gun work, buy TRUED felt wheels.

DO NOT run at excessive speeds.

DO NOT run against the grain.

DO NOT use a sharp instrument to crack the "head".

DO NOT soak in water.

DO NOT store in a damp room.

DO NOT polish without abrasive at the periphery.

Further, before going into the better quality polishing processes, make absolutely certain that your motor is very well bolted to its table or pedestal. Do not try to use a flexible shaft as they do not run true and in the same vein, be sure your polishing arbor is absolutely true.

Why all this "true" business? Any chatter in your wheel's surface will result in chatter marks in your polished surface.

As you are now set up for "Master" quality work, the thing to do is turn out some work justifying the name. Here's how:

All guns which have been handled much have a few pits in them - perhaps there are some which don't but I've yet to see a gun which does not have some - even those belonging to the most avid gun crank, unless he has always used moisture displacing and fingerprint neu- tralizing oils. So it is up to you to determine just how deep these pits are. If they are quite deep, place one of the soft eight inch felts on your arbor, mark the end of it with the figure "140" and apply some 140 grit to the wheels periphery.

The barrel offers the greatest problem to the beginner - especially if it were one of the Model 39's which have the flat sides on the tube. These flats take a little more time to bring to a true polish because you dare not ride too hard as rounded corners will result.

If you have started with the 140 grit, polish the flats at a 45 degree angle. Do one at a time and polish it full length. When you come to that little area where the barrel screws into the receiver, turn the barrel at right angles to the axis of the wheel and with gosh-awful steady nerves polish each individual section, remembering to use that old "down-and-around-and-up-against" business. It is difficult to do on such a small surface but otherwise you'll make gouges.

And speaking of gouges! When you first start using these felt wheels, you'll discover why gunsmiths leave home. Your work must be held at right angles to the periphery at all times, for if not, the fast cutting edges of the wheel will make very deep cuts into your gun's surface. These can only be removed with considerable extra work at cross polishing. As soon as you discover you've made one of these cuts, remove it. If you forget and polish over it in the regular manner, you'll have some beautiful ripples in your finished job. And don't think a gun nut won't discover it. I know! I've caught the devil more than once for thinking I could get by in a slipshod manner before discovering that there is just one way to treat a gun and that is HONESTLY.

As this gun is a take-down model, be sure and put the two parts together before polishing the receiver. This is really a sweet little gun to work on in that the receiver's area is small. But during your first passes you will find that the case hardening assumes a silvery color quite unlike that on regular steel or heat-treated steel. If you do a reasonable amount of polishing, you will go under this skin the first pass or two.

Don't polish the small parts with the 140 grit. It is just a waste of time. They can be done much later.

The next step, now that you have all the marks left from the 140 grit, is to completely remove them if you are striving for the "Master" finish. If you wish an intermediate finish, remove "most" of the polishing marks, and those polishing marks you do leave must be of such microscopic fineness they won't show in the finished blue job.

Regardless of where you are going to stop, go over the gun completely with the 240 grit. The theory is this: if you are going to proceed to a mirror finish, adjust your angle of polishing so that you will end up parallel to the bore and at right angles on the receiver if there are protrusions thereon; or parallel to the action if that action's lines are flush. If you are going to stop before getting that far, you'll want to end up the same way as far as polishing direction is concerned.

You've gone over the gun at a 45 degree angle with the last 140 grit pass, so with another 8 inch soft felt (and marked with 240) go back over the gun, but this time go at about a 10 or 15 degree angle to the bore and action. Remove ALL the 140 grit marks.

This request for a different felt wheel for each grit may sound rather odd at first inspection, but it is impossible to clean a wheel completely and then add a finer grit. Nothing is more discouraging than to be polishing along with a real fine grit and suddenly produce a scratch as wide and deep as the Grand Canyon from a grain of grit left in the wheel.

As this is an intermediate job, you can bring your polishing operations to a rapid close. Make certain that the metal is in the pure "white", no pits or mars left. These little gremlins have a habit of showing up at exactly the tail end of the last polishing pass just when you think you are all done. So make sure the gun is thoroughly and 100% covered with nothing but 240 grit marks, then turn to your small parts.

Seeing as how you are getting a little more pay for this job, examine all the inside parts. If they are rusty, throw them in with the parts which show and give them a good buffing; if they are dirty from old fouling and grease, put them in a special basket for a good run through your de-greasing tanks at the same time you are preparing the other parts for bluing.

Screw heads, pins and the like can be cleaned darned fast on the 240 wheel, but use lots of common sense while doing it. In the first place, you can burn hell out of your fingers if you ride too hard; and in the second place, don't make them lop-sided. Hold them in the fingertips and spin or hold them in the tool you can make up, and then put back in the box for final polishing later.

The next and last grit for the intermediate finish is with the 400 grit. Use about four 8" x 3/8" loose muslin wheels on your arbor. Break them in with an old file as you did with the 45 ACP and apply the grit to the wheel. As before, it will take a little work to get a good amount on the periphery. When you get some there, let the wheel run awhile to insure the polish setting hard and then go over the gun at about a 35 degree angle to the bore. Keep applying polish to the surface of the wheel, letting it set up so that you've a hard but flexible polishing surface. Again: don't ride too hard, but keep riding until nothing shows but plenty of 400 grit marks.

A blow to your pride: actually you are NOT removing all the 240 grit marks in this intermediate priced job - you are just rounding them off so good that they don't show.

After you have done the above, start polishing parallel to the bore, but ride your work hard. Get sort of a buzz-saw sound to it. And for gosh sake remember to make full length passes on the barrel. When you get to the action shoulder, sort of "snap" the work away from the wheel. A little practice and you can do this without leaving any slap marks.

In case it is the round barrel variety, do your HARD polishing when traveling at the 35 degree angle and take it light all the way through the parallel passes.

In regards to the next to the last paragraph - after you have gone over the barrel riding hard, finish off with a very light pass. At the action shoulder hold the barrel at about a 70 degree angle to the wheel and make a real fast turn, forcing the barrel down at the same time and end up with the barrel parallel to the wheel. The resulting polish marks will be indistinguishable in the final blue job.

Go to the small parts again and final polish those which were from the inside of the gun, dip in oil, and return to your work bench. The parts which are to be blued should be polished lightly with the loose wheel and put into the bluing basket. The finger lever had best be rough polished with the same tool you should have had made up for the ACP. Then go over the outside of the lever with the 400 grit on the loose buff using the "Swing" turn described above for polishing the lower curves.

Warning: Be mighty cautious, brother, when putting a sharply curved surface over a polishing wheel's periphery. A week ago I tore the front of my pants clean to the skin doing that clever little trick and I didn't like it. The buff caught the spanner wrench I was making and had I been an inch closer would have been gutted like a fresh caught fish. So in the real deep recesses of any finger lever or up between trigger guard and handle of a pizzle, get a good grip on the part and press the "hillside" part against the wheel with the depression or valley down and let the wheel work its own darned way into the small space. A couple of times at this and you'll see it is simpler than it sounds. (Figure 11)

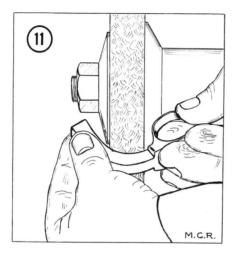

Before proceeding to blue this gun, examine it closely for frost marks, for if you have done this as you should, our resulting blue will be superior to most factory jobs.

Now to get on with getting a mirror finish. Go back to the close of the instructions concerning the 240 grit. After being sure that all 140 grit marks are gone, take the medium felt and mark it with "400" and head it up with that number. This finer grit is harder to handle in that if it is too moist it will harden dead smooth and not cut worth nothin'.

To make the story better, why not go ahead and blue that Marlin and get your money, then take a S&W Military and Police and see what we can do with that? No use in shooting the whole yarn on one 22 rifle, for if you've been a good boy so far you have turned out a finish not to be sneezed at and can go on from there to any rifle or shotgun made and do the same. In one way, shotguns are easier to handle in that the barrels come off easily which is always an advantage in any man's language.

Before tearing that Smith & Wesson down, or any other pistol as far as that is concerned, make up some screw blanks for the side plate. Do this by getting some fillister head machine screws and grind the heads down to size and file a slot in the top for taking out and putting back in. Cut them to length and when polishing, put the plate on and use these screws. Using them completely eliminates funneling around the holes, does not damage the original screws and they can be used several times before they are so damaged they need to be discarded.

Take the grips off, carefully lift off the side plate and remove the entrails. (Figure 12 shows this step on a Colt, but the technique is the same.) Completely strip the cylinder and crane and return the crane to the frame in its original position. This being a S&W, drive out the barrel pin, lock bolt and lock bolt pin as well as all sights which will come off. (S&W calls theirs a "yoke", and not a "crane", but you get the idea!) And as long as this is the super-duper job, remove the barrel - refer to Baker or Vickery if you don't know how, and if you don't have BOTH books, lay your work aside, buy them and read them clear through before reading another word of mine. Then get yourself busy and lay the frame on a smooth brass or steel block and drive out the frame lug. Whazzat? It's the little "what-cha-ma-jigger" which sticks out on the left hand side of the frame and is there to prevent the cylinder from coming back and biting you when doing the extracting job.

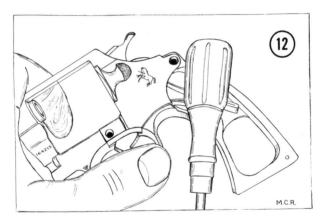

Pick up the hammer of this gun and look at it. If the case hardening finish is in good condition, tenderly place that hammer in the "not to blue" box and pick up the trigger. Ditto on the preceding. "If the case hardened finish is rusty or worn," you ask. If you can't figure that one out, you're lost! Polish and blue!

Yeah, and take out the cylinder stop plunger, spring, and screw! On some of the heavier models of the same brand, you'll find there is a "dobiddy" on the bottom of the crane which locks it up when it is up and is called "yoke stop" and "yoke stop spring". Rusted in? Okay, take a 1/2 mm drill and drill a wee hole (and 1/2 mm is dinged wee) right about where you think the plunger is and then take a scribe and force the plunger out...all this is AFTER you have tried tapping it, soaking it in penetrating oil, and swearing it out - none of which generally works.

So now you have a pile of parts with perhaps the trigger and hammer in the "no blue" box. Put all the rest of the parts in the "to blue" box and stumble over to your polishing table. Take the "no blue" box with you.

Start with the barrel. Probably has fixed sights and always has the locking bolt housing lug sticking down at the bottom. There are several particular spots on this particular hunk of tubing where you can blow your stack - around the sight, the locking housing and the milling from there back to where it goes up agin' the frame.

Start with the front sight. Examine the periphery of your "240" soft felt wheel and see to it that it has good sharp edges to it and CAREFULLY polish the sides of the blade, then carefully polish the barrel for about a quarter of an inch each side of the blade parallel with the bore. Then turn the barrel at right angles to the wheel and do fore of the blade and about an inch aft. Take it easy aft and don't ride, or it will end in a ripple. Turn the barrel over and look at the lug. Purty! It's a dinged nuisance to polish. So stand close to the wheel and hold the barrel perpendicular to the ground and slowly and carefully polish the recessed part of the lug and the adjacent area of the barrel. (Figure 13) Polish enough of the lug that you can then turn the barrel at right angles and cross polish the rest of the housing. Now, polish the front of the housing, but be careful that the edges of your wheel do not cut into the barrel. Let the back or rear end of it go as is, unless rusted - in which case, give it some of the same.

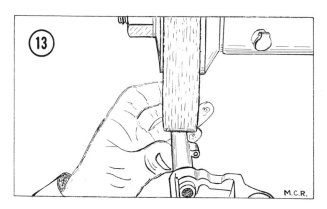

The flat part which is formed on the barrel immediately above the extractor rod had better be draw filed (Baker or Vickery tell you how) and the sides of this protuberance should be polished with the edge of the little one inch felt bob you have chucked onto the end of your grinder. The polishing of this recess is the reason you removed the barrel, bub, so do it up brown after all that work. Anything but a perfect job would be a waste of time.

Polishing the barrel can be best done with the 240 grit at a 30 degree angle to the bore, being careful not to bump the fine edges of the sight nor the housing underneath. When you come to the largest part of the barrel, that wee bit which continues on beyond the frame without changing shape, turn the barrel at right angles and give it a quick, even spin. There is a rather sharp shoulder on some S & W barrels which can be darned easily slopped up. So, take it easy.

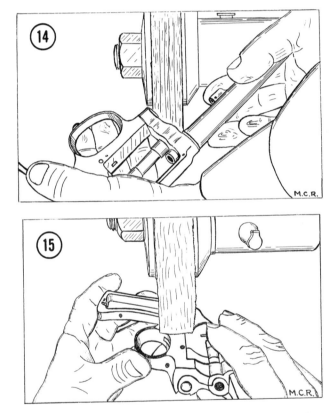

Now to the frame. A quick look will show you why the frame lug was removed. It would be absolutely impossible to polish around that projection without doing a slug of damage. Also examine the front end of the frame and yoke. How in hell would you polish them if the barrel was still on, if that barrel happened to be a six incher? (Figure

14) And if you don't have the crane - yoke, darn it - in place, put it there now and also have sense enough to use a screw long enough on the side plate that it locks the yoke tight, else it will be flopping around like a wet sock when you are polishing other parts of the frame. (Figure 15)

I hope you have had the grace to read the preceding stuff about polishing other guns, so will not go into too much detail about the actual polishing with the 240 grit on the frame. Just remember that old stuff about "around and around and down - up to and on down and back again." And, if you want the guy that owns the gun - if he is a gunnut (and everybody that owns more than one gun is bound to be a gunnut) - to really love you like a two inch sirloin steak DON'T buff out the monogram on the frame. There are times when you'll have to, of course. But usually the only reason it is buffed off is because us gunsmiths get in a hurry to get done so we can go chuck hunting or some other non-profit enterprise.

Would be a good idea to make yourself up an eight inch soft felt with a "rounding" periphery. Try and make it an exact half circle - (if the wheel is one inch wide, then give the round face a one inch diameter.) Best thing in the world for getting in between most of the trigger guard and handle. (Figures 16 & 17) You might want to call it a "grip" but it is a handle to me.

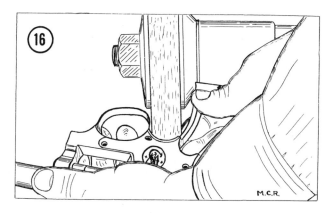

The top strap, barrel band, and yoke millings are powerful hard to buff, sir, and had best be approached with due caution. Hold the frame exactly perpendicular to the ground and work them over. You'll have to do most of your polishing with the edge of the wheel, so be careful in your round and round motion that you do it in a true fashion or the result will look like a plowed field. Of course, if you are in the business of bluing for keeps, get some 1/2" felts for this particular

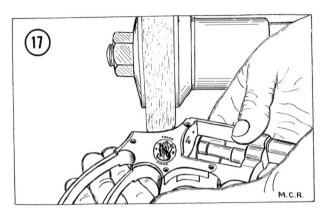

job. If you want to get snooty, you can shape them with a rasp in much the same manner a tool maker shapes a lathe bit to cut compound stuff and thus save yourself a lot of headaches and worry. (Figures 18, 19 & 20). Maybe this is getting too fancy for most of us...but it sure works swell.

Don't forget to polish the inside of the trigger guard. The sharp curve on the front of it and the front strap are best polished with that round face wheel I suggested, but can be nicely polished with the same wheel you used for the inside of the trigger guard.

Next major obstacle is the cylinder. More cylinders are done sloppily than any other part of the gun. Of course, they look nice when the gun is new but did you ever polish a new cylinder, even lightly, with your 400 grit loose buff? No? Try it some time. You'll be amazed at how completely you were fooled by the fact that the deep polishing

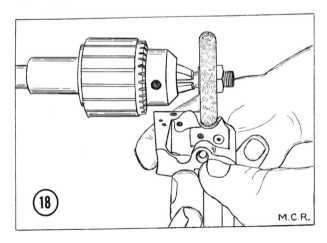

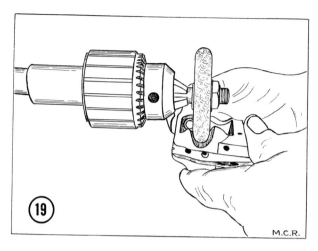

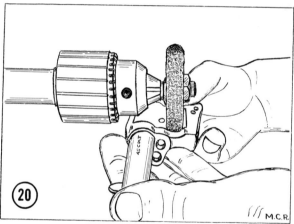

marks went round and round the axis of said cylinder and went past unnoticed.

Take a lesson from the above and govern yourself accordingly. Personally, I don't believe in it for the "Master" finish, but do do it often on the cheaper finishes.

Regardless, hold the cylinder with the bore parallel to the axis of your polishing wheel and polish the area between the flutes, (Figure 21) then with the cylinder on a good piece of dowel pin or brass brazing rod, hold it to the periphery of the wheel at a thirty degree angle, letting it spin (but snubbing it lightly with the thumb), polish the area from the end of the flutes to the end of the cylinder. Holding at the

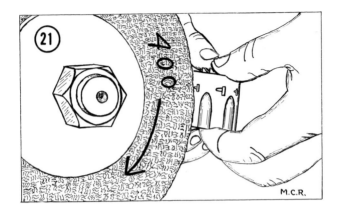

same angle, proceed on to the metal between the flutes. Remember to hold it firmly, though, and don't begin playing fire truck with the noise - don't let it travel that fast. (Figure 22) Doing this absolutely prevents rounding the end of the cylinder or funneling the cylinder stop holes.

The flutes make some guys gray-haired when they try to polish them and other guys gray-haired when they see how other guys do polish them. There is just one really good way to do it and that is with a small felt wheel shaped as shown in the pictures, and used as shown. (Figures 23 & 24)

The hammer and trigger were probably rusty or worn so tackle them next. The flat sides are easily done in the same manner as the frame, but the inside curves are another problem, especially with the hammer. Write a supplier of polishing parts and get one of those little felts like your two eyes see in some of the other pictures. If you know of a better way, fer gol's sake, let's have it. (Figure 25)

Guess that 240's the major parts, so secure your eight inch medium felt with the "400" on its side to the arbor and get to work. Without going over the same stuff in words, you proceed to do it with the wheel. Polish all the barrel parallel to the axis of the bore and change your angle about twenty or thirty degrees when working on the frame. Cylinder? Return it to the rod and holding it at a forty-five degree angle, spin the whole business without too much pressure being sure this time to go over the entire cylinder and remove all the former polishing marks. Be careful not to let the thing start vibrating with you when polishing the fluted area or you might round the edges of the flutes.

Take all your small parts - side plate screws, extractor rod, locking bolt, etc., etc. - and examine them closely for signs of rust or failure on the factory's part to polish. Those internal parts which are only pol-

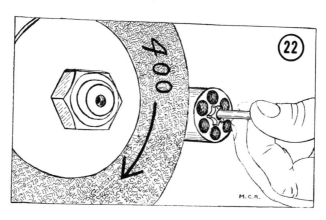

ished on the side which shows will work much better if polished on both sides. So, with the 400 grit lightly polish off the mill marks, etc., and bring to a clean "white." This applies especially to the rebound slide, hand bolt, and bolt as well as the cylinder stop. The other parts, if nicely polished, will greatly enhance the quality of your work and more than please your customer.

These 400 grit marks which now cover your gun are really quite shallow, but you can make them less shallow and speed up your final polishing if you will go over the entire gun with 400 grit on an eight inch loose muslin wheel. Do this in exactly the same manner as described previously except that on the barrel and cylinder, travel in a line direct with the bore and at a thirty degree or forty degree angle on the frame.

Just a reminder: when polishing with the felts on either side of the

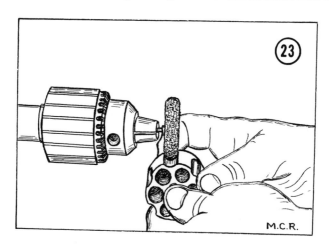

frame, do so with wide, all inclusive sweeps from grip to cylinder flange, doing it in a swinging motion, not attempting to do all that bordering the flange in one grand power sweep, but up to - down and around - and over again.

You will, in time, discover that this is one swell way to get a gun up to the cheap and medium priced jobs - using the felt up to the final pass with the loose buff and 400 grit polish - for the gun can now be be blued and turn out very, very nicely.

To get the "Master" finish, tho, you need two more buffing wheels: a felt wheel as large in diameter as your motor will handle (eight inch on 1/4 to 1/3; 10 inch on 1/2 to 3/4 and 12 inch on one hp.) and a correspondingly large loose muslin buff. The extra diameter greatly speeds up your surface cutting speed without any increase in depth of grit cuts.

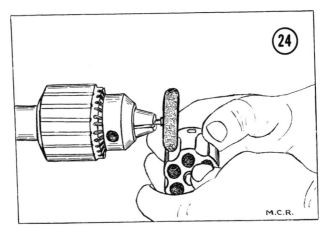

(Note: Since the original writing of this article, the use of #500 grit polish has come into more common use. Although we usually went directly from #400 grit - with all the former polishing marks completely buffed out - directly to #555 "Stainless Steel Polish" on a hard felt wheel, the intermediate #500 grit polishing step can be used. This step would be done as follows: on a 6" or 8" soft felt wheel use the #500 polish, polishing the gun at 45 degrees to the bore. Follow this with #500 grit on a loose muslin wheel at right angles to the bore to remove all the grit marks. - Bob B.)

A "rock hard" felt will give the best results when used with any of the so called stainless steel polishes, which, by the bye, are far superior and much less messy than the "rouge" and "tripoli" polishes formerly recommended. They generally come in three pound cakes and sell for

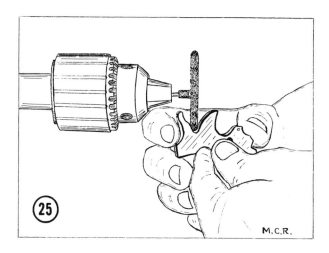

about a buck and a half - some less, some more. But they last a long time and are more than worth the chips.

Mount your hard felt on the arbor and mark it with the trade name of the finishing polish you are using. Go over the gun and all the small parts with this polish. At right angles to the axis of the bore, thirty degree angle to axis of cylinder and at right angles to the line of fire on the frame. Do the hammer and trigger in straight lines with line of fire.

Should you, by chance, try using a softer felt than the above, you must be mighty dinged careful, toots, or you will do something you didn't believe possible - the polish seems to build up in front of the actual polishing surface of the wheel as it spins and digs itself into the steel, resulting in minute gouges. When this happens there is but one thing to do - start with the 400 grit again and work back up to where you did your dirt.

Former polishing marks really stand out like a brick whatcha-may-call-it in a fog in Cincinnati from now on and the thing you have to do is remove all of them. If you have been of sharp eye and patient nature, you properly followed instructions and did remove each preceding polish mark with each new grit. If you did, you won't waste much time with this, the next to the last step. Otherwise, about the best thing you can do is go back and start all over - saves time, wheels, polish, and disposition!

When starting in with this stainless polish, dig out a clean pair of gloves and reserve them for this one grade of polish. You have undoubtedly worked a lot of abrasive into your other gloves and don't think for a minute that stuff won't raise particular hell with a piece of highly polished steel!

It'll take you some time to get the surface of the gun worked down to a point where it looks like you are getting somewhere. But do that you must. Every little grit scratch must be polished off, and when you discover you've left a lot of pits in the gun don't feel too badly about it for even Rome wasn't built in a day, the book says. Just start over again. Do the small parts next.

Polishing the cylinder on this hard felt wheel is best done without spinning. Do it at a sharp angle from your former pass with the 400 grit. I personally found that traveling quite closely parallel to the bore is best.

Heave a sigh of relief and put on the big loose muslins, apply the stainless and polish it up parallel to the bore, right angles on the frame. Then go over the small parts and bring to a high luster. The cylinder can be given a beautiful finish by spinning it at right angles to the periphery of the wheel until all polishing marks disappear. Dip the small parts not to be blued in oil. Put those to be blued in the bluing basket and you are ready to do the last half of the job...blue the durned thing!

Quick Reference Summary

In the foregoing article, two distinct methods of polishing are discussed: the quick "Cheaply as Possible" method, and the "Master Mirror Finish" method. The following tables give you the equipment needed for each method, plus the individual steps and the general directions of polishing for each grit. If in working on a gun it is evident that some of the coarse grit steps can be eliminated - because there are no bad pits or rust spots or the like - just be sure to keep in mind that at each successive polishing step all grit marks for each step are removed before going on to the next finer grit...and that the direction of movement of the piece across the wheel must be alternated not only with each grit, but most importantly, at the next finer grit. For example, if you start out with a gun in good condition on #240 polish, polishing at 30 degrees to the bore on the barrel and at right angles on the action, you must on the next finer grit polish at parallel to the bore on the barrel and at 45 degrees on the action, and so on up through the final polishing with #555 on the loose muslin wheel.

Polishing Cheaply as Possible:

Need: 4 6" x 3/8" Stitched Wheels
8 6" x 3/8" Loose Muslin Wheels
1 tube each 140 and 240 Polish

1. On 3 or 4 6" Stitched wheels put 140 polish. Travel perpendicular to wheel axis, then parallel with axis on frame/actions.

2. On 4 Loose Wheels put 240 polish. Travel lengthwise, then at right angles to axis to remove all former polishing marks. If working on a shotgun, put the 240 polish on 4 loose muslin wheels instead of stitched wheels. Gives a "Frosted" look for no-glare in the field. (This 2-grit polishing job is the "Standard" grade finish.)

"Master" Mirror Finish Polishing:

Need: 2 Soft Felt Wheels, 6 or 8"
        1 Medium Felt Wheel, 6 or 8"
        1 Hard Felt Wheel, 8"
        8 Loose Muslin Wheels, 8"
        1 tube each of 140, 240, 400, (500) and 555 Polish

1. On 6" or 8" Soft felt wheel - 1750 rpm - use #140 grit on rough guns; #240 grit on average guns - to remove pits, mars, etc. Travel at 30 degrees to bore on barrel. Travel at right angles on action.

2. On 6" or 8" Soft felt wheel use grit #240 following #140 - or #400 on a 6 or 8" Medium felt wheel following #240 - and polish parallel to bore on barrel and at a 45 degree angle on action. Remove all former polishing marks.

3. On 4 6" or 8" Loose Muslin wheels use grit #400 at right angles to the entire gun to remove all former polishing marks. (If you are working on a rough gun on which you started with #140 polish on soft felt, then #240 on soft felt, be sure to use 400 on medium felt before before using the #400 on loose muslin.)

***The gun can now be blued for a good standard finish without using finer than #400 grit. (This is the "Pittsburgh" grade finish.)

4. For "High" mirror finish, continue with the optional #500 grit on a 6 or 8" Soft felt wheel, polishing at 45 degrees to the bore. Follow this with #500 on Loose Muslin wheel and travel at right angles to remove all grit marks.

5. On 8, 10 or 12" Rock Hard felt wheel use #555 polish at 45 degrees angle to bore on entire gun and remove all the #500 polishing marks. Be sure NOT to overheat!

6. On 4 8" Loose Muslin wheels use #555 grit and polish either parallel or at right angles to the bore. Continue - without overheating - bringing the gun to mirror finish. (This is the "Master" grade finish - the very best.)

Note: Muslin wheels should be at least 1" wide or more at periphery. Stitched muslin wheels can be used instead of Felt, but Felt wheels give a smoother finish.

Some Random Shots in the Dark

When the grit on the polishing head becomes spotted and rough, one of the wheel truing bricks is the best thing I have found for removing the old polish from the wheel. The edge of a worn-out hacksaw blade is next best and an old file brings up the rear.

Don't try and apply grit abrasive to wheels which have been subjected to oil or grease-base abrasive. It won't work.

Rouge, if used on hard felt with too much pressure by the operator against the piece of steel being polished, will lap into the surface of the steel and show color variation when blued.

Heat-blued parts such as Colt hammers, etc. had best be polished off even if they look in excellent condition, prior to bluing. This heat blue has a tendency to turn light green when blued by many of the modern processes.

You will find that steel used by some of the major firearms manufacturers will take a much better polish than the steel of their competitors. Trade names need not be divulged but once you have done master polishing on all the various arms you will be able to draw your own conclusions.

Do not be disturbed by the forge marks which will show in the surface of the steel on some of the older models of a certain brand of well known arms. The cause for these "strata" is not my business, but it will be well for you to know that you cannot polish these out, and that they will show color variation when blued. In some instances of old army guns of the same make, the "strata" is quite pronounced in that certain layers of it will be pitted much deeper than their companion layers. When this happens, polish the gun as best you can, pickle lightly to remove the rust, repolish and blue. The gun will probably look like something the cat has drug in but this is absolutely not your fault.

When polishing the trigger guard of some of the cheap rifles, watch the metal closely. This pertains to detachable trigger guards in particular. In many cases they are pot metal or aluminum painted black and will not only disappear in your bluing tank but will, in all probability, completely ruin the bath.

Don't forget that inhaling very much of the abrasive dust can be mighty hard on the lungs so a respirator is recommended, as is a suction type dust collector.

Some of the real old octagon barrels look real well if draw-filed with a real fine file without any further polishing.

Don't polish brass on your stainless buffing wheels and then immediately polish steel for small particles of brass might adhere to the steel surface and show up as specks in the blue job.

The finished blue job is no better than the polishing job which precedes it, and I repeat, *the finished-blue job is no better than the polish-*

ing job which precedes it.

Guns which have been nickeled and then stripped properly, clean up very nicely and easily as a general rule and should not be turned down by the gunsmith for fear of not turning out a good job.

Real cheap guns had better be passed up. Heaven only knows what kind of steel or cast iron went into their construction and the results you will get bluing them will probably make you so ashamed you won't let the fellow pay you - and even then you have established yourself a bad reputation. And weren't even paid for it!

Removable target sights are best prepared for bluing with a medium cut file. File the metal lengthwise on the sights and perpendicularly on the ends.

A beautiful sand blast effect can be had by carefully pickling the top strap in the 10% sulphuric acid solution before bluing the gun. During the polishing process be very careful not to let the wheels touch this pickled surface. After it is blued, it will look very attractive. This goes for the tops of hammers or a shotgun housing, etc. and surely offers a decided advantage to the man in the field who has tried to eliminate as much glare as possible.

When doing welding on gun parts, attempt to use steel similar to that of the original part. Different steels are prone to show different shades of color when blued. This can be very embarrassing in the wrong place.

Do not be too worried about grit marks between trigger guards and front strap or inside trigger guard or any other sharply curved surface. These marks do not show up very badly after being blued.

Do not attempt to pickle front sights which contain mirrors for the purpose of deflecting light on the sight bead. That may sound like a silly precaution, but I have heard of it happening in three various shops under the handling of excellent gunsmiths and all have the same result. The mirrors either dropped out, flew away or were 'et by the goblins - anyhow they couldn't be found.

If you must hire kids in your shop, don't put them to polishing - let them start in dismantling or assembling guns. Polishing is too important a process to trust to the youngster, unless he is an exception rather than the rule.

After the buffing wheel has snatched three or four pieces from your hand and slammed them against the floor with resulting expected damage, you will probably put a rubber mat or some pieces of cardboard beneath the wheels, or if you can take advice, do it before you ever start polishing.

It greatly adds to the appearance of a gun to leave some of the small parts mirror-polished after the rest of the gun is blued. I refer particularly to sides of hammers, or plunger pins, some extractors, some safetys, etc. You will have to let your own artistic nature govern your actions on this score but don't be afraid to try it.

Following are drawings showing the basic steps in polishing a pump or auto shotgun action. Pay particular attention to the special felt bobs used to correctly polish the various contours.

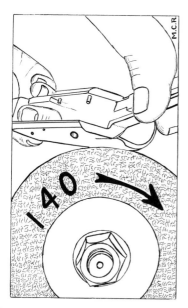

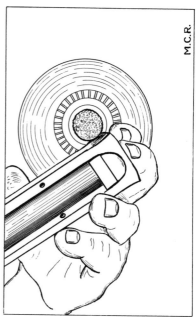

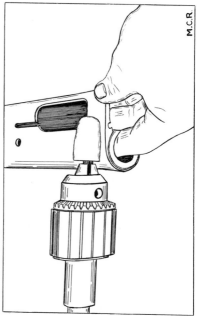

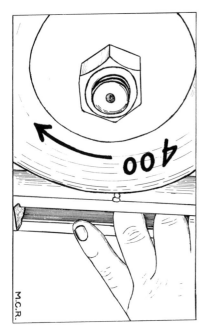

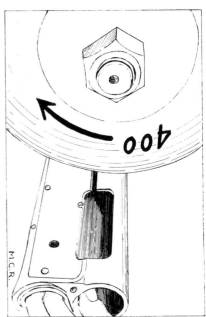

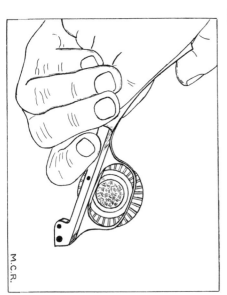

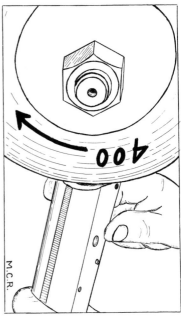

CHAPTER 6

BLUING - HOT & COLD

DEAR MR. BROWNELL:

Some time ago - about three weeks to be exact - I received an order of bluing salts. Since then, I have been getting my guns polished and ready to blue. Last night I, and a doctor friend of mine, attempted to blue the guns and I must say our results were discouraging to say the least.

I followed the instructions quite carefully, but not carefully enough, for this morning I discovered that I had made an error or two. But perhaps you would be interested in hearing what happened.

We put the bluing solution together as per the instructions on the wife's electric range, and as the guns were already clean the "Doc" and I sat back while it was warming up and enjoyed a spot of giggle water he had uncovered. That was the only enjoyable moment of the evening. Didn't think about stirring it, and of course it boiled over.

Doc and I each grabbed a dipper of water and dumped it in to cool it off. As it says in the instructions the results were "eruptive." Solution spattered all over the wall, on Doc's new wool hunting suit and on the linoleum. We turned the heat off and started cleaning up the mess before the wife found her stove covered with the stuff. What a laugh that was. As we wiped the solution off, we brought the stove's finish off right along with it. That not only applied to the stove, but also to the paint on the wall - and the linoleum has holes in it this morning and Doc just called to report that his new woolen hunting suit looks like rats built a house in it during the night.

Rather than admit defeat we tried once more. This time we brought it to a gentle boil, as per the instructions, and when the temperature was right placed the guns in. They hadn't been in the bath more than a couple of minutes when there was a hell of an eruption and the solution went all over the kitchen again. The plugs that Doc had encouraged me to place in the ends of the barrels had blown out. I removed the guns from the bath and Doc and I poured the stuff down the sink and swore to heaven above, never to try such a stunt again, thinking that our troubles were over. But, now it developes that the damned bluing solution has settled into the outside sewer trap, so now the plumbers are on their way to dig it up.

I wonder if you will blue the guns for me before I have to spend another hundred dollars or two to discover it is a good idea to leave every man to his business?

Very truly yours,

L.H.B.

P.S.: Are the soft, rotten spots on Doc's bird-shooting boots due to the solution getting on them? Sure ruined!

- Name withheld...for obvious reasons!

AND MAY WELL WE ASK, "WHY GUN RE-BLUING?"

No other activity or line of work in a gun shop or sporting goods store teaches the mechanics of a gun better than re-bluing. To re-blue a gun one has to completely dismantle it piece by piece and each of the hundreds of varieties of guns that one handles has its own peculiarities. After one has handled about so many guns the whole theory of a gun's mechanical operation becomes ingrained in one's mind, never to be lost. Further, continued handling of the more popular guns soon leads the gunsmith to know, almost automatically and without looking, which pieces are worn, which pieces should be replaced.

There is also a money-making feature - not only is re-bluing fairly profitable but it also gives the dealer or gunsmith an opportunity to become better acquainted with his shooting customers. Nothing pleases a gunnut more than to have his favorite and heart-loved gun made like new by a gunsmith; and, as a result he is inclined to look up to the man who worked such miracles - for bluing does seem to be magic to the uninitiated. So! As sights and scopes, slings and gun cases are needed the sportsman not only buys from the man who did up his gun, he brings along his friends.

The original cost of setting up a bluing shop is not great nor is it necessary to buy a lot of unnecessary crap. Bluing tanks, burners, some bluing salts and cleaner, polish and some wheels, and you're in business. From then on buy as you need - don't buy unless you do need.

The quality of a blue job depends entirely on the man doing the bluing - little on the salts!! If you have a man who will do a masterful piece of polishing, have all surfaces true and bright, corners sharp, no funneled screw holes and ground-off screw heads - if he is careful to clean the gun properly just before bluing - if he will follow the instructions that go with anybody's salts - well, he'll get bluing jobs that are out of this world.

Bluing can be fun and profitable - full time or part time. Shooters are always looking for gunsmiths who will give them honest work.
- *Bob B.*

OXYNATE NO. 7 BLUING INSTRUCTIONS

Since the dawn of time sportsmen have been spending more hours cleaning and caring for their shooting and hunting equipment than has ever been spent using this equipment. Even King David of Biblical fame cared for and practiced with his side-arm, the sling; the Yeomen of England and the Longriflemen of New England realized that to live was to insure the reliability of their equipment.

The urge to care for your gun, to keep it in top flight condition, was born in you. The caveman had little truck with a rotten club - or an Indian much use for a bow that had lost its spring. How many millions of hours do you suppose our ancient ancestors spent in rubbing oil into their bows or hacking at that club point so that when the time did come for use it would be ready? Yes, the loving of guns and the desire to keep them in perfect condition is a basic part of man's construction.

Until recently the art of re-bluing guns was a closed secret to a very few Masters who were willing to take the time and pains to go through the lengthy process necessary with older methods of gun bluing. It required hours of patient rubbing and scrubbing, rusting and burnishing, to get a finish that would be durable and yet attractive. These older finishes, when properly applied, are still things of beauty.

Modern day living costs and higher standards of living make it impossible for the average individual to devote the multitude of hours necessary to produce a finish on a single gun that these older methods require for perfection. Solutions are now available which make it possible to produce beautiful and durable finishes with but a fraction of the work and chemical skill.

Bob Brownell, president of Brownell's Incorporated, is largely responsible for the revolution in gun re-bluing that has occurred in the gunsmithing field during the last 25 years. Prior to his introduction of "How-to-Blue" in the columns of *The American Rifleman* the average hobbyist, gunlover or gunsmith either had to turn down blue jobs or send them to the gun manufacturers. Those who did attempt the work were required to use sweat and back-break on a job that was too often thankless and unsatisfactory. The presentation of "How-to-Blue" did indeed prove to be a boon to the gunsmith.

Since the introduction of "How-to-Blue" or Oxynate "7", as it is now called, a great many other brands of bluing solutions with a variety of publicity and promotional claims have been shoved at the shooters and gunsmiths. Regardless of how much the chemical sells for or how much is spent on advertising it, it serves but one purpose - to blue guns.

Oxynate "7" Blues Guns

The finish is simple and easy to apply. When properly handled it will color the types of steel found in firearms; does not alter the characteristics or dimensions of the steel, and yet, is inexpensive. Once you have mastered the simple technique of Oxynate "7" you need not spend money and time worrying about other solutions. None of them will do anything that Oxynate "7" won't do. No company will stand behind their customers with the satisfying completeness as that given by Brownell's. Bob Brownell's care for his customers built the business to its present levels - the entire force of his company are bound to carry on this tradition of service first.

Even of more importance to the prospective user of bluing solutions, as well as to the old timer, is the world famous chemical organization at the disposal of customers of Brownell's. Not only does Brownell's maintain access to a production laboratory establishment, but the company from whom they buy the basic material is the largest of its kind in the world, having plants in every major country on the globe.

In view of the foregoing it would be senseless for us to make promotional statements about our chemical bluing products. Our entire organization and financial set-up are dependent upon the good will of the gun lovers of the world. This attitude of giving the whole story has resulted in there now being over 5,000 gunsmiths and gunnuts constantly using Oxynate "7" with ever increasing success.

Part of this success with Oxynate "7" is that no matter what kind of trouble you can get into - no matter what problem may stump you - Brownell can supply you with the answer. To put it into his words, "You can't think up any situation so brain-bursting in the bluing business that it hasn't happened to me - only more so." In addition, gunsmiths are constantly writing Brownell's to tell them about the solutions they have found to problems in their own shops, and new techniques and procedures are always being tested and perfected in Brownell's own testing facilities as well as in the laboratories of the compound's manufacturer.

So, the instructions contained here are not one man's findings, or one laboratory's specifications. Rather, they are the compilation of all the information passed on by those 5,000 gunsmiths and hobbyists, plus all the technical dope. This means you are getting several hundred years worth of experience all in one dose - an asset most products cannot claim, and really the only asset that is of value to you as a gun bluer!

OXYNATE "7"

When Oxynate "7" is used according to the instructions a beautiful finish can be assured. As the finish is a part of the steel itself, it will not chip off, check, crack, and is as flexible as the steel.

The deep penetration of Oxynate "7" provides maximum durability and acts as a rust preventive and lubricant to the surface of the steel, rounding off, as it does, the microscopic edges, leaving the surface smooth, yet without any dimensional change to the surface.

Parts are not damaged in any respect by the process. Even the accidental leaving of a part in the bath for months has found no change in the parts.

So the following can be said of Oxynate "7";
1. It is easy to handle.
2. The finish achieved is beautiful and uniform.
3. It is easy to operate at low temperatures without complicated or difficult procedures.
4. It causes no dimensional changes.
5. It is fast-acting, requiring less in-tank time.
6. It makes a durable and lasting finish.
7. Finish color is the highly desirable midnight blue-black.
8. Set-up cost is low and per-gun costs stay low.

Operating instructions are simplicity themselves:

Single Tank Method

To mix, per gallon and a half of solution: Place three and a half quarts of cold water in the tank and slowly add ten pounds of bluing salts. In cases where more salts are being used per mixture the same proportions should be carried out. Care should be used in adding, for heat is generated by the dissolving of the salts, and too large a quantity at one time may cause the solution to boil or erupt. Stir frequently until salts are dissolved.

When salts are dissolved, turn on the heat source. When the solution starts to boil stir thoroughly and note the temperature. If it is below the required operating temperature range of 285 to 295 degrees F. add more salts until the density of the solution is raised, thus increasing the solution's boiling point; or, permit the solution to boil until enough moisture is precipitated out of solution to cause a higher boiling point.

The bath starts to color steel at about 285 F. but is most efficient on common gun steel at from 290 to 295 F. Surface coloring will be completed in approximately 15 minutes - when the gun can be removed from solution - and maximum penetration is complete at the end of thirty minutes.

That is all there is to it. Faulty results, poor finishes, and miscellaneous gremlins are human errors and no fault of your bluing solution. It is therefore wise for you to read the chapter on "Professional Technique" where-in preparation and completion are graphically presented for your personal benefit.

CAUTION: Oxynate "7" is caustic. Always wear rubber gloves when working with it. It is also advisable to wear a plastic face shield when the bath is in operation to prevent damage to face or eyes, which could prove permanent, should the very hot solution come in contact with your face or skin.

In case of serious accident call your doctor. Advise him to treat the same as for bad lye burns. External: Flush with acetic or boric acid and water. Internal: Sweet oil, stomach pump and neutralizers for caustic alkali.

Oxynate "7" attacks leather, wool, skin. Wear cotton clothing, rubbers and other non-animal clothing when working in your bluing room.

Two Tank Method

The average gunshop or hobbyist will have little use for the two tank method of gun bluing. However, in instances where a great many nickel steel or special alloy steel parts are to be blued, a two tank method may prove an economy.

The operator should prepare two bluing tanks instead of one with adequate heat source, barrel racks, thermometers, etc.

Tank Number One: To every ten pounds of bluing salts add four quarts of water and adjust water to salts ratio so that the solution boils at from 278 to 285 F.

Tank Number Two: To every ten pounds of bluing salts add three quarts of water and adjust water to salts ratio so that the solution boils at from 300 to 310 degrees F.

Procedure: With **both** tanks boiling at their proper temperature, insert the parts to be blued in tank number one, after usual chemical cleaning, for fifteen minutes. A temperature of 280 degrees F. is usual procedure. After the parts have remained in the tank for the required time, transfer them immediately to tank number two and leave there for fifteen to thirty minutes. Rinsing and oiling operations are the same as with the single tank process.

Advantages of the two tank method: With a few rare exceptions, any steel you may attempt to blue will not take on a red cast at the Tank Number One temperature of 280 degrees F. After the metal has been brought up to the 280 degree color, it can then be safely heated, in Tank Number Two, to 300 to 310 degrees F. at which temperature practically all the alloys (except **True** stainless steel) will blue.

Note: Where ample time is available, this same method can be used with but one bluing tank in the following manner: adjust water to salts ratio so solution will boil at 280 degrees F. Immerse the parts and leave in the solution without adding water. After a period of boiling, excess moisture will precipitate out of solution and the temperature of the bath will gradually rise to 300 or 310 F. after which the guns can be withdrawn fully colored. (This method eliminates the purchasing of extra salts, tanks, thermometers, etc.)

PROFESSIONAL TECHNIQUE

The methods of preparing a gun for bluing are varied, some simple and some complicated. If the home bluer is equipped with a polishing outfit his troubles are lessened to a great extent and he can carry out the work as listed below, which is for the gunsmith. If not, the steel must be sanded by hand to a high luster before bluing. Emery paper works satisfactorily for this, starting with 150 grit, then 240 grit and finishing with crocus cloth to a bright finish.

For practical purposes the gunsmith should equip himself with a good polishing outfit and do all polishing and preparation by power equipment. This is gone into detail later with all steps fully described.

It has been said, and justly so, that the better the polishing job the better the blue, for with this method the appearance after bluing depends entirely on the gun's appearance before bluing. The higher the luster before, the higher the luster of blue after immersion.

Dirt and Grease

The first step after polishing and before bluing is to be certain the piece to be blued is absolutely clean. You often hear of naptha or other gasoline products being recommended for cleaning, but experience has shown that the use of any gasoline during the process is courting trouble. There is always the possibility of a bit of the oil being left on the surface of the steel, resulting in grey streaks in the finished product. The best that can be recommended is "Dicro-Clean" which completely saponifies all dirt and grease. It is strong enough to do the job and if handled according to the following instructions cannot possibly harm the steel.

Use five ounces (by weight) to a gallon of water. Heat to between 180 degrees and a slow rolling boil and then immerse the parts to be cleaned. Leave in the cleaner for approximately 10 to 15 minutes, after which the parts should be removed and placed into a tank of clean soft water and scrubbed well with a vegetable cleaning brush.

When thoroughly scrubbed, examine the parts under a strong light for signs of puddling around screw holes, barrel rings, etc. If no oil slick or puddling appears the parts can be assumed clean. If oil is present, return the parts to the Dicro-Clean 909 for another minute or two and repeat the above examination.

Regardless of claims to the contrary: In bluing, cleanliness is perfection assured.

After cleaning in Dicro-Clean 909 the steel is chemically clean. Do not allow parts to stand in open air or in water for longer than is absolutely necessary. The oxygen in the air and the free oxygen in water will attack the steel and cause it to rust very rapidly. This rust might not be evident to the naked eye, but will show in the form of black specks or white specks after the gun has been blued, rinsed, and oiled.

Rust

Rust or scale should be removed with a good rust remover or if that is not available mix up a solution of 10% sulphuric acid and heat. A few minutes in this will do the trick. Any strong acid pickle should be avoided if at all possible because of the etching action of the acid on the surface of the steel.

Tanks

The bluing process tank should be made of mild or stainless steel with welded seams. A common black steel bread pan is satisfactory for pistol work, providing the pan is large enough. The average pistol tank should be six inches wide, six inches deep and 16 inches long. For rifle tank, 40" is minimum and even then some old Krags will take tanks up to 44".

All equipment coming in contact with Oxynate "7" should be made of steel. If your tanks are made of zinc-covered steel, this zinc can be removed by washing the tank thoroughly with a muriatic acid solution until all zinc is gone. Non-steel tanks will weaken your bath. A good temporary tank is made from steel barrels cut in half.

Occasionally galvanized rinse tanks will cause trouble. This comes about in the following manner: Due to the chemical composition of your water it is possible for electrolytic action to set up when the steel gun parts are placed in a galvanized tank. This results in a mild transfer of zinc from the tank to the gun. End result is white specks in the completed bluing job.

CAUTION: It takes less than .001 oz. of free copper per gallon of solution to completely deplete a bluing bath.

Bluing Operation

The following suggestions are the result of experience and are set forth to be of assistance to you in establishing your own operational technique.

After cleaning the gun, it is placed in the bluing tank when the temperature reaches the optimum bluing range of 293-295 F. and left there for from 15 to 30 minutes. Move the work around in the heated solution occasionally to insure full circulation around the parts. Maximum success will be achieved if parts are suspended in the bath by wires, in wire baskets, or laid on rods suspended from the edges of the tank.

Suspension of Parts

Why suspend? Contact with the edges of the tank will cause excessive heat conduction to the parts, thus making them red and contact points do not come in contact with the bluing solution and therefore won't blue. Vegetable strainers made of steel or iron wire are ideal for suspending small parts. For large parts, weld yourself up some baskets from welding rod with short legs on each corner and a handle. Be sure to remove plating with a mild Muriatic Acid solution.

For barrels, get yourself some quarter inch drill rod or welding rod and bend them into big "U"s the size of the inside of the tank, bending hooks into the "U"s legs to hold the bottom of the "U" an inch from the bottom of the tank. Make two of these. They are removable and should be kept out of the way when not in use. When in use be sure and not put them so far apart the barrels won't rest on them.

Handling Barrels & Actions

Then make some two-armed "L"-shaped affairs to use as handles for manipulating the barrels in and out of the various tanks. Stick one end of the "L" into the receiver end, use the other leg of the "L" as a handle and there you are. Blisters avoided.

Temperature Rise

During the operation of the bath the temperature gradually rises. This is due to the evaporation of water from the bath, which raises the density of the bath and causes the temperature to increase. Were this increase to be permitted to continue, parts already in the bath would not be affected, but parts put in at the higher temperature would take on a decided red cast.

Water should be added to the bluing solution with caution. It is best accomplished by using a long handled dipper. Fill the dipper about two-thirds full of soft water and immerse it in one end of the tank until the lips of the dipper are flush with the surface of the bluing solution. Then tipping the dipper to one side, gradually pour the water out and at the same time and with the same motion sweep the dipper full length of the tank. This will avoid excessive spluttering and minor explosions encountered when water is added in other manners.

Temperature Control

Up to a certain point the temperature of the bath should not be regulated by regulating the heat source. When first turning the fire on under the tanks, turn them on full blast until the solution starts to boil, then turn the fire down until the bath is barely bubbling full length.

Repeat: The bath operates most efficiently when it is just bubbling full length with the temperature reading 293-295 degree F. after thorough stirring.

If the solution temperature is too high, add water slowly to lower the boiling point; if too low, let excess moisture boil off. In other words, you are controlling the boiling point of the solution by the addition of water rather than manipulation of heat source.

Adding Salts

The only addition of salts needed will be to keep the level of the bath at a sufficient height to conveniently cover the work. The only loss incurred in the bath's strength is from drag-out - or solution carried away when parts are removed from the bath. When the level does become low, estimate the required amount of salts needed and add. Do not add salts when guns are in the bath, nor add water until you have reheated the solution and noted the temperature.

Starting the Bath

When starting the bath after cooling, the salts in the bottom of the tank should be stirred with a steel rod to break up the crystalline settlings, to insure even dissolving of the cold salts. You will note, here, that the solution starts to boil at about the same temperature it did when you last shut it off.

It has been found that after long periods of storage that the solution often takes on moisture from the surrounding air, thus thinning it. When this happens either boil off the excess moisture or add a few pounds of salts to the solution. Justify the density.

Removing from Bath

After the parts have been allowed to remain in the bath for the determined length of time, they are withdrawn and examined for color. If satisfactory, rinse in an adjacent tank of cold water. After being thoroughly scrubbed and rinsed to remove all traces of solution from recessed areas, the parts are transferred to a pan of boiling water and allowed to boil for ten minutes to insure the dissolving off of all excess traces of bluing solution.

Several gunsmiths have advised that they believe they get a little more durable surface if the boiling step is eliminated. After rinsing in the cold water, the parts are gently dried over an open flame and wiped with a soft cloth.

All parts are then transferred to a final tank of oil. We recommend our Water Displacing Dipping Oil which is moisture displacing, everlasting and gives the gun a beautiful protective coat when you hand it on to your customer.

PECULIARITIES OF THE HOT PROCESS

The following bits of general information would be found out by any operator of a bluing establishment through experience. The more experienced you are **before** you start, the more proficient you will be with your first job. Acquaint yourself well with these "kinks", for forewarned is fore-armed.

1. Do not attempt to blue aluminum chokes or sights, stainless steel, magnesium. Stainless steel barrels are best sent direct to the manufacturer as are the new light weight receivers made of special alloys and appearing on some of the newer guns.

2. When buying bluing salts be sure to buy enough to allow a full inch of solution between the parts to be blued and the bottom of the tank, and a full inch over the parts being blued. The bluing business is a very enjoyable one; do not be so frugal that you ruin your work by not having enough volume of solution to adequately cover and surround the guns being blued.

3. Excessive Foaming: Foaming of the bath is to be expected

unless you are trying to blue aluminum or pot metal, in which case the bath is being ruined! The best thing to do when you are having foam trouble is TURN DOWN your heat source to a point where the bath is just barely bubbling up and down its middle and directly over the burners. Then stir often and when you put the parts in to be blued, be sure and swosh them around a bit - thus insuring thorough contact between bluing salts and metal. Too vigorous boiling is to be avoided.

4. About Plugging The Bores: DON'T! The government ran several tests at Rock Island Arsenal several years ago on a series of blued bores as compared with unblued. With this method of gun bluing, it was found that the blued bores gave longer barrel life and better muzzle pressures-very slight, of course, but proves the point. Just be **SURE** and scrub them thoroughly after bluing to remove all traces of salts. Further: These modern solutions are hard on wood and the heat inside the barrels expands the air and the plugs blow out very easily. **Dangerous.**

5. After Rinse To Neutralize Salts: A dilute chromic acid rinse used following the cold water rinse after bluing will neutralize any traces of bluing salts still on the gun, will greatly toughen the blued surfaces, and will make the gun's surface much more rust resistant... DO NOT USE CHROMIC ACID IF CYANIDE HAS BEEN USED in the bluing bath. The combination is DEADLY POISONOUS. To add chromic acid, mix at the rate of 8-1/2 oz. chromic acid per 100 gallons of water or a .06% solution. Operate the tank at 200 degrees F., or slightly under boiling. Immerse the gun for one to two minutes only.

6. How Many Guns Per Batch: The answer to this one depends on one jillion, two hunnert million different things. First: the main reason the bluing baths don't last as long as they might is the constant heating and cooling. Were you to turn your bath on and leave it on you would get many times more hours of service. Second: If you use city or hard, lime-bearing water, you shorten the bath's life. Third: The carrying over of cleaner into the bath rapidly shortens its life. Fourth: Did you try to blue aluminum, pot-metal? Or have you busted a mercury thermometer in it? Or did you try bluing too many double barrel guns (more later about this) without the use of sodium cyanide? Are your tanks made of WELDED (not brazed) black iron? How much dirt and foreign matter settles in the tank when put away for a long time? Do you stir it well - break the settlings loose from the tank's bottom - right after turning up your heat source? Fifth: The bath, under well regulated and controlled supervision, will blue many many guns. You can figure less than 1 per cent per hundred pounds depletion from bluing action. In other words, there are many things which will cause your bath to go down a lot faster than just bluing.

7. When To Throw A Bath Away: The very minute it has stopped serving its purpose. Your time is too valuable to fiddle around trying to wring the last damned drop of bluing qualities out of a bath. If it has gone down from things not its fault (and thus your fault) don't blame it. Also when you start encountering too much of what we call 'yellow mud' in its bottom or too many settlings sticking into milled-out recesses - throw it away.

8. How Much Volume Should The Bath Have: That is best answered by comparing your bluing ambitions with any other business. If you are going to go into the bluing business as a business, get enough volume to your bath that every time you add another gun you won't chill (and thus shorten the life) your entire volume. If you're doing just a job at a time once in awhile, you can get by with a gallon or two of mixed solution. If you are going to blue several guns get enough solution that you can go places with it. Skimping on volume of your bath is a very poor place to practice economy, for after all is said and done, that is where-in you expect to find the golden egg.

9. Bluing Double-Barrels, Triple-Barrels, Soft-Soldered Ribs, etc.: The Addition of 96-98 Sodium Cyanide to the bath will greatly retard any chemical action between the bath and the solder or tin, therefore making it possible to do the job. However, we do not advise bluing these guns for another reason: The outer shells are quite thin, the inner shells, or where the barrels come together, quite thick. This results in some of the steel getting hot almost immediately when immersed in the bluing bath and the inner or thicker steel heating more slowly. The net result can mean a warped barrel or a popped-off rib due to the almost thermostatic action of the steel - the thin parts expanding rapidly, the thick slowly.

A SIMPLE CROSS CHECK METHOD

Actual shop and laboratory experience has shown that 99% of all bluing failures are due to one of three causes: Improper heat, faulty water, incorrect cleaning methods. The remaining 1% of failures are due to faulty bluing solutions and a host of other remote causes.

To Check your own procedure when unsatisfactory bluing jobs are coming from your shop:

FIRST: Check your thermometer in a can of boiling water. It should read very close to 212 degrees F. If, after taking into consideration your altitude above sea level (and unless you live in the high mountains, this will have little effect) you find the thermometer incorrect, immediately contact the manufacturer of the instrument. If you bought it from a reputable firm, it should be replaced at no charge.

SECOND: If your thermometer is correct, take a few pieces of steel, polish thoroughly and, with your entire bluing process in operation, wash the steel with soap and water, rinse in rain or distilled water and immerse the piece in what is given as the correct operating temperature of your solution. If the steel does not blue, the fault will lie in your solution. As a second check, suspend another piece of steel in the solution without washing, rather wipe it off with Energine or equivalent. Still no blue: solution or personal method of operating the solution is at fault.

THIRD: Should the piece blue, then take another piece of polished steel, clean as previously. But this time run through your rinse tank only, using the water you generally use, scrubbing with whatever brush you generally use, leaving it submerged in the water for every bit as long a time as you do guns when bluing. This is IMPORTANT. Then transfer the piece to the bluing solution and leave there as long as you do gun parts. If the piece does not blue, the trouble lies in your water OR you have left the clean part in the rinse so long that it has started rusting as a result of having been chemically clean and coming in contact with free oxygen in the rinse water.

FOURTH: If the piece blued after rinsing in your regular rinse, take another piece of steel and run it through your cleaner, but do not run through your regular rinse . . . . rinse it in distilled water and blue. Be absolutely sure of leaving the piece in the cleaner as long as you do gun parts. THIS IS ALSO VERY IMPORTANT. Transfer to the bluing tank and observe the results.

There is no need of going any further, because the above outlines what you are doing and how you should proceed. You see, you are cross-checking one step in your bluing operation against another, eliminating each operation as you go until you find the one that is at fault.

If none of the above works: Write the suppliers of Oxynate No. 7 and give a FULL AND DETAILED account of every step. Don't write him as some do "I tried to blue a gun last night and couldn't. I insist you tell me by return mail what is wrong." There is just as much sense to that as there would be to going out and trying to start your car. It doesn't start so you call the garage. Could the mechanic tell you what's wrong with your jalopy if you just told him you turned on the key, stepped on the starter, wheels went around and around and nothing happened? Of course not.

CONTROL

Mal-Function & Probable Cause   **Remedy**

OVER-ALL GREY CAST

1. Too low an operating temperature.

Check thermometer for correct reading - Be sure solution is boiling at 285-295.

2. Solution approaching depletion.

Replace with fresh solution.

3. High nickel steel content.

Hold solution at normal operating temperature for 15 minutes then allow temperature to increase up to 310 F. and leave part in bath for 15 minutes after it has taken on proper color.

4. Presence of oil in rinse water.

Double check water supply - examine surface of water for presence of oil-slick.

GREY STREAKS

1. Presence of oil or dirt on surface of metal.

Check cleaning operation, water supply for presence of oil or excessive dirt. Examine parts immediately prior to immersion in solution for signs of puddling around ramps, holes, joints.

OVER-ALL RED CAST

1. Too high an operating temperature.

Check thermometer for correct reading - be sure solution is not boiling too actively.

2. Attempting to blue high carbon steel at too high an operating temperature.

Very high carbon steel will blue best if initial immersion temperature is approx. 285 F. Allow temperature to increase to approx. 295 F. before removing.

3. Allowing parts to come into contact with sides or bottom of tank.

Suspend parts in bath to overcome this fault.

RED STREAKS

1. Allowing parts to come in contact with sides or bottom of tank or other large parts in solution.

Suspend parts correctly in solution.

2. Presence of spot hardening in metal.

Scrub parts in clean water and return to bluing solution until correct color is achieved. A slight temperature increase AFTER parts have started to color will speed up the action.

MOTTLED RED COLORS

1. Attempting to color Cast Iron without taking proper precautions.

10 Minute immersion of parts in rust remover immediately before chemical cleaning prior to bluing will generally overcome this fault. Sandblasting of parts prior to bluing will also give the same relief.

RED/PURPLE COLOR

1. Generally occurs on Mauser bolt stop springs and Extractor springs.

Suspend parts in bluing bath when solution is still cold and allow to remain in bath until day's work is completed. Will generally take correct color. If not, bring to mirror polish and do not blue. Gives nice effect to gun.

YELLOW/RED COLOR OR SCUM ON SURFACE
OF METAL AFTER BLUING

1. Attempting to blue case-hardened parts without sufficient pre-polishing and cleaning.

Polish part thoroughly prior to bluing. Short immersion in rust remover will generally overcome this trouble.

2. Presence of foreign matter or oil in water or on gun's surface.

Check water supply and cleaning procedure.

UNBLUED SPLOTCHES

1. Presence of caked polishing compound on metal's surface.

Scrub parts thoroughly with brush after cleaning but prior to immersion in bluing solution.

SILVER SPECKS IN FINISHED JOB

1. Overexposure to cleaning solution.

Either decrease strength of cleaner or shorten exposure of part to the cleaning solution.

2. Leaving parts in rinse after cleaning prior to bluing for too long a time.

Free oxygen in rinse water will attack the chemically clean steel and cause oxidization after a very short period of time resulting in a multitude of specks in the finished job. The use of lye is the most common offender.

FAILURE OF SOLUTION TO BOIL AT 295 F.

1. Faulty Thermometer.

Check thermometer in can of clean boiling water. It should read 212 F.

2. Solution too strong.

Cautiously add water to the solution, stirring after each addition until sufficient water has been added that solution will boil at desired temperature.

SOLUTION BOILS AT TOO LOW A TEMPERATURE

1. Faulty thermometer.

Check thermometer in can of clean boiling water. It should read 212 F.

2. Solution too weak.

Either add a small amount of salts at a time until strength of solution has been properly increased to correct density or let solution boil until sufficient water has been precipitated out in the form of steam and the solution brought to proper boiling point.

3. Long storage during damp weather.

Modern bluing salts are very hygroscopic in nature. They will take on a great deal of moisture from the air and thus increase balance of water to salts.

SCUM ON THE BATH

1. Natural Chemical Reaction.	Do not remove from solution unless it has turned brick red - then just remove red portions. If entire bath is red, it is depleted and should be renewed.

EQUIPMENT

Before spending any money on bluing supplies or equipment may we suggest you do some introspection? Are you going to blue one or two guns, a dozen or so, or do you plan on making the work a profitable hobby or full time occupation? The answers to the foregoing are important to you. From those answers you can better determine just what you should spend in starting up.

Regardless of what your answer is, do not plan on buying all your equipment in one fell swoop. Get the basic supplies first and get the BEST. Then, as time goes on, add just those items you HAVE to have and again, get the best. In this way, you will eventually have the best equipped shop in your locality. But if you plan on buying all the equipment at one time, you will necessarily economize on certain items which is going to create unnecessary stumbling blocks for you in the future.

The minimum requirements for bluing a gun or two are as follows: (and it may interest you to know that Bob Brownell blued several hundred guns with no more equipment than this minimum requirement list. He does not recommend it, but it can be done with care.) Ten or twenty pounds of bluing salts, some bread pans for pistols, a longer pan for rifles, some wash tubs for rinsing, a three-burner kerosene stove, the wife's deep fat thermometer, a half-dollar's worth of emery cloth and a lot of determination...and USE THE BEST POSSIBLE CLEANER - such as our 909.

Setting up a gun shop, either professional or hobby, for re-bluing is worth a lot of serious thought on the part of the gunsmith. Re-bluing is the foundation on which many successful gunsmith businesses are built...it gives the gunsmith a chance to show his artistic ability, for a beautifully blued gun will create more comment among shooters than anything you can do other than build a beautiful stock... and there are many more hundreds of guns needing re-bluing than are needing new stocks.

The first thing for you to determine is JUST HOW MUCH DO YOU WANT TO SPEND? When deciding that, remember that no mechanic or artist can do good work with inferior tools. On the other hand, don't go in over your head. Maybe the shooters in your locality are going to need a lot of education before they start bringing in guns in sufficient quantity for you to justify spending a lot of money at the start.

Practical Items:

Salts - at least 25 pounds, and 50 would be better.

Oxynate "D" to add to the above to cut down fumes.

Polish-O-Ray - Nos: 140, 240, 400, 500 and 555.

Bench Grinder or motor to convert into a polishing machine.

Thermometer.

One to five tanks depending upon how heavily you're going into the business.

Three soft felt wheels for the polish.

Four muslin wheels consisting of at least three sections to the wheel.

Assortment of felt bobs for trigger guards, sharp angles, etc.

A roll of No. 240 emery cloth for places wheels won't reach.

Source of heat (kerosene, gas or electric).

Pedestal polishing lathe if you are going full time.

An ounce of 96/98% pure sodium cyanide to be added to the bluing bath (again, **WARNING: Deadly Poison**).

A large mouth jar for vinegar or mild acid - into which you dip your hands when you get fouled up with the bath...but remember, if it is a strong acid and any cyanide gets into it, you have the same results as a gas chamber: sure death.

Now, do not let yourself be told that one salts is going to make your blue job come out regardless of how little work you do on the gun! The entire success of your bluing venture depends on YOU and the work YOU do.

POLISHING SUPPLIES

And Their Use

Inasmuch as the attractiveness of your completed blue job is largely determined by the quality of your polishing job prior to the actual re-bluing, too much stress cannot be placed on the polishing equipment to be used.

When making your decision as to which type or brand of polish you are going to buy always bear in mind that a polish which dries to a hard, brittle surface will invariably cause deep scratches in your work, making it necessary for you to spend untold hours of needless additional polishing to get the finish you want.

Brownell's Polish-O-Ray is the answer to the gunsmith's prayers and dreams. It does not get glass hard, does not emit offensive odors when in use, is exceptionally fast cutting and above all, it is grease-less. Polish-O-Ray can be applied to your polishing wheels when running at operating speeds, thus assuring an even, true cutting surface. It polishes fast and leaves a good smooth surface that will not gouge the metal.

Practically all the leading gunmen of this country and Canada use Polish-O-Ray exclusively in their shops. It is indeed with a great deal of pride that we point to these users and the volumes of praise they write Brownell's regarding its superlative qualities.

Polish-O-Ray comes packed in two pound tubes with metal ends and foil lining to retain the proper moisture content. Before opening the tube, prepare a storage container in the following manner: Obtain a wide mouth jar such as peanut butter is packed in. Be sure the mouth of the jar is wide enough to permit insertion of the tube. In the bottom of the jar place a piece of cloth or a handful of sawdust. Dampen this so that it feels damp but not wet. When the Polish is not in use insert it into the jar with the open end of the tube resting LIGHTLY on the dampened material. If storage is to be prolonged, pack damp paper around the open end of the jar and sides of the tube and store in a cool damp place.

How to Use Polish-O-Ray

Tear off the unmarked metal cap from one end. Be sure and leave on the end showing grit size. Then, using a pair of pliers, tear the paper down one side of the tube for approximately 1/2". The tube is now ready to be pressed against the polishing wheel.

Before applying the Polish-O-Ray to the wheel, be sure that the wheel is in proper condition to receive the polish. For satisfactory performance of the polish and the polishing operation, the wheel must be in balance with the surface true. An old cabinet rasp should be used to break in new muslin wheels and a heavy, coarse carborundum stone is ideal for truing up felt wheels.

Turn on your polishing outfit and with the torn side of the tube down, press the open end against the face of the spinning wheel. If the wheel is new and never used before, hold the polish against the surface for a few seconds and remove for a few seconds. Repeat this several times until the surface of the wheel commences to take on the polish. When this occurs, press the tube against the wheel, hold there until sufficient polish has built up on the wheel and then remove the tube with a quick upward motion.

The above may sound complicated, but in actual practice is quite simple.

Once the wheels are broken in they will not throw quite so much polish over the floor and walls when polish is being applied. A certain amount of throwing will always occur, however, so for cleanliness sake, it is best to have dirt catchers above and behind the wheel.

As the polish wears down, apply a little more from the proper tube. Do not try to polish without sufficient polish on the wheels. In damp weather it is often necessary to let the wheel run for thirty to sixty seconds after applying Polish-O-Ray before it will be dry enough to perform properly. Attempting to polish with green polish on the face of the wheel only transfers green polish to the surface of the metal. This must be washed off with water when it occurs.

R. P. M. recommendation: 6" to 8" wheels, 1750 r.p.m.; Up to 6", 3,500 r.p.m.

Polishing Process

A very satisfactory finish for hunting guns can be had by using nothing more than Grit No. 140 Polish-O-Ray, one felt wheel and a one inch muslin wheel. Process as follows: first, go over all parts to be blued with the 140 polish on the loose muslin wheel until all dirt, old blue, rust, etc., has been removed. Then go over these parts with Polish-O-Ray on a 6" or 8" soft felt wheel to smooth the surface. When all pits and blemishes are removed, return to the muslin wheel and polish the deeper grit marks out.

The only practice necessary to get a nice finish as described above is in learning how to take the parts from the wheel without grit slap marks. To do this, remove the parts with a very fast and snappy downward motion from the wheel.

Higher gloss finishes, up to mirror finish, can be obtained by going to succeedingly finer grits and finishing off with the No. 555 mirror polishing compound. Instructions on the polish tube give a step by step process that will insure your success if followed.

For Mirror Polishing

Step 1. On 8" or 6" soft felt wheel - 1750 r.p.m. - use grit No. 140 on rough guns - No. 240 on average guns - to remove pits, marks, etc. Travel at 30 degree angle to bore on barrel. Right angles on actions.

Step 2. On 8" or 6" soft felt wheel use grit No. 240 following No. 140 or No. 400 on 8" or 6" medium felt following 240 and polish parallel to bore on barrels and at a 45-degree angle on actions and remove ALL former polishing marks.

Step 3. On 6" and 8" loose muslin wheel use grit No. 400 at right angles to entire gun and remove all former polishing marks. The gun can now be blued for Standard Finish.

For High Mirror Finish

Step 4. On 6" or 8" soft felt wheel use grit No. 500 and polish at 45 degrees to bore. Follow with grit No. 500 on loose muslin wheel at right angles to remove grit marks.

Step 5. On 8" or 10" or 12" rock hard felt use No. 555 at 45 degree angle to entire gun and remove the 500 grit polishing marks.

Step 6.   On 8" loose muslin use 555 parallel to entire gun or at right angles. Bring gun to mirror finish.

NOTE: Muslin wheels should be 1" wide (or more) at periphery. Stitched muslin wheels can be used instead of felt, but felt gives smoother finishes.

- *Bob B.*

OXPHO-BLUE

Oxpho-Blue for re-bluing and the touch-up of guns was designed originally for the occasional re-bluer. It does so many things so remarkably well that it is threatening to revolutionize the re-bluing industry. For looks the re-touched finish was not intended to approach the beauty of the well polished, hot blued gun. It has developed, however, that in the hands of a careful craftsman not only is the Oxpho-Blue finish beautiful, it is also more durable and weather resistant than any other known chemical or rust-type finish.

As Harold MacFarland, well known gunwriter and gunbuilder says about Oxpho-Blue: "For the production job I use the hot tank method. But when I want a particularly fine job on either my own or customers' guns, I use this stuff. Naturally I have to charge a little more but it surely is worth it."

Method of Application for Retouching

Retouching where gun is worn bright and rust is not serious: -

1.   Wipe off excess oil and grease. Do NOT attempt to remove all traces of oil from surface of gun. For retouching (ONLY) it is better if a small trace of oil is present on the surface!

2.   Dampen a cloth pad, such as a 12 ga. cleaning patch with Oxpho-Blue and vigorously rub the areas which have worn bright until they turn the color desired to blend in with the rest of the gun's finish. You will note that the Oxpho-Blue removes traces of rust and transfers the rust to your rubbing pad. You will also discover that the steel actually blues under the oil.

Many gunsmiths have found that a very easy way to re-touch a gun is to proceed as follows:

Get one of those shoe-shine cloths at a dime store. Dampen it with Oxpho-Blue and blue the gun simply going after it as you would shine your shoes. This is an excellent method to prepare low value guns for resale...or make attractive a gun a pet customer has brought in for repairs.

NOTE: The above method does not make an exceptionally durable blue. It is so simple to apply, however, taking just a few seconds as it does, that this is no objection.

Retouching Badly Rusted Spots

Either remove rust with emery cloth and polish or follow the method explained below:

Take a pad of No. 0 or 00 steel wool and saturate it with Oxpho-Blue. Keeping it saturated, briskly rub the rusted area until all traces of rust are floated off. Then, without permitting surface to air dry, wipe dry with a clean cloth. Then with a DRY piece of steel wool briskly burnish the area until it turns a bright gunmetal grey color.

With a small cotton pad slightly dampen the area with Oxpho-Blue, wipe dry and burnish with dry steel wool. Repeat until desired color is reached. For details on obtaining proper color using this method of application, read below under "Over-all re-bluing".

NOTE: THERE IS NO AFTER-RUST WHEN USING OXPHO-BLUE SO IT IS UNNECESSARY TO RINSE WITH WATER.

For Over-all Professional Re-bluing

1. Polish and clean gun in the usual manner.

2. Do NOT polish the surface too brightly. The procedure used in applying the Oxpho-Blue will produce a bright surface and the action of the chemical will be better if the surface is slightly matte in texture before starting. No. 140 grit Polish-O-Ray is sufficiently fine.

3. Make a large, very loosely wound cotton swab on a wooden swab stick such as your doctor uses to swab your throat. Pour some Oxpho-Blue into a cup and mop on generous quantities of the chemical, dipping the swab into the liquid with each pass.

4. When the surface of the gun is holding as much liquid as you can apply without excessive run-off, wait about 30 seconds or until the liquid has turned a messy-looking black color.

UNDER NO CIRCUMSTANCES ALLOW THE CHEMICAL TO DRY ON THE GUN THIS FIRST PASS.

5. Wipe dry with a clean rag and rub with the rag until thoroughly dry.

6. Burnish the surface of the gun with No. 00 steel wool. Rub very hard. You will not take off the finish with steel wool, it is that tough. Rub until you have a bright gunmetal color.

What you now have is a bright Parkerized-type finish which is just tougher than the dickens, resistant to wear and rust and fairly thick. The secret is to now blue or blacken this grey finish without going back to its grey color. Proceed as follows:

Take a piece of cotton about the size of the end of your thumb and just barely dampen it with Oxpho-Blue. Squeeze this pad between thumb and index finger and shake out all excess chemical. Now dampen the surface of the colored steel and wipe dry with a clean cloth. Burnish briskly with steel wool. The color will now be similar to that of the old-time Colt blue.

Repeat this dampening process for deeper color.

Remember, the secrets which only you who read this know are:

1.   Use a lot of chemical for the first application and a minimum for the following applications.

2.   If at any time you go from the blue color back to the original gunmetal color, you have applied too much chemical in your coloring steps. (In all steps but No. 3 above, you are actually coloring the finish achieved in step No. 3!)

SUGGESTION: Practice a time or two on pieces of scrap barrel to get the technique which will make your bluing jobs famous with all your gun trade.

OXPHO-BLUE will stain the skin yellow. Remove with Clorox.
- *Bob B.*

SLOW RUST PROCESS OF BLUING

The coloring of metals dates back many centuries, and one of the processes much used is rust process bluing. This method imparts a dark-blue to bluish-black to black on metals, usually steel. The process, properly performed, is fairly complicated and requires attention to detail as any well-informed, practical craftsman can testify. Today, with modern steels and processes, the practice is usually reserved for soft-soldered barrels or complete arms where cost is no object.

As with any job, getting the proper start is most essential. Barrels are usually chemically stripped of all old finish, thus saving polishing time, but, more importantly, preventing loading or glazing of the polishing wheels with the old finish being removed. Ribs, top and bottom, and sides are always hand-polished with suitable tools designed to fit the areas being worked on. When nicking or pitting is present, files or hones must be used to remove these defects to prepare the metal for proper smooth polishing. All ribs must be tight and not leak during the process, as barrels are usually handled in units of six, and greasy water leaking from any rib on any of the six under process can spoil the whole set. Loose ribs must, therefore, be properly resoldered before bluing is possible. Dents, either inside or out, must be removed as must all pitting or other defects. The degree of polish on the barrels may be either a true mirror or a velvet type finish and is dependent upon many things, among them the customers' wishes, the type of solution used for the bluing, and the method of inducing rusting, either natural or artificial. Some solutions bite the metal to initiate action and will always result in a velvety finish, even on highly polished work. Other solutions work in a milder fashion and will maintain any degree of polish given the steel throughout the process.

After the above details have been attended to and the piece polished in accordance with the customer's wishes, the bore is wiped dry and greased. Water pump grease gives the best possible results because it makes a good, stable coating which does not melt and run during the bluing operation. Apply with a bristle brush which has first been dipped into boiling water to 'limber' up the bristles. After greasing, suitable plugs are driven tightly into the bores and serve as both handles and as plugs. Any good commercial cleaner for metal may be used, and I favor the commercial preparations over lye as a cleaner, for lye has the nasty habit of causing spotting unless removal to a clean tank of boiling water is quickly done after the lye-bath. Even after cleaning in a commercial cleaner, I have never been able to get a good, deep color without using an extra cleaner consisting of air-slaked lime added to water until a brushing consistency is obtained. This is simply brushed carefully over the very hot barrels upon their removal from the tank of commercial cleaner. The lime solution dries on contact and may be brushed off, taking with it any remaining traces of grease or oil. A final rinsing with boiling water, preferably from a hose, prepares the barrels for coating with the slow rust solution.

Many solutions are suitable for the coating of the barrels, but I prefer one that colors the barrels a light blue or black with the first coating. Many solutions do a fine job but do not impart any color until several coats have been applied. Thus the barrels may have spots that do not receive coats but which are not discovered until after several coats have been applied. The following solutions have always given me perfect satisfaction:

1. Does not bite on application -
Copper sulphate, 183 grains; Nitric acid D.142, 110 grains; Selenious acid, 110 grains; Distilled water, 1/4 pint.

2. Bites slightly on application -
Copper sulphate, 22 grains, Hydrochloric acid D 1.16, 9 grains; Sol. Ferric chloride 29%, 102 grains, Ferrous sulphate cryst., 73 grains; Distilled water to make 1/4 U.S.A. pint.

3. Bites to start action -
Copper sulphate, 110 grains; Sol. Ferric chloride 29%, 55 grains; Alcohol 90%, 64 grains; Nitric acid D 1.42, 27 grains, Spirit of nitre, 27 grains; Distilled water for 1/4 pt.

The solution is applied to the hot barrels, and for this I like a small sponge, not sopping wet, but well-moistened. After a complete coating, including the small crevices along the ribs, the barrels are set aside to rust. I use a cigar case humidifier to maintain a controlled temperature of 75 degrees. Care must be taken that too much moisture is not present as water drops on the work will ruin the job at any stage. After the barrels have evenly rusted, they are boiled for thirty minutes to kill the action of the solution and to convert the rust to black oxide. They are then carded either by hand or by using a cleaned hair wire wheel. Carding must be thorough but light so as not to remove the color that has started. The above operation is carried through from three to eight times with the average being six. With controlled humidity the operation can be completed in four to six days, and with natural rusting, depending upon the climate and season, in two or three weeks. After final color is achieved I like to boil barrels for forty minutes, then card off with the hair wire wheel, motor driven. After the last carding operation, the barrels are coated with cylinder oil and left for thirty-six hours to cure and set.

In thirty-six hours the barrels should be well-cured and set up, and it is time to inspect the finished product. All oil is wiped off the barrels, the plugs are removed, and the bores are carefully cleaned out. Final inspection is done out-of-doors in hard, direct sunlight; no artificial light is ever safe to use for this most important inspection. If the barrels pass this test and have a good, deep, even finish, then the bores are polished. Mating surfaces with the receiver are polished into the white and the job is completed.

If muzzle plugs stick, and they often will, the only safe way to remove them is with a hard dowel nearly bore-size. All plugs do not stick, but there is usually one that requires the use of the dowel rod. Anything smaller than bore-size is risky to use and may well jam between the plug and the barrel, producing an outside dent; this must be avoided as there is no simple cure for such a disaster.

Many of the frames that accompany the barrels are of cast or malleable material that either does not blue at all or else blues very poorly. These may be left in the white or colored by some means to resemble factory color case-hardening. Of course, if of good steel, the frames may be blued by any method, and even modern methods make a fairly good match. Of course, malleable frames encountered on current factory-produced guns are best returned to the factory for the tricky color hardening process, which is too tricky to be done privately. For home use the formula given in Harold McFarland's book on gunsmithing is the obvious choice. It is safe and wears well.

Finally, correctly assemble and grease the entire job, including bores and exterior surfaces, with Rig.

There are very few bugs that crop up in this work, and usually cleanliness and attention to detail will give a truly beautiful job. As with any worthwhile project, this one requires time, care, and above all, a little common sense.

- *J. A. Wingert, Waynesboro, Pennsylvania*

NEBRASKA HENS

And then there was this meat market in Fremont, Nebraska, that ran this ad unintentionally: "Young Dressed Hens, absolutely clean and ready for the rooster."

- *Bob B.*

AND HELL FROZE OVER. . .

We-uns who live between the south end of the Texas Panhandle and the North Pole have been having a winter so far to end all winters. Keep this up and that famous brass monkey is going to lose his nose, toes, fingers and ears as well! As this is being written, snow is practically knee deep here in Iowa, thermometer is pushing Zero and the pheasant and quail hunters have had their fires of ardor smothered, and that's almost like summer compared to what's happening on further north. Early fall and it was too hot to hunt, late fall and it's too cold... Stooding in bed has its advantages. But there are light sides.

Got a letter from Irv Benson, he who lives on the Minnesota/ Canadian border and had to cut a hole in the outhouse roof last winter because of the deep snow. "You-all might be interested in how my first attempts with Oxynate No. 7 came out," he wrote. "I had asked a fellow near here to weld up a tank framework to allow the burner to be hung underneath; however he couldn't get at it in time, so I had to make a rather 'flexible' arrangement, strictly temporary, of course. The wife had overheard the customs officer giving me the word on his bluing precautions, and I was politely informed that the house was closed to bluing activities -- the word 'spatter' caused the most grief. At any rate, I moved into the emptied ice house, set up the tank on four barrel sized chunks of green birch with a grate for cross support, and then slung the pipe burner under the tank with several turns of rabbit snare wire on each end, around the tank and under the burner. I swiped some coat hangers, took off the finish with emery, and used these for barrel hangers. Not having any proper screen to make a parts basket, I hit on the idea of making the basket out of a section of fiberglass cloth with a coat hanger rim. Seemed to me that this glass cloth was strictly non-anything, and the salts would have no effect on it...that was a mistake, as after exactly three minutes at 285 F. the basket fell apart like a busted Coleman mantle. All this proves that fishermen with fiberglass boats shouldn't blue firearms while on the lake... All this took place at 10:00 P.M. one snowy night, and it must have been quite a sight - a kerosene lamp and the burner making an unearthly glow in the empty icehouse, empty except for me and some 1728 cubic feet of steam...We do some odd things up here, and some of the oddest must take place around this island."

(Note from Bob B.: We decided here at the office that if we'd been up there lost and come stumbling thru the snow onto that scene that there was just one conclusion we could come to: we'd died in our travels and were coming into the gates of hell! Bluing tanks and all!! - Anyhow, Irv got some beautiful finishes on the guns he was doing -- naturally..!)

- *Irv Benson, Ontario, Canada*

HOT BLUING WITH AN ICE WATER PLUNGE

A fellow had a rifle here last night that my Dad had reblued several years ago. Thought I'd drop you a line since my Dad passed away last June in Tennessee. He had a gun/machine shop in Ripley; his reblue jobs were out of this world and seeing that gun last nite reminded me just how good a gunsmith he was and what a closely guarded secret he had on using hot blue.

Here goes: when he was bluing, after the solution got hot and the parts began to take, he would remove the hot parts from the solution and immediately plunge them in a tank of ICE water; from this ice water back into the solution until they got real hot again, then back into the ice water. Usually he did this three times. After the final heating they went to the rinse and then into a tank of HOT quenching oil. This off-beat method would give a blue that looked a foot thick and was without spots or fading, due to different hardness of various parts... Thought you'd like to pass this on to the fraternity.

- *Harry E. Jones, Torrance, California*

BLUING & ICE WATER

You know Brownell, you and I have been doing business ever since you started in. Auggie Pachmayr and I were very close friends and he taught me many things about guns - case hardening, bluing and the like...In his instructions to me in 1939 he definitely stated to quench your parts in ice water at least 5 times, which I have always done which gives a big difference in depth and lasting power.

- *L. D. Machamer, Coeur D'Alene, Idaho*

BLUING AND ICE WATER

I tried using Ice Water (Ice Cubes) during the bluing as per one of your Kinks - Finish is Fantastic. (Note from Bob B.: By the way, Mike is working up an instruction manual on gunsmithing for his grandson!)

- *Mike Poitras, Lindenhurst, New York*

BLUING THOSE "HARD TO BLUE" PARTS

Whenever I have one of the classic hard to blue parts that I just can't get to blue any other way, I put it into the bluing solution while it is still cold, and go ahead with my bluing. Usually, by the time I am finished, the part will have a really good deep blue.

Don't know why this works, but always has for me in Oxynate No. 7. Cannot say for any of the other bluing salts as haven't ever tried them!

- *E. L. Hunter, Meeker, Colorado*

BROOM BLUING

"A few comments on your Oxynate No. 7. We carelessly dropped a broom in the bath during the last bluing operation. In a few seconds it was baldheaded but the handle came out the most perfect blue you ever saw."

The above came off an order from Gabriel's Shooters Service. When I read that bit of news there was just one thing to do: write and ask what in the ever-loving blue-eyed world he was doing with a BROOM in the bluing tank area. Right back came an answer - but he never did tell me how-come the broom. He did say, tho, that: "I did notice that quite a bit of red dross formed on top of the tank when the stuff cooled off and was wondering if I was doing something wrong when I caught my mother-in-law sneaking in and dipping her fingers in the bath to remove her finger nail polish. It removed the polish, all right, but even at 285-F. it didn't harm her fingers as I noticed when she speared the last pork chop on the platter that evening at dinner..."

- *Gabriel's Shooters Service, Eau Claire, Wisconsin*

BROWNING

Tell your clients to use a soda water rinse following the use of your Plumb Brown just before oiling to prevent after-rust when browning barrels.

- *Dale M. Guise, Gardners, Pennsylvania*

BLUING SMALL SCREWS AND PARTS

To hold small screws while bluing, try bending a compression coil spring - like an old striker spring - in a 'U' shape and insert the screws between the coils of the spring. Then place the spring with all screws, etc in a Brownell's Bluing Basket!!! Works great.

- *Dave Nelson, Willow Springs, Missouri*

GRIPE! GRIPE! GRIPE!

Pappa Bear came downstairs one morning and discovered that his bowl was empty. "Someone has been here and eaten all my porridge," he roared...Little Baby Bear come downstairs and found his bowl empty, and cried, "Someone has eaten all my porridge!"...Whereupon Mamma Bear walked into the room and bellowed, "Gripe, Gripe, Gripe...that's all I ever hear around here. I haven't even made the damn porridge yet!"

- *Al Abramow, Rochester, New York*

THERMOMETERS

Ho, Boy! Thanks for the answers, but you threw me for a loop about that purple finish (he was getting when bluing and had written about). Bob, I was about ready to skin you Sunday...Ran that tank again, some came out fine and others no good. Talk about a solution that bites! You should have told thick headed me that the SOLUTION was too hot when I placed the parts in the tank. I thought you meant when you said "running your heat too high" that I had my FIRE turned too high after the tank was loaded!! Anyway, after two nights til 3:30 A. M. and 4:00 A. M. (those of you who have ever blued know what he means - we all been there at one time or another) I began to wonder about my thermometer. So I checked it against a cheap one I use in my pistol tanks and they both checked the same... This may not happen again in years BUT I have two thermometers that are both off the same amount - about 17 degrees - and maybe you should put it in the Newsletter that if a guy is getting purple and checks against one thermometer and still gets the same reading, he should check against a third one just to be SURE. (Note from Bob B.: The above couldn't happen once in ten blue moons - but it does bring out a very good and important point: if you are getting purple colors, the operating temperature of the bath is too high for the steel being blued and some thermometer checking or bath correction is in order.)

- *Taylor's Gun Shop, Abingdon, Illinois*

SOLUTION SPATTER

That "spatter" business has been a bugger for Lo! these 20 years I have been in the game. Looks like we might have the foaming end of it cured tho, thanks to Miles Baker who put us onto a solution - we call it "OXNATE NO. 7 ANTI-FOAM". Here is how Miles uses it: "Use 8 drops to the gallon. You can drop it on the surface and it will never mix, but put some in a bottle of water and shake it up and it mixes well. I put some in my water before adding chemicals, and then about every-other time I add water to control temperature. I shake some up in a Coke bottle (10 drops) and add a little of this and have no foam what-so-ever . . . sure saves on mess, burners, dispositions and what-all."

- *Miles D. Baker, Simons Island, Georgia*

JUST ONCE MORE . . .

Writes Joe Head, "Here is one of those crazy ideas which you all like. When the bluing salts in the tank get to such a low level that as the water boils out in order for it to get hot enough to blue guns and exposes parts of guns and they won't blue and it botches the whole job and you are out of salts waiting for more and want to get by once more with the low level - I always just keep plenty of limestone rocks handy and when the level is getting too low add them in the end of the tank to raise the level. Seems that the limestones even help the color. Anyhow, it's a way to get by just once more . . ."

- *Joe Head, Mangum, Oklahoma*

CAST IRON WATER DIPPERS

Don't use same in your bluing bath - they'll cause troubles, but plenty. We had one H of a time running down what was wrong with a fellow's bluing operation and it finally settled on the DIPPER he was using, fer Pete's sake. Who'd ever thought of it, but that so-called cast iron job must of had a little of about every known kind of metal in it. He went to a porcelain one and he had no more troubles! Golly!!

- *Bob B.*

"WATCH THAT WATER" FOR YOUR BLUING TANKS

This may never happen to you - but if it does, maybe the following will tell you "why"!

We heard from a gunsmith who had just mixed up a fresh batch of Oxynate No. 7, that as soon as he put a couple of rifles into it, it started bubbling violently and turned all the parts a bright green. Not only was the color still on the guns after taking them out of the bath, but it turned out to be extremely hard, was unaffected by steel wool or any of the other normal mild abrasives and was finally removed only by complete repolishing. Also, the metal surfaces were etched as though they had been dipped into an acid bath.

We contacted our factory immediately, and after considerable head scratching, the chief chemist told us that he believed, in view of the action of the bath, that there must have been some type of acid involved. Furthermore, the most commonly used acid in bluing set-ups is Chromic Acid, which would bubble violently when in contact with steel, give it a hard green color and also completely spoil the bath for further bluing.

As nearly as any of us have been able to conclude, the gunsmith either reversed his rinsing procedure, putting it through the after "hardening" rinse before he put the steel into the tank and carried over the Chromic Acid. Or, he took water from his rinse tank (Chromic Acid Rinse) to fill or replenish his pre-rinse tank or even possibly to mix the salts with in the first place!

- Wayne Fleming, Montezuma, Iowa

DIRECTIONS FOR USING DICRO-CLEAN NO. 909

Dicro-Clean No. 909 is designed for use by the gunsmith to properly clean firearms prior to the bluing operation. It may be used in any welded steel tank, heated by gas burners, steam coils or electric heat element immersion units. A concentration of 4-ozs. to the gallon will clean guns which have been polished and buffed in the usual manner. If heavy greases, cutting oils or storage type rust inhibitors are present on the gun's surface, a concentration of 8-ozs. to the gallon is recommended. Operate the cleaning solution at temperatures of 180 to 212 F. Average cleaning cycle time should average 5 to 10 minutes.

After gun and parts have been cleaned they should be transferred to a tank of clean water and completely immersed. Baskets of small parts should be thoroughly agitated. Wearing clean rubber gloves to eliminate any possibility of finger prints on the work, scrub larger parts such as barrels and actions with a clean bristle brush. Examine the large parts for signs of "puddling" - if the water does not adhere smoothly to the surface of the metal but comes up in "puddles" there is still grease, oil or silicon on the surface. Return the part to the cleaner for a few minutes and repeat the rinse, scrub and examination. If this condition persists, either increase the concentration of No. 909 in your cleaning bath or increase immersion time.

Sudden appearance of puddling following immersion in a satisfactory bath is an indication the cleaning bath should be replaced.

NOTE: - it must be remembered that steel that has been cleaned in Dicro-Clean No. 909 is chemically pure on the surface. This means there should be no delay between final cleaning and immediate immersion in the ready bluing bath. Any undue delay will allow the free oxygen in the water to start acting on the clean steel, forming small spots of rust which will show up as tiny white specks on the blued gun from a few hours to a few days after it has been blued, oiled and assembled.

With Dicro-Clean No. 909 there is less smut and grease traces left on the inside of deep holes or gun barrels than with most other methods, thus eliminating the contamination of bluing solutions. Life of the solution is about twice that of other hot or boiling cleaners. It is also safe to use on brass and similar metals.

- Brownell's Incorporated, Montezuma, Iowa

LENGTHENING BLUING SALTS LIFE

I have not changed my salts tank since I put in the first batch I ordered from you 4-5 years ago. I do strain the bottom of the tank EACH TIME I use the bath, and then add salts to keep the bath at a boiling point of 285 degrees to 310 degrees F, and deep enough to cover the work amply.

- *Donald Anspach, Denver, Colorado*

BOIL THAT CLEANING SOLUTION

For some time now - 70 guns worth at least in the last 18 months - I have been boiling the H out of the 909 Cleaning Solution before ever putting in the first gun. Then, when I'm ready to blue, I get her going again and take the parts out of it at boiling or near boiling, immediately immerse them in good clear tap water at room temperature, and right into the bluing tank. Keep on using the cleaning solution until it finally gets to looking murky, then toss it out and start a new batch.

The guns come out beautiful - better lookin' than I can get them by using the 909 at room temperature. And besides, my present tank of Oxynate No. 7 has been in use over 2 years so far, and I think with the boilin' cleaner, it isn't ever going to wear out!!

- *Bob McDaniel, Caruthersville, Missouri*

PASS AROUND THOSE CIGARETTES

Maynard Buehler says "Some men like their women to be like a cigarette - long, thin, easily set aflame and readily discarded. Other men like their women to be like a good cigar - full-bodied, luxuriant, expensive. While other men prefer their women to be like a good pipe - something to fondle, caress and set aside for future reference. Now, a man may give you a cigarette, he may offer you a cigar - But - he will NEVER LEND YOU HIS PIPE!!"

- *Maynard Buehler, Orinda, California*

CRYSTALIZED BLUING SALTS

The boys may be able to use this suggestion . . . . after shutting my bluing tanks off when through, I stir up the Oxynate No. 7 mixture about 2-1/2 hours after it cools. Then, about every two or three days I stir again. It only takes a couple of minutes and it will never get hard and settle on the bottom of the tank.

- *L.E. Franey, Delmont, Pennsylvania*

"GOLDEN BLUE"

While on the subject of cleaning - makes one think of bluing, and bluing brings up a new method discovered by J.D.C. Smith that goes to whit: "I ran upon a new slant, by accident, which involves one of our pet cats. I'd been using the same old 85-13-2% stew-pot for a long time and on finishing up some old muskets awhile back, I had to go out to the ranch in a sudden and sure forgot to put the top back on the old stew-pot.

"I got back several days later and fired up again, polished up a couple of old irons and dunked 'em in the brew. After I figgered they was well done, I drug them out and, what do you think! They were the purtyest golden red with a blue-hue you ever saw -- plumb beautiful. I rushed madly in the back way to show them to the wife and expound on my great ability of mixing the proper chemicals, exact heat control and all that. Now, Bob, much to my humiliashion, she told me that after I had left for the hind forty, one of the cats had fallen off the rafter into the bluing pot and that after it had cooled down a bit they had finally got old Tom out of the pot and cleaned up the splashing and buried what was left of Old Tom in the back lot. Old Tom was sort of yell-o rusty red color - sure did make a purty finish on that shootin' iron but the Sheriff tells me that the S.P.C.A. won't let me market the process . . ."

(Note from Bob B - General Julian S. Hatcher, past director of the Technical Service of *The American Rifleman*, read the Newsletter about J.D.C. Smith who got the beautiful colors in his bluing solution because the family cat got boiled up in his tanks. The General wrote that "this isn't the first time a tom cat has added greatly to the things of life.")

 - *J.D.C. Smith, Alice, Texas*

STORING OXYNATE NO. 7

A good many of our customers, for one reason or another, do not find it advisable to keep their Oxynate No. 7 solution in the tanks all the time. Irwin Baird was faced with this problem and came up with the following answer: "Up until a few months ago, storage of No. 7 gave me fits; in spite of a rather tight lid I was constantly having trouble with water gains and losses, especially in the summer. I finally got hold of a couple of glass jars from the storage batteries of a wind charger and decided to try one for the salt solution. These jars hold about five gallons and have a big - 8" by 10" opening at the top, so they are easy to fill and empty, even with the 'mush' in the cooled solution. A double layer of Saran Wrap seals the top and solves the problem. Not only have I gotten over the water exchange problems, but the salts show less signs of deterioration than they did when tank stored."

(Note from Bob B.: Be sure and have the salts cooled before pouring into the glass or you are apt to have bluing solution all over the floor and you -- and you know how wives love that! Not to mention eating up your shoes and toes.)

 - *Irwin L. Baird, Lawrence, Kansas*

BLUING TANK COVER

Finally got tired of the water evaporating out of the bluing tanks between "cookings", so went down to the local welder and had him make me up some black iron lids that fit down over the cleaner and bluing tanks with a 3/4" to 1" lip overhang. Had him put me a strap-iron handle in the middle for easy off and on.

Now, I can keep the dirt and junk from falling into the tanks, and can quit worrying about the neighbor's big tom who likes to come over to the shop and walk around looking the place over . . . Don't want a 'golden' blue! (note from BB - Be very sure you do NOT use galvanized for the lid. Not only will the zinc ruin the solution, but frequently the basic metal is copper bearing, and it definitely will spoil the salts!)

- *C.J. Weber, Jr., Sheffield, Illinois*

A ZISCHANG-TYPE BLUE

This I discovered while using your Oxynate No. 7: Polish the gun as usual to a fine finish using about 400 grit and then swab all parts liberally with #30 motor oil. Take a soft wire brush wheel 6" diameter, .003 wire, at 1500 rpm, and go over all the parts with the oil still on the surface. Polish in one direction until covered and then reverse and polish in the other direction. Wipe off the oil and clean and blue as usual. Finish will be a very slightly deeper blue than the older Zischang Blue but will have the same translucent appearance.

- *Charles A. Graham, West Alexandria, Ohio*

NICKEL STEEL & SPRINGFIELDS

On some Springfields a guy can have trouble with red color. Here's what I do: Put the gun in at a temperature of around 285 and hold it there for about 20 minutes. You will then note a purple color or reddish color. When this happens, let the temperature go on up to around 300. Then, let the temperature start back down to about 290 and you will see no traces of red. Then I take it out. Man, is it even and beautifully blued. I have blued nickel and steel barrels this way.

- *Loran Edler, Heber City, Utah*

BLUING NICKEL STEEL AND CAST IRON

Leave the nickel steel in to cook for as long as you can stand it. Will eventually get as black as anything else, just takes longer!

For cast iron, I soak it in properly mixed Rust Remover for about 2 hours before putting it in the salts. Always turns black for me then.

- *Richard A. Turgeon, Sioux Falls, South Dakota*

BLUING DCM SPRINGFIELDS

Fired up last night to blue some of the last D.C.M. Issues.

Found something you may not know about bluing those vari-hard Springfields. Barrels came out perfect after 12 minutes at 290 degrees but every action had a different color until we ran across this procedure. We put them in at 280 degrees, left for ten minutes; then poured on the heat to 315 degrees and held there 10 minutes . . . then lowered temperature to 290 degrees. PERFECT.

- *George Ferchaud, Baton Rouge, Louisiana*

BLUING CARBINE TRIGGER GUARDS

Can be blued by removing from the salts, dunking in cold water and returning to the salts several times during blue process .

- *Henry Hensil, Buckhannon, West Virginia*

BLUING M1 CARBINE TRIGGER GUARDS

M1 Carbine trigger guard housings, I understand, are made of copper bearing steel. I put them in Rust Remover after being polished and then into sulfuric acid dilution and then blue. Came out OK.

- *Jack Thompson, Birmingham, Alabama*

OXYNATE NO. 7 WITH STEEL WOOL

Was bluing a Browning Auto the other day and had it in the tank for about 25 minutes at 285 degrees when a customer walked in and we got to swapping lies. By the time we quit, the heat had run up to 305 and the barrel had the nicest 1-inch red streak all the way down one side.

I had a pad of #0000 steel wool on hand, so clamped it in a clothes-pin and after dipping it into the salts solution, rubbed it the full length of the barrel real hard. The red streak disappeared, so went ahead and just rubbed down the whole barrel with the pad while I was at it, and put it into the rinse water.

Bob, you wouldn't believe how great that barrel looked. Think it is one of the very best jobs that I have ever turned out. The old fellow I did the work for sure was much surprised and pleased, and I figure if I can please him, I can please them all.

- *J.W. Bulwan, Alliance, Nebraska*

BLUING NEW WINCHESTER MODEL 94's

DO NOT attempt to blue the receiver frames of the recently made Winchester Model 94's. At the February 1966 N.S.G.A. Show in Chicago, I asked one of the factory men about this and his advice was: "The best thing to do is tell your gunsmith customers to send them back to the factory for re-bluing. There is something about the metal in the frames of the first run of those that will cause him all sorts of problems."

End of quote. The fellow surely wasn't fooling! We've had a flock of letters about them that we couldn't answer --everything on the gun blues but the receiver.

- *Bob B.*

BLUING THE WINCHESTER MODEL 94

I think I have found a simple answer to bluing the cast iron frames of the new Model 94 Winchesters. I leave them for about two hours in the tank, cooling them down every half hour or so in a vat of cold water. They come out a blue about the same as the old single shot 22 frames and shotgun frames, turning spotted purple and finally turning black.

Have also found that these frames do not ever polish up very well. The surface has a definite grain to it that does not smooth out.

- *Don Mott, Douglas, Arizona*

GRAY FINISH ON GUN RECEIVERS

Clean receiver in rust remover then immerse for 6 to 8 seconds in a solution consisting of 20 parts water and 1 part nitric acid. Rub with soda to neutralize further action. Protect with gunlock varnish or good oil.

- *John Rohner, Boulder, Colorado*

FROSTED GRAY FINISH

Many times when bluing certain pistols and rifles, I've wanted a frosted gray finish on the receiver - either the sides of the receiver or all of it. I've found the best way to get this is to go ahead and blue the gun in the usual manner. When the job is complete, and prior to final oiling, paint the areas to be gray (using a regular paint brush) with rust remover. When the color you want develops flush with oil. Then thoroughly re-rinse in water and re-oil. The finish looks great and shows no tendency to rust or discolor.

- *John Rohner, Boulder, Colorado*

RUST REMOVER TANK

I suppose I was the last to figure it out, but just in case I was not, a plywood vat, well lined with fiber glass like I had left over from a boat makes a fine vat for your rust remover.

- *J.M. Points, Rockport, Texas*

"COLD" CASE HARDENING COLOR

Ray Fisher gave a Single Action as purty a case hardened color job as you could ever hope to see . . . warmed up the frame until it was a trifle too hot to handle and then took a cotton swab and dabbed Perma Blue all over it, inside and out. Every color of the rainbow!

Oxynite 122 will do the same.

- *Ray Fisher, Des Moines, Iowa*

CASE HARDENING FOR COLORS

Leland Wheeler was kind enough to pass along his method for case hardening. Takes a bit of practicing, of course, and all the proper precautions must be taken so's you'll be around to enjoy the fruits of your labors:

"Mix the following as a quench - 2 ozs. sodium nitrate; 1-oz. sodium nitrite; 1-qt. distilled water; 1-oz. sperm oil . . . multiply the foregoing to make up one or two gallons as required. Place this quench in a cast iron or wooden tank. A steel tank does not work well as you get too much flake rust which eats up your chemical. This is the base formula and the sodium nitrate or sodium nitrite (or both) may have to be increased to get the desired color.

"Place work to be colored in a pan made of 10 or 12 ga. steel or cast iron. Heat in gas furnace to a dull red. When part is starting to turn red, apply potassium cyanide and heat until entire surface is covered with fine foam. Any part not covered will have a black oxide finish. Quench in the above solution.

"REMEMBER: POTASSIUM CYANIDE IS A DEADLY POISON - SO BE CAREFUL.

"Do not heat too hot as the higher the heat the less color . . . the longer the work is heated the deeper the case. Confine case hardening to low power rifles, shotguns and the like . . . . DO NOT case harden the bolt or receiver of a high-power rifle, but leave them to the expert with the best of heat controlled equipment.

"When not in use the quench should be kept in a glass container with a tight lid or stopper as exposure to the air will oxidize it . . . . This method works well on either low carbon steel or malleable.

"The rust bluing and procedure I use is the #1 formula as given in James V. Howe's book."

Comments by Bob B.: There are a couple of other methods for getting such colors as above. One is the professional method, which I have never used. It consists of packing the parts to be case hardened in a cast iron pot with bone-black or commercial hardening (heat treating) compounds. The pot and all are heated to a dull-to-cherry red. A tank is prepared with snaked air pipes in its bottom into which hundreds of small holes are drilled. The tank is filled with a quench similiar to that used by Leland.

Just before dumping the contents of the iron pot into the tank of quench, the air is turned on. This allows myriad bubbles to work up through the quench - making swirls of colors on the parts as they fall thru the quench to the bottom of the tank -- this is a very old method and probably much out-dated.

Another method - and one we used to use in the shop ourselves - was to polish the parts as tho for bluing but only bring to about a 240 Polish-O-Ray grit finish. Then, with a cotton pad dobb bits of cold gun blue over the frame. With a bit of practice a very suitable color can be achieved. Once you get the knack, you can heat the metal up to just below sizzling - good and darned hot - and apply the chemical. This gives even a better and more durable finish. Does take more practice, tho! - - -

- *Leland A. Wheeler, Milford, Illinois*

SAND BLAST FINISH

To put an excellent sand blast finish on a gun that looks "real nice" and you don't have access to a sand blaster, have the following mixture made up: 1/2 Gal. Butyl Cellosolve and 1/2 Gal. Phosphoric Acid.

Take one or two pints of the above and pour into a tank of water. After polishing parts, like you were going to blue 'em, plug bores at both ends, cylinders, etc., and boil them in this tank of mixture for thirty minutes. Rinse thoroughly in cold water, go into hot rinse, then into bluing tank for 60 minutes and treat same as usual bluing job. It gives a beautiful black "parkerized" job and is durable. Like "a thing of beauty is a joy forever". It is a beautiful job that will last forever!

(Note from Bob B.....reaction unknown on nonferrous metals. Watch it!)

- *Charles Degenhart, Marysville, California*

ALUMINUM BLACKENING

I have resorted to "Pappy" Kodak's brush-on lacquer for aluminum blackening which dries to a dull black and does a nice job...let me further add that this is a very dull finish and easily rubbed off; however, one can add a nice gloss endurance by a wax or by stock sheen and hand buff with soft cloth. The lacquer cannot be sent parcel post, however.

- *Smith's Custom Loading, Pittsburgh, Pennsylvania*

IT'S A MATTER OF VIEWPOINT

From the Mongo-Nkundo and Ba-Nkundo tribes of Africa: "The man who is not hungry says the coconut has a hard shell."

BLACKENING ALUMINUM

I do it with heat...First polish up the part good and then use a bottled gas torch to heat the part about as hot as the wife's iron. I then apply the blackening solution with a swab and use fine steel wool after a couple of coats. Then repeat. With care, I get a finish that looks anodized.

- *George Murchison, Kawanee, Illinois*

BLACKENING ALUMINUM

With your aluminum black and the following method, I've had pretty good luck. To get a good color, it is absolutely necessary to remove all oxide from the aluminum. First I polish with small buffs to remove paint, oxide and corrosion. Oxide begins to form instantly on the aluminum and will prevent coloring so I wet the aluminum with the blackening solution and use a steel wire brush in a hand grinder to remove the new oxide and allow the blackening to proceed. It is necessary to keep the metal wet and use a speed reducer on the hand grinder so that centrifugal force will not throw off the liquid. Use a steel brush, as a brass brush will leave a residue on the metal. I then use a hard wax to preserve the finish - maybe this will help somebody with the same problem.

- *Kem's Craft Shop, Streator, Illinois*

SOLDERING BLACKENING

Custom Craft Combat Grips came up with a new one - I should be surprised but after dealing with gunsmiths for nearly 20 years, nothing surprises me anymore - just amazes me. Says he: "We're currently running a quantity of conversions on 7MM in the Model 95 Mauser for one of the mail order houses in L.A. and one of the operations is to cut off the barrel, turn for a band front sight and crown. The sight is sweat-soldered on, and that durned Aloxo Black is just the ticket for getting a deep blue on freshly machined metal that is still hot from soldering. I have found that the stuff works best at the temperature it takes to just jell the 50-50 soft solder. You can pass this on if you think it is worth mentioning. Just stumbled onto this trick by grabbing the wrong bottle at the start of the job. Thought I had Oxpho-Blue in my hot little fist.

(Note from Bob B.: In case you don't know it, Aloxo Black is not even supposed to commence to color steel or soft solder. It is the gunk we sell you-all for touching-up scratches on black anodized aluminum frames and parts. You guys keep on and one of these days one of you is going to goof on a rifle barrel and turn it into gold bar stock! If you do, just be sure and remember how you did it and tell me first.)

- *Custom Craft Combat Grips, Pasadena, California*

COLD BLUING

I have found it a big help when using Oxpho or other similar blues, after buffing or sanding, to thoroughly wash metal with ordinary household bleach, let dry, wool down with #000 steel wool and blue. Results are excellent.

- *William H. Vinson, Jackson, Ohio*

CLEANING STEEL WOOL FOR CARDING

All instructions for using any of the cold or hot bluing processes are quite positive about the need for keeping all traces of oil away from the work. In one step in the carding (steel wool rubbing) operation in the rust or cold blue method of bluing this can cause a multitude of problems, for steel wool as it comes from the factory is oil soaked! Under no circumstances, therefore, should steel wool be used in the bluing process without first soaking it with alcohol, touching a match to it and burning out all traces of the oil.

- *Bob B.*

MORE ON SHORTENING

A midget went to the Doc holding his hands between his legs. Doc said, "What's the trouble?" Midget said, "Doc, I am so sore I can hardly walk.' 'Get up on the table and I'll have a look,' said the Doc. So, the midget did, and the Doc got a big knife and took a couple of cuts, then told the Midget, "Get up and try walking." He did, and told the Doc, "You sure cured me, but what did you cut off?" "Two inches off the top of your overshoes," said the Doc.

- *Warrens Gun Shop, South St. Paul, Minnesota*

OXPHO BLUE "SHINE"

Have you tried taking a piece of cotton cloth about 6 - 7 inches long and wetting it with Oxpho-Blue and using a "shoe shine" stroke to put it on the barrel? If you don't have the rag too wet it goes on good and is easy to match up with regular blue when spotting. I have tried a couple of times to give guns that I have worked on a quick going over as above on the worn areas on top of receiver and where the case usually rubs on the barrel. Not a blue job, but just makes the gun look better than the owners have seen them for some time. Maybe drum up a little business, maybe kill it, don't know.

- *Vernon Drake, Staples, Minnesota*

BLUING RAGS

I found out something about your Oxpho-Blue that might help some other guy. I was wetting my rag from the bottle and re-wetting the same rag. Results nicht sehr gut! I poured the stuff into a dish and never returned a used swab to the dish. The results are good - up to marvelous.

- *E. J. Edwards, Creswell, Oregon*

OXPHO-BLUE ON SOLDERED DOUBLE GUNS

That stuff does a nice job on soldered double guns when fully polished and cleaned - in fact, I'm about ready to stop hot blue since I've been using this...it wears, too.

- *R. L. Patton, Providence, Pennsylvania*

"HOT" OXPHO-BLUE

Say Friends and Fellow Gunschmidts! I have stumbled on to the darndest discovery ever. I had a steel butt plate to blue the other day and I didn't want to fire up my tanks for such a small job. So, having no Dicropan, I proceeded to rust blue it, using a Coleman stove and a pan of water. But the darn "Tiger Sweat" I'd brewed up a couple of years ago in my pot still had gone sour on me. The only thing around the shop that would blue a quick job was some Oxpho-Blue. So! I tried it the same way I would use a rust blue. I got the finest blue I ever saw. Looks like a fine job of heat bluing. No more mixing for me on rust blue jobs - the Oxpho works faster than anything I've tried. Three applications...

- *Charley Newel, Lewiston, Idaho*

DICROPAN IM FOR DOUBLES

Dicropan IM is a steel blackening chemical we sell to industrial manufacturers for specific applications (including one of the parts going into the Space Probe Satellites!) but because of its nature, have never promoted it for the gun trade. Mr. Orville B. Bell, Gunsmith, obtained some from us and developed it for use on double barrel shotguns. Since running the following in our Newsletter we have received several letters from other gunsmiths who bought and tried and all had excellent results.

Mr. Bell's Instructions: -

"Polish and clean gun by the usual method. Boil parts in clean water. Make a nitric acid solution of 1-oz. of acid to 10 ozs. of water. Take parts out of boiling water and swab thoroughly with this solution until cool and return to boiling water for 10 minutes. Mix 5-ozs. of water and 1-oz. of Dicropan IM for your blackening solution.

"Take parts out of boiling water and swab on blackening solution with a cotton pad, rubbing vigorously until parts are cool. Apply more solution until surface is wet. While surface is wet with blackening solution, take fine steel wool and rub hard all over. Return to boiling water until hot. Remove and card off loose rust and repeat blackening solution application operation. Return to tank and let boil a few minutes. Remove from tank and card off rust and again return to tank and heat. Remove from tank and while barrel is still hot apply heavy coat of good upper-cylinder lubricant as used in automobiles. Leave this on at least 2 hours. After cured, remove oil and apply wax or light gun oil. This method has worked for me with best results. It also works on cast iron and case hardened parts, although you have to pickle longer with acid solution."

- *Orville B. Bell, St. Louis, Missouri*

FIBERGLAS DICROPAN TANK

No N.R.A. Convention would be complete without the smiling countenance of Paul McKnight Deeley, past president of the New Jersey Gun Collectors Association, member of about every other association you can name and quite a gunsmith in his own right. Visited with him about Dicropan and when he got home he wrote how he made his own Dicropan tank:

"Just finished a little job which I thought might be of interest to you. In scouting around for a container to use for your Dicropan I did the following: First, I made up a simple wooden box to serve as a mold or form. I smoothed the outside of this box and then smeared it with release agent and proceeded to cover it with glass cloth and resin much in the same manner as if I were covering the hull of a boat. I built this up to a thickness of somewhere between 3/32" and 1/8". After the thing was thoroughly cured I slipped it off the form and, Viola! I had a light and strong fiberglas tank. Came out nice and was actually less trouble than trying to line a metal or wooden tank. Perhaps you would like to pass the idea along..."

- *Paul McKnight Deeley, North Plainfield, New Jersey*

STEEL IM TANK

...took three valve covers from Buick straight eights, cut the ends out and welded them together and then got some polyethylene storm window covering, laid in three layers of that and got two nice tanks out of the deal for IM bluing.

- *Neil Finney, Beloit, Kansas*

DICROPAN IM

What is the nature of Dicropan IM that keeps you from promoting it to the gun trade? I have just used it in two A3's and one 03 and also on an Enfield and got what looks like black nickel jobs. Takes more than 2 coats, though, using the method Mr. Bell used on shotguns. Please tell me more about this stuff - I think I am going to like it.

- *W. E. Beckstrom, Eureka, Montana*

DICROPAN IM FOR DOUBLES WITH STEEL WOOL RUB

I am getting wonderful results with your Dicropan IM for doubles. I have been using it for a year. I use two applications of the nitric acid first and then three applications of the Dicropan IM (as Mr. Bell says). I tried four the last time and it wouldn't take. The last one ran off the barrel like rain off a tin roof. The first application - I rub hell out of it with steel wool. After that it works fine.

- *Harry Franey, Delmont, Pennsylvania*

DICROPAN IM TO BLACKEN DIE-CAST GUN PARTS

Sometimes in rebluing work we run across these blankety-blank guns with die cast parts...the factories paint them black, but who wants to make with a paint brush and call it a blue job? Anyway, in casting around for something that would color this stuff and resemble a gun finish, I happened to see the bottle of Dicropan IM on the shelf, so I says to myself "what have you got to lose?...all it can do is dissolve the d--ed thing."

I hand sanded the part with 240 grit abrasive cloth and applied the IM cold to cold metal and kept it wet and kept rubbing until it was as black as it was going to get. When it dried I put some gun oil on it and heated it with the torch until it was just hot enough to be uncomfortable to the hand and to try to thin the oil and work it into the pores of the metal. Then I rubbed the metal with my hands just as you would a gunstock. It came up with a pretty nice sheen. I tried applying Dicropan to warm and hot metal but this did not work out nearly so well.

- *J. L. Anderson, Tipp City, Ohio*

DARKER DICROPAN FINISH

If you want a darker and finer grain finish on your Dicropan blued gun, mix as follows: 3-oz. of concentrate; 5-ozs. of water and 1-oz. of Methanol. Methanol is pure alcohol without any additive so you cannot use rubbing alcohol or the like. Generally speaking, you can get the pure stuff at paint stores and most of the time from gas stations as radiator anti-freeze. If you get it from a gas station be sure and read the label and be sure there is no rust preventive or anything else in it but Methanol! The slight addition of alcohol also helps overcome faint traces of oil which might appear on the surface of the solution after use. This oil can be removed by laying a piece of clean paper on the surface of the solution (or piece of clean cloth) and letting it blot up the oil. Other concentrations are:

6-oz. concentrate --- 10-oz. water --- 2-oz. Methanol --- 18-oz. total
12-oz. concentrate --- 20-oz. water --- 4-oz. Methanol --- 36-oz. total
24-oz. concentrate --- 40-oz. water --- 8-oz. Methanol --- 72 oz. total
48-oz. concentrate --- 80-oz. water --- 16-oz. Methanol --- 144-oz. total

- *Bob B.*

DICROPAN FOR LAYOUTS

Use Dicropan for lay-out fluid on parts you are making. You can see your lines and handle all you want without rubbing off.

- *Thomas P. McCormick, Bellaire, Ohio*

DICROPAN ON FORGINGS

One of our customers couldn't get a Husqvarna floor-plate to blue with Dicropan. We had him send it in to us and Wayne got nervous and started fiddling with it. Discovered that it was forged and that with a 5-second immersion he got a beautiful blue. We then tried some other forgings and found that from 5 to 8 seconds was best on all of them and that if you went over this immersion time you were in trouble. Of course, it figures. On all forgings the grains of the steel are much more open than on machined or stamped steel.

- *Bob B.*

T-4 ON DOUBLES

Just used your Dicropan T-4 for the first time on a set of double barrels. From past experience I wasn't even expecting the stuff to work. I am surprised as hell! It looks better than a slow process rust blue.

- *Dal Lutz, Orlando, Florida*

T-4 ON STAINLESS STEEL

I blued a stainless steel barrel with pure T-4 by just heating the barrel in water and then putting on the blue just like cold blue and it came out real nice.

- *Francis M. Antonowicz, Minneapolis, Minnesota*

CHAPTER 7

SPRING MAKING

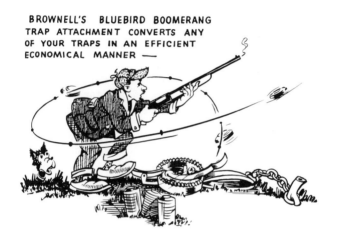

BROWNELL'S BLUEBIRD BOOMERANG
TRAP ATTACHMENT CONVERTS ANY
OF YOUR TRAPS IN AN EFFICIENT
ECONOMICAL MANNER —

SPRING MAKING

Here is a method for making springs that I've been using for 40 years and it suits me best. Heat the spring to a light cherry red and plunge in water at about room temperature. Now stone it bright, as it will be hard as H--. Now, with a slow heat, bring the part to a dark blue. Air cool. I have successfully made many, many springs with this method.

- *D. L. Shaffer, Mercer, Missouri*

TO MAKE SMALL SPRINGS

To make small springs, saw and file to shape from old auto springs, taking care not to heat metal to darkening temper if they are ground. This is much easier than shaping from steel and then tempering. The

tough car springs make a really good gun spring, so I have found.
- *Dorsey Williams, Jefferson City, Tennessee*

GUNSMITH SPRING MAKING TECHNIQUE

The following method of spring tempering was the life-long trade secret of John Frazier, top flight master gunsmith. When a youngster and an apprentice toolmaker, it was taught him by an old English craftsman. Of some 3,000 plus springs he made during his active gunsmith career he had only three break that he knows of!

"Heavy 'V' springs are best forged and finish filed and ground to shape. Be SURE all lines are absolutely true and all tapers are similar to a 'buggy whip'. Beyond the end of the taper of one leaf, leave part of the original steel size, this to be used to hold the spring while hardening to prevent heat bleed-off if the spring itself were held with pliers.

"In a dark or unlighted corner of your shop, heat the spring until it just shows red color and then quench.

"Then, take a regular quart motor oil tin can and with a hammer, pound in one side of the can making an indentation deep enough to hold the spring - which is now filed or ground to final exact shape and dimensions.

"Place the spring in the indent in the can and cover it with regular motor oil. With your torch, set the oil on fire and let it completely burn up. Then throw a handful of dry asbestos over the spring to keep it dark for a couple of hours. The spring has now been properly tempered and heat soaked. As John puts it: 'You either have a spring or you don't. A complete compression in your vise will darned soon tell you!'"
- *John Frazer, Clariton, Iowa*

SPRING TEMPERING

About every so often someone writes in wanting to know how to temper the steel we sell in those kits in the catalog. The piano wire ones, the compression ones and the wee flat ones should form okay without tempering but in case they do not hold for you and do need tempering, here is the procedure I always followed on all the small sized ones:

Heat red and forge to shape. Forging aligns the molecular structure. Bending does not. Heat to a dull cherry red and IMMEDIATELY push into a can of slacked lime being held as close as possible to the spring while being heated. Leave in the lime until thoroughly cool. Heat to a bright cherry red and quench in brine, stirring vigorously until cold. Polish bright and proceed as follows:

Lock your torch in your vise with the flame shooting straight up - and make it a small flame. Hold the spring quite a ways from the tip of the flame, turning it constantly. Soon it will turn a yellow color and then gradually turn brown and finally it will turn a dark purple (550 degrees F.). Immediately quench it in cutting oil or motor oil, stirring vigorously. This is for the heavier springs. For lighter springs, keep on heating until it turns dark blue (570 degrees F.) and quench in oil.

Now, squeeze the spring as flat as it will go in your vise. If it breaks, make another.

- *Bob B.*

"POREJOHN" TEMPERING

Here's an item from us boys who are 'Porejohns' and can't afford a furnace or pyrometer for tempering flat springs. Shape it and polish 'er real bright. Take it into the kitchen and put it on the burner of Mama's electric stove, edgewise. It will nearly fit the curve of the rods and you can color temper real well. No flame to distort your vision. (Commercial: If you would use the Tempilaq shown in the catalog you could even hit your temperature closer - better than a forge!)

- *Bob B.*

SPRING TEMPERING FLAT SPRINGS

"Incidentally, that flat stock that you sell is the best that I have had for a long time. (#149 Assortment) The spring stock that we used to get from England & Germany was very fine but I believe this is just as good. I do not know what temperatures your supplier recommends, but I have good luck with 1450 F, quench in oil and draw to 550 to 600 F." Note: Ben also makes "V" wedges to drive between the red hot folded steel to properly form top lever springs as for a Smith double. Removes guessing!"

- *Ben C. Lary, Jacksonville, Florida*

TEMPERING - COLORS AND TEMPERATURES

If you never know for sure what temperature you want to heat a part or tool to get a particular grade of hardness, the following table gives you all the dope you need. Not only does it list the major tempering temperatures, but also gives the color the steel turns when it reaches that temperature, and the tool or part that is usually tempered to that particular degree of hardness.

If you are a little color blind like me - or just don't trust yourself to tell the difference between "faint yellow" and "pale yellow" - you can use one of the temperature indicating liquids that you just paint on the piece. When the specific temperature is reached that you have applied the indicator for, it will melt sharply, and you can quench.

Here are the tempering colors and temperatures.

420 F. Very faint yellow
Drawing dies and punches and gun parts subject to friction, but no shock
430 F. Very pale yellow
Wood gravers, checking tools.
440 F. Light yellow
Chambering reamers
450 F. Pale straw yellow
Hand reamers, rifle action-pins.
460 F. Deep straw yellow
Milling cutters, machine reamers, points of triggers and sears.
500 F. Yellow brown
Twist-drills, firing-pin body only
550 F. Dark purple
Gun hammers, flat springs, extractors, screwdrivers, cold-chisels
570 F. Dark blue
Firing-pin noses, light flat springs, small screwdrivers.
- *Frank B.*

OVERHEARD
On a Park Rapids, Minnesota, party line: A gal named Olga was telling a friend she was having trouble with her canning: 'The yuice is so loose that the yelly won't yam . . .'
- *Lyle Kjer, Grantsburg, Wisconsin*

ELECTRICITY
Like the electrician said: Electricity won't kill you -- it just tickles you to death!
- *Dick Erickson, Bridgeton, New Jersey*

STENTOR HOT ROLLED TOOL STEEL
Carbon . . . 0.90%   Manganese . . 1.60%   Silicon . . 0.25%

STENTOR Tool Steel was not only recommended to us by Carpenter as "best" for the gunsmith trade, but also by several leading gunsmiths and parts & tool manufacturers. It has the widest safe hardening temperature range of any tool steel made, good machineability, superior hardening accuracy, excellent tolerance and finish and about the same wear resistance as Green Label.

HEAT TREATMENT
TO HARDEN: Heat parts to 1425/1525 F. If controlled furnace is not available, use 1450 Tempilaq . Hold at this temperature a few

seconds and quench in OIL. 5W straight motor oil makes a satisfactory quench.

TO DRAW: You will receive maximum combination of hardness and toughness with Stentor when drawn to 375/400 F. Use same technique as with Green Label below.

SPRING STEEL & LIME DRAWN DRILL ROD FLATS

Use regular hardening and drawing techniques described in all the gun books when handling these steels.

- *Bob B.*

GREEN LABEL TOUGH TIMBRE STEEL

Carbon . . . 1.20%   Manganese. . 0.20%   Silicon . .0.20%

Green Label Tool Steel Drill Rod is the best of the Carpenter line of rod for wear resistance, giving extreme toughness, will hold its size better when brine quenched than high quality, straight carbon tool steels! Sizes 3/16" round and smaller, when quenched in oil, will behave similar to top quality oil-hardening tool steel such as Stentor.

Not only are the Green Label sizes standard for practically all requirements, they also represent 99% of all pin sizes for all guns shown in *The Encyclopedia of Modern Firearms* - which were all tallied to determine sizes listed.

HEAT TREATMENT

TO HARDEN: heat parts to 1450 /1500 F. If controlled furnace is not available, use 1450 Tempilaq . This temperature is slightly higher than a cherry red. Hold at this temperature a few seconds and then immediately quench in a 5-10% brine solution. If oil hardening is desired on parts 3/16" and smaller, quench in any good pure 5W motor oil.

NOTE: If torch is used, have flame on "soft" side.

TO DRAW: You will receive maximum combination of hardness and toughness with Green Label when drawn to 350 /375 F. This is too low a temperature to use "color". Use furnace or Tempilaq . If higher temperatures are used, see suggestions in the gun books.

NOTE: - as with "Stentor" Steel, Carpenter Steel Co. technicians advised us to tell our gunsmith customers to use the recommended draw temperature for all tools and parts before going to any higher draw temperatures.

- *Bob B.*

THE NEW DEODORANT

E.A. Bixby wants to know if we have heard of the new deodorant, "Gone"? You rub it on, he says, and then you disappear, and all the people stand around wondering where the smell is coming from...

- *E.A. Bixby, Mt. Pleasant, Michigan*

HARDENING WITH MERCURY

Was advised years ago by chemist friend of the dangers of Mercury vapors. Your teeth will fall out first and then more serious complications. No joke! Suggest you discuss it with your local M.D. or chemist. I have been using it for years but with the shop well ventilated. Use small, 1-oz. liquid container. Heat carbon tap DULL RED and not bright red. Bright red makes it very brittle and the cutting teeth on your tap will powder at the slightest vibration . . . Also, you can break off a standard carbon drill to about 1/2" flutes and treat the same way for hard receivers (I don't believe in spot annealing).

- *Carmichael's Sporting Goods, Tuscon, Arizona*

FILE HARDENING COMPOUND

I don't know if there are any commercial file hardening compounds on the market at the moment - but if you need one, here's how to make it. Mix equal parts of regular baking flour, bone black, some charred leather-dust from your local shoe-makers, and a good slug of salt with enough water to make a thick paste. Have used it myself hundreds of times. Heat the file a bit and gunk it into the mess. Get a good pile of it on the file, and then gradually heat up the file, being careful not to blister the goo. Heat to a red color, bend the file to any shape desired, then heat to red hot and quench in brine. Works that simple. The goo stinks like sin while you are heating the file - and be careful not to burn it, char only.

- *Bob B.*

GENERAL HARDENING AND TEMPERING INSTRUCTIONS

The degree to which steel may be hardened depends primarily upon its carbon content, and the higher the carbon content the more it may be hardened. Alloy steels, due to their chemical constituency, normally are lower in carbon than a straight carbon steel that may be hardened to the same degree. The addition of alloying elements to steel broadens their usefulness by increasing abrasion resistance, shock resistance, tensile strength, ability to retain hardness at elevated temperatures, and many other desirable features.

Steel, to be hardened, must first be heated to a point slightly above the critical temperature, held at that temperature just long enough to assure a uniform diffusion of carbides throughout, and then quenched in a suitable medium such as water, brine, or oil.

Any means, such as gas, oil, gasoline, coal, coke, or electricity, may be used to heat the steel to the desired temperature, providing that excessive amounts of either carbon or oxygen are not surrounding the heated steel, as this may cause carburization or decarburization. A SLIGHTLY smoking flame is usually recommended. Prior to heat-

HARDENING COLORS FOR CARBON TOOL STEEL

Color	Degrees F.	Degrees C.	Color	Degrees F.	Degrees C.
Black Red	900	482	Bright Cherry	1500	815
Dark Red	1000	538	Salmon	1600	871
Blood Red	1100	593	Orange	1700	926
Dark Cherry	1200	648	Lemon	1800	981
Medium Cherry	1300	704	Light Yellow	2000	1093
Cherry	1400	760	White	2200	1204

TEMPER COLORS FOR CARBON TOOL STEEL

Color	Degrees F.	Degrees C.	Hardness	Hardness Rockwell "C"
Faint Yellow	420	215	Extra File Hard	63
Light Straw	435	225	File Hard	62
Dark Straw	465	241	Knife Hard	60
Yellow Brown	490	254	Extra Hard	58
Purple	520	271	Hard	56
Dark Blue	570	299	Half Hard	53
Blue Grey	620	326	Tough (Spring Temper)	50

These charts are approximate and for Carbon Steel only. Colors will vary slightly with steel analysis and with the length of time held at the desired temperature.

ing, surface scale or oxides should be removed to assure uniform hardening.

After the section to be hardened has been brought to temperature, quickly immerse it in either water or brine if it is a water hardening steel, or in oil if an oil hardening steel. Continue to move the steel around in the quenching solution until it can be held in the hand, after which it may be tempered.

Tempering is the process whereby both the brittleness and hardness of steel is decreased, and is performed in almost all cases of heat treating. After a section has been hardened and while still hand warm, shine or polish a part of it, normally the cutting edge, so that tempering colors may be watched on the surface. Reheat until the temper color corresponding to the desired hardness is obtained, and again quench in the proper medium until cold.

- *Bob B.*

CHAPTER 8

DRILLING & TAPPING

"SPORTERIZED" SPRINGFIELD

DENTISTS PRICKERS

"You are aware of the crow-bars dentists use in fixing your chewing equipment," writes H. Hamilton. "Well, they break a lot of them and will give them away for the asking. They come in dozens of shapes and sizes with octagon handles about 4" long . . . .Handiest things around the shop for reaching in after springs, aligning pins, making tiny screw drivers, etc."

- *H. R. Hamilton, Syracuse, New York*

OLD DENTIST BURRS

Bob, am sending a broken dentist bit to show you. These small affairs, if wound up to high speed, will cut a broken tap and are of great value to drill out broken parts, too. Dentists throw them away . . . . They'll drill thru the Enfield like butter . . . .

- *Bob Showers, Moses Lake, Washington*

GO SEE YOUR DENTIST

Next time you're in to see your local drilling contractor and oil-well locator (the dentist) see if he'll give you some of his left over broken and bent dental probes and the used burrs not fit for teeth anymore.

The burrs work fine for all sorts of grinding operations, and you can make anything from small punches to chisels, engraving tools, burnishers, etc. from the probes. They're excellent steel and you can easily do anything you want to with them in the way of making special purpose tools.

Don't forget the local Doc's and Vet's either, for they have lots of old scalpels that make fine special stock working knives.

- *Joe Waring, Comanche, Texas*

CUTTING HARD RECEIVERS

I use 3mm H.S. dental burrs to cut hard receivers. Run them about 600 rpm with lots of oil - will cut any of them.

- *Ken Parmele, Little Falls, Minnesota*

CENTER DRILLS

On the phone - "If you'll take one of those small double-ended center drills and grind one end to #31 wire gauge size and the other end to #28 wire gauge size, they make the best possible starting drills for sight screws. Positively rigid and will not bend or walk on the curved surface of a barrel or receiver."

- *Red Arrowwood, Hampton, Iowa*

THE RUSSIANS ARE REALLY OUR FRIENDS

Two wealthy gunsmiths fell into an argument about whether the Russians were really our friends. The one who maintained that they were said, "Why, I'll bet that I could ride a Russian ship to Russia, tour the country -- even Siberia -- and return, and nothing at all would happen."

The other called his bet, and being wealthy gunsmiths, the sum was set at a million dollars.

Two weeks later, as the Russian vessel left New York harbor, the ship's Captain called the American from his cabin. "Ve haff cable for you from New York," he snarled, glaring at the fellow, "Read it!"

The American looked at the telegram, which was signed by his friend.

"If you can't shoot Khruschchev," it read, "try for Mikoyan."

- *Fred Moulton*, The American Rifleman

CENTER PUNCH FOR DRILLING

Grind a 3-Square point on center punch for centering holes for drilling scope mounts. This will eliminate walk and give better starting cut for drill.

- *Joyce Hornady, Hornady Bullets, Grand Island, Nebraska*

ARMOR PIERCING CENTER PUNCH

I keep a few of the 30 caliber armor piercing bullets on the bench to use for center punches. Make really good ones by simply grinding down the hard centers. Given a good rap they will even mark a hardened receiver - usually!

- *Bob Blackburn, Fort Worth, Texas*

SPOT ANNEALING - ELECTRICALLY

...this one has been in use for a long time - because it is good - and is worthy of repeating. "...to help deal with hardened receivers without using a torch. Useful and gets the job done every time...Using a carbon out of a flashlight battery, sharpen it down on the tip to a drill point. Hook carbon to one side of battery (plus side), preferably 12 volt, and the ground wire to the barrel or action. Be sure and have the carbon securely held to the place on the receiver that you have to drill and tap. Clamp the lead wires to the battery and wait until the usual color changes take place on the receiver. This gives a small but thorough annealing of the part to be drilled..."

- *Bob Emery, Tulsa, Oklahoma*

DO-DRILL

Among some of the things we have added is some stuff called "Do-Drill". This is a heavy, compound drilling agent that smells like an oil refinery on a foggy night. It was developed for use by the precision manufacturing industry for drilling tough and hardened steels and alloys. Like so many other things, we ran across it because of one of our customers.

Roscoe Ormiston, gunsmith from Brooklyn, Iowa (14 miles from here) was in, mighty happy over a scope mounting job he had just done. He had tried everything under the sun to drill a receiver with absolutely no luck - even tried the material we mentioned last Newsletter, "And that wouldn't work, either," he said. Then a relative of his gave him some of this other stuff and to use Roscoe's own words:

"That drill went into that receiver like butter - honestly. All four holes and the drill was still as sharp as new. And here is the best part of it. I tapped all four holes with but one tap and when I got thru you couldn't tell the tap had been used...Just like tapping a real soft barrel."

- *Bob B.*

DRILLING

And while on drills, Ray Davis says: "Here is an item that the boys will bless you for if you see fit to pass it on. This morning I drilled holes with a #60 wire drill through a piece of old automobile spring leaf without drawing the temper and without busting a drill!

"Tried the same stunt with larger drills, and put them thru that 3/8" spring leaf like it was lead. The secret: Dip the drill in Permatex 300. In the case of very small drills be sure to re-apply before the drill runs dry. You will immediately regret all the hours of frustration that I am sure you have known when you have tried to tap or drill a 'glass receiver' that you did not want to spot anneal.

"Wish I could take credit for the tip. A local fishing friend who is a damn good mechanic found out first by accident, and proved it by experiment, and passed it on to me. Permatex was so grateful that they gave the man a whole case of Permatex. Whothahell wants to drill that many holes?"

- *Ray Davis, Morehead City, North Carolina*

A .22 CALIBER HOLE

One of my recently disowned friends was building a sort of shadow box around one of his kitchen windows this last winter and needed to drill a hole. So instead of driving a quarter of a mile to get a drill of the right size, he took the board he was working on, marked it off as if to drill it and took it out in the yard. There he leaned it against a tree, got out his trusty .22 rifle, and "drilled" himself the hole right where he wanted it.

(Note from Bob B.: Sure would like to see this friend make up some peg-boards for over his bench. Bet he'd use a 12 gauge with Mag loads!)

- *Brent Keefer, Fayette, Ohio*

CHIP CLEANING

As you know, Bob, in drilling for a scope in any type of jig, it is best to remove the chips in the hole as you pull out the drill and start in the tap. These little things are really hard to get out. You either drag the air hose over and blast chips over a 30 foot area, or make like a $3.00 bill boy doing a job through a picket fence blowing 'em out by mouth.

So, found a better way! Buy one of those large ear syringes at the local drugstore. Now bend a 3" piece of copper tubing (1/8" diameter) in a 90 degree. Put some epoxy cement on one end and insert this in the hole in the syringe. Let dry. Cut end off until you have a section about 1-1/2" long extending downward from the bend. Put this tip in the jig hole and give a quick hard squeeze. Chips cleared away without blowing them over a half-mile radius. Handiest little bugger you ever saw!

- *Ralph Walker, Selma, Alabama*

CARBIDE DRILLS

Those special ground carbide drills are by far the best I've used to date - over 300 holes with #31 in '03A3, M/70, etc. and still cuts but will need sharpening soon. How good can they get?

- *Jerry Shannon, Spanaway, Washington*

SHARPENING CARBIDE/TUNGSTEN

I note everyone is praising Carbaloy or Tungsten Carbide bits - and well they should, but most seem dazzled about sharpening them. Common old Sears & Roebuck sells a Silicon Carbide wheel that will sharpen the H---- right out of them. Maybe this will be of help to some of the boys.

- *Bob Puryear, Memphis, Tennessee*

CARBIDE DRILL TIPS

If you'll just use a wee bit of common sense when drilling with them, they should give mighty good returns on your investment and save a jillion ulcers. Goes thru an A3-03 like a regular drill in soft steel. The special drills should NOT be used in soft steel. They will drill all the way thru hard steel, but do remember on guns like Krags just to use them on the hard surface and soft steel drills (regular drills) for the insides.

- *Bob B.*

BROKEN CARBIDE DRILLS

Here's an easy way to repair those expensive carbide drills that do such a beautiful job of drilling the hard receivers - and break sort of easy at times.

Grind the broken ends of the pieces on an angle, so that the two pieces fit together with an angled overlap. Now, chuck one piece in the headstock and the other in the tailstock of your lathe. Bring together until the parts just touch and carefully silver solder (Be sure to cover the lathe ways!). Be sure to flow a little of the solder in the upper parts of the flutes for added rigidity. When cool, unchuck tailstock and slide out of the way. Start the lathe, and file the silver solder down flush with the drill shank. Check accuracy with dial indicator - and when right, the drill is ready to go.

- *Jim Melchor, Norfolk, Virginia*

EASY TAPPING TECHNIQUES

Like anyone else, I have busted a tap or two in bottomed holes and nitric acid is about the only thing that will get 'em loose so that the hole is not ruined, but an easier method for bottomed holes is to heat a carbon tap nearly white hot and quench in mercury. This produces a glass hard tap that will cut threads in the hardest M/70 or 03-A3 and if broken, a smart blow using a hammer and flat end punch will shatter it so that it can be bounced out in small pieces.

Another idea that saves me money - don't throw away broken carbon taps. Just leave them as broken and when tapping hard receivers, start threads with well worn tap, switch to new, sharp carbon tap and get a couple of threads started full depth. Then chuck the broken tap in your jig and carefully start it in. Done properly, the longest end picks up the couple of started threads and the whole d---- thing winds through so easily it scares you...

- *Jerry Shannon, Spanaway, Washington*

TO STOP TAPS STICKING IN HARD RECEIVERS

To put a cutting edge that will cut a good clean thread and not stick in a hard receiver, don't leave more than 3 threads on the tap... in other words, grind it off! It is quite easy to grind a tap if you turn it so that you are looking at the flat end. The greater the angle, the more surface there is to bind. You want only enough to start the tap through. I find that drill bits work better too if ground on the least angle.

- *Richard A. Turgeon, Sioux Falls, South Dakota*

BROKEN TAPS

Those solid pilot carbide drills will drill a tap out of a bottomed hole slick as a whistle. You have to be careful and I have chipped a drill that way - but who cares about a four buck drill when you have a tap broken off in a Hundred & Fifty buck gun!

- *Jim Brusaw, Casper, Wyoming*

BUSTED TAPS

I recently read in the Newsletter about using the carbide drills to get broken taps out of a gun. The gent who wrote also mentioned that you can chip a drill...you can! Recently I found myself in that unenviable position with a busted tap in a very expensive smokestick--Agony! I chipped one drill (hence my order for another recently). I started over and used plenty of Do-Drill and got 'er out with no sweat and no chipped drill...

- *Joe M. Waring, Comanche, Texas*

BROKEN TAPS

Maynard P. Buehler, Buehler Mounts wrote, "Those split point drills are good. I've been selling them for years. Agree with you about HSS taps. People are nuts. Carbon taps are 2 to 3 points harder on the Rockwell 'C' scale to boot...Next time try a little HNO_3 to loosen a broken tap."

(Note: Nuts, just called the local druggest and HNO_3 is nuttin' but nitric acid. Wouldn't wonder but what Maynard has something there at that!!)

- *Bob B.*

BROKEN TAP REMOVAL - THE HARD WAY

I broke a 6-48 tap off in a rifle action (rear) and couldn't budge it any way I tried. Finally I took my smallest welding tip and carefully heated the broken tap to a bright, almost white-red, then cut the acetelyne off but left the oxygen on. That tap boiled out of there like crazy. Nothing was left but a bunch of carbon which was no trouble to remove. The threads weren't even hurt. Sure enuff advise using this as a VERY LAST resort only and don't blame me if it doesn't work.

It surely did for me and got me off a real hook. Hope this gets someone out of a jam sometime.

- *Cal Duke, Shreveport, Louisiana*

FIGURING THE CORRECT DRILL SIZE FOR WOOD SCREWS

When joining wood with screws, it is necessary to bore pilot holes, especially in hardwoods. With pilot holes, screws are easier to drive and there is less chance of damaging the screws or the wood.

Bore holes large enough to freely accommodate screw shank in first piece of wood. Bore holes slightly smaller than thread diameter to a depth of half the length of threaded portion in the second

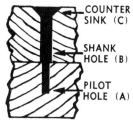

COUNTER SINK (C)

SHANK HOLE (B)

PILOT HOLE (A)

No. of Screw	PILOT HOLES (A)				SHANK CLEARANCE HOLES (B)		COUNTERSINK (C)
	HARD WOODS		SOFT WOODS				
	TWIST BIT (Nearest size in fractions of an inch)	DRILL Gauge No. To be used for maximum holding power	TWIST BIT (Nearest size in fractions of an inch)	DRILL Gauge No. To be used for maximum holding power	TWIST BIT (Nearest size in fractions of an inch)	DRILL Gauge No. or Letter To be used for maximum holding power	NO. OF AUGER BIT To Counterbore for sinking head (by 16ths)
0	$\frac{1}{32}$	66	$\frac{1}{64}$	75	$\frac{1}{16}$	52	—
1	—	57	$\frac{1}{32}$	71	$\frac{5}{64}$	47	—
2	—	54	$\frac{1}{32}$	65	$\frac{3}{32}$	42	3
3	$\frac{1}{16}$	53	$\frac{3}{64}$	58	$\frac{7}{64}$	37	4
4	$\frac{1}{16}$	51	$\frac{3}{64}$	55	$\frac{7}{64}$	32	4
5	$\frac{5}{64}$	47	$\frac{1}{16}$	53	$\frac{1}{8}$	30	4
6	—	44	$\frac{1}{16}$	52	$\frac{9}{64}$	27	5
7	—	39	$\frac{1}{16}$	51	$\frac{5}{32}$	22	5
8	$\frac{7}{64}$	35	$\frac{5}{64}$	48	$\frac{11}{64}$	18	6
9	$\frac{7}{64}$	33	$\frac{5}{64}$	45	$\frac{3}{16}$	14	6
10	$\frac{1}{8}$	31	$\frac{3}{32}$	43	$\frac{3}{16}$	10	6
11	—	29	$\frac{3}{32}$	40	$\frac{13}{64}$	4	7
12	—	25	$\frac{7}{64}$	38	$\frac{7}{32}$	2	7
14	$\frac{3}{16}$	14	$\frac{7}{64}$	32	$\frac{1}{4}$	D	8
16	—	10	$\frac{9}{64}$	29	$\frac{17}{64}$	I	9
18	$\frac{13}{64}$	6	$\frac{9}{64}$	26	$\frac{19}{64}$	N	10
20	$\frac{7}{32}$	3	$\frac{11}{64}$	19	$\frac{21}{64}$	P	11
24	$\frac{1}{4}$	D	$\frac{3}{16}$	15	$\frac{3}{8}$	V	12

Sizes of holes recommended for average application. Slightly larger or smaller holes may be required.

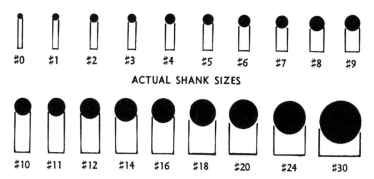

ACTUAL SHANK SIZES

#0 #1 #2 #3 #4 #5 #6 #7 #8 #9

#10 #11 #12 #14 #16 #18 #20 #24 #30

To determine sizes of Wood or Tapping Screws - Lay screw flat inside parallel lines shown below each exact-size screw shank shown above.

piece of wood.

Screw length should be at least 1/8" less than combined measurements of materials being joined.

- Bob B.

"WRENCHING-OUT" STUCK SCREWS

Squirt a little liquid wrench or pour on some Coca Cola (No kidding, Maytag Auto-Washer Service branches use Coke to loosen and remove stuck splines, screws, nuts, etc.)

Fit one of your Magna-Tip screw driver bits into the screw slot and snug up the assembly in a vise. Put a wrench on the bit and the screw just walks out. The frame of a carpenter's vise has enough 'give' or spring to allow the screw to unscrew a half turn, then loosen the vise

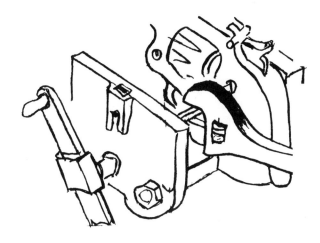

a little touch and wrench the screw out some more. (With regular bench vise, you will need to loosen the vise a bit as you unscrew.) -By the way, did you ever try to unscrew the unscrutable?

- *M. C. Ray, Cleveland, Ohio*

STUCK SCREWS WITH BRAKE FLUID

I use common hydraulic brake fluid to loosen rusted or frozen screws. It is the best penetrating oil I know of. I also use it to clean up corroded and rusty barrels, lock plates, etc. To clean out an old barrel, use the finest steel wool obtainable on a rod. A little scrubbing does wonders.

- *C. V. Baker, Massillon, Ohio*

RUSTED SCREW REMOVAL

John Frazier was in telling about a badly rusted gun he had to take apart. So bad that if you twisted the screws they'd up and break. How did he get it apart? Soaked it in water. Says the screws practically fell out - has used the same on muzzle-loaders for years with equal success. If he runs into something he can't give the water soak treatment - then he heats it up and applies a bit of beeswax... has never failed him yet and John has been actively gunsmithing for more years than most of us have seen since the diaper stage!! And he can still go out and break his 24 birds or fit a Drilling stock so close you can't squirt water between wood and metal - even under pressure.

- *John Frazier, Chariton, Iowa*

MISTAKES

As the effervescent David Wyer puts it: "Learn from the mistakes of others for you can't possibly live long enough to make them all yourself!"

- *David Wyer, Muleshoe, Texas*

FOREIGN SCREWS

Fit brace screwdriver exactly to screw but use Jacobs headstock chuck from lathe as handle - never had one fail to come out easily this way. (Note by BB: I have used off-set screwdriver (ratchet type) with gun & screwdriver locked in vise. Loosen vise a hair and turn screwdriver. The toughest screws can be turned out this way.)

- *Ben Barton, North Newcastle, Maine*

SCREW REMOVING

I used to make up a screwdriver bit from drill rod, harden and draw it, and put it in the chuck of my drill press. Then I put the gun

- or whatever I am swearing at at the moment, in the drill press vise and bring the spindle down into contact with the screw slot and tighten the spindle lock. By rotating the spindle in reverse by means of the chuck key, out comes the screw, forcing the spindle up as it loosens. Never have had it fail. Was a lot of work making up those bits until you came along with those tips for the Magna-Tip screwdrivers. They are a natural for a job like that. Many thanks to the guy who invented that little jewel.

   - *Tommy Munsch, Prior Lake, Minnesota*

OF SCREWS AND CHIPS

I place a small screwdriver with a magnet attached near the handle inside holes I've drilled and tapped to remove the pesky cuttings. Beats blowing them and gettin' 'em in every eyeball you've got ...Lastly, I've made up a plate 3 x 6 x 1/8" of 4120 steel, drilled and tapped 4 x 40, 6 x 40, 6 x 48 and 10 x 32 holes in it. (Note: Can suggest also shotgun 3 x 56) When ya' need to grind a screw down, it can be screwed through the proper hole to the desired length and ground square. If it isn't screwed up tight enough to keep from turning while grinding it, it can be held by simply chucking a tap wrench down on the head of the screw flush with the back side of the plate.

   - *Bob McDaniel, Caruthersville, Missouri*

CHAPTER 9

TIPS FOR SPECIFIC GUNS

HOW TO MAKE YOUR RIFLE SHOOT BETTER!

The secrets of a really accurate rifle are many and varied. Here are some tips on how you can do the job yourself.

Hundreds of would-be hunters last season bounced out of bed hours before dawn, shouldered their rifles and set out afield with just one idea in mind - to bag an old mossback buck for the mantle or a fat young yearling for the deep freeze. • But more often than not, things just didn't work out. • Not a few neophyte nimrods came back after several days of hard hunting, disillusioned about the whole business because they missed a choice shot at just about the trophy they had dreamed about. • What was the problem? • "I jerked the trigger," some will guess, or, "maybe it was buck fever," or, "could I have flinched?" • Well, it could have been any one of these things, especially if the individual is only an occasional hunter who seldom fires his rifle more than a few times a year in the field.

The first consideration in accuracy is, of course, the ammunition. For the very best, hunters should handload their game loads, making them tailored to their individual rifles. Target shooters have no choice. Factory ammunition, at least that being produced under current standards, just won't deliver sufficient accuracy for match-winning scores.

This isn't to say that commercially-produced ammunition is of poor quality. Cartridges produced on the assembly line are better today than ever, but mass production methods don't contribute to exacting uniformity in the loaded round, and uniformity is essential for superior accuracy.

Handloaders can weigh a batch of brass on their powder scales and select several cases which weigh within a few tenths of a grain of each other. This test is based on the idea that the heavier the case is, the thicker the wall of the brass is and, hence, the smaller the volume of the case.

For top accuracy, for target or long range varmint shooting, use only the cases of almost exactly the same weight and you'll all but eliminate those unexplained "flyers" that seem to take off on a course all their own, for no apparent reason.

If you don't plan to handload, however, you can at least make a suitable compromise. When you go to the range, take several brands of ammunition with various bullet weights, because you can bet they won't all shoot exactly alike. One brand, or one bullet weight, will almost certainly group better than the others. And just because one load shoots well in your buddy's gun, doesn't mean the same thing will happen in your rifle, even though both guns are identical.

Do your shooting from a bench-rest, if at all possible. Shooting prone, using sandbags, is acceptable but there's no substitute for a rock-steady position atop a sturdy bench with sandbags supporting the butt and forearm of the rifle.

Shoot three-shot groups at first, to eliminate the majority of types being tested. Then, when you've narrowed the field to a couple of brands or bullet weights, shoot a few five-shot groups to be sure you're making the right choice.

It's important that you do this experimenting under almost perfect conditions. That is, when there is little or no wind blowing, and preferably in the early morning or late evening when mirage (heat waves radiating off the ground which can usually be seen through a telescope on a sunny day) is less of a problem. Unless you're a top flight conditioned shooter, wise to the effects of wind, mirage and light changes, you'll never be able to "dope" the changes which can alter your point of impact considerably, even at 100 yards, and invalidate anything you're trying to prove.

This process of finding the correct load for your rifle isn't really as complicated as it might seem, and once you find one type of ammunition which outperforms all others, you're in much better shape than the fellow who buys a brand simply because he likes the color of the box.

It's a good idea, though, to know where shells of a different brand will group in your gun so you won't be completely stymied if the only ammunition retailer in town happens to be sold out of your brand the day hunting season opens.

Often, a load is worked up for a gun before hunting season and the rig performs without fail at every trial. When the season ends, the once-or-twice-a-year hunter usually sacks up his rifle and pokes it in the closet to wait for "next year."

But next year, his "pre-season check-up" reveals that the old gun just won't produce those mouth-watering groups it once did.

A good place to start is the scope, but if the mounts and bases are all right, and they usually are, you've got trouble.

If you're serious about wanting to solve your problem, the next step is to pull the barreled action out of the stock and check the bedding. If your barrel is free-floated, be sure the stock isn't bearing against the barrel anywhere. Wrap a piece of paper around the barrel and slide it all the way back to the receiver ring, or recoil lug. It should slide freely, to be sure clearance is sufficient to allow for barrel expansion caused by heat from firing several rounds. Insignificant as this sounds, such trivialities can play havoc with accuracy.

If the barrel is bedded solidly to the forearm, you need to be sure the wood isn't exerting too much pressure on the barrel at any point. You can do this by smoking the metal parts over a kerosene flame or, better yet, coating them with a mixture of Prussian blue and oil and replacing the barreled action in the stock. Darker smudges or indentions in the wood indicate areas of excessive pressure. Use a fine-grit sandpaper to work down high places in the stock's barrel channel.

Particular attention should be given the recoil lug. It must contact the wood evenly at all points (it need not touch on the front or either side, however) or accuracy will almost certainly be erratic. Often, the best remedy for a poor fit here is to bed the lug with any of several fine compounds, such as fiberglass bedding kits produced specifically for that purpose.

And, it might simplify matters to rebed the entire action if the bedding has really gone sour. Coat the wood behind the recoil lug with the compound, also dab a little in the inletted area where the rear tang rests. If the action is a flat-bottomed type, such as a Mauser, Sako or Winchester, coat the wood under the flat bottom of the receiver to insure a perfect fit there.

Be sure to follow directions for using the bedding compound. If called for, coat all metal parts which are likely to touch the compound with some type of release agent, such as paste furniture wax, or you'll cement your barreled action and stock forever.

An often overlooked cause of erratic groups is the screw (s) that hold the barreled action in the stock. Could be they're bearing against the wood in such a way as to act as recoil lugs, and this situation can produce those hair-pulling groups with three or four shots in one little cluster and another hole out by itself in left field.

Once you've worked up a load for your rifle and tuned it up as suggested, you're ready to head for the range again. Chances are you helped things considerable - if you did a good job. But if the thing still refuses to shoot, you've got no choice but to look somewhere else for your problem.

At this stage of the game, a suspicious glance at your barrel might be well-advised. Sadly, many barrels have been ruined through neglect or just plain carelessness.

Too many shooters don't realize that a rifle barrel just won't stand constant shoddy treatment and keep shooting like a new one. Fellows who sit down on a hot summer day and ring off 15 or 20 rounds time after time with barely a pause to reload can just about forget any hopes of top accuracy in the future. When the barrel gets so hot you can hardly touch it, you're already doing permanent damage, many experts claim. Shooting rapidly, keeping the barrel hot, and failure to clean the tube regularly subtracts thousands of rounds from normal barrel life.

Careless cleaning techniques are responsible for a large number of ruined barrels. All rifles should be cleaned from the breech whenever possible to minimize chances of scratching the barrel with the cleaning jag. A scratch near the muzzle is almost sure to destroy any consistent accuracy.

More serious, however, is a scratch near the center of the barrel. If the damage is near the muzzle, a gunsmith can solve the problem by simply whacking off the tube behind the scratch and doing a re-crowning job. But if the spot is located near the center of the barrel, you've got troubles that only a new barrel will cure.

If you have to rebarrel your action, it helps to know a few "ground rules" before plunking down the price of a new barrel. If you demand really top accuracy, and if weight is not problem, then forget about the little pencil-size tubes that look so attractive in rifle advertisements. Buy something that will measure from .600 to .800 of an inch on the muzzle and you'll just about triple your chances of having a real tackdriver.

Don't worry too much about the length, either. World records were broken in the light varmint class of National Benchrest Shooters Association competition last year with guns having 18 and 19 inch barrels. For most purposes, a compromise between these carbine-length tubes and the ultra-long 30-inch jobs is probably the best choice.

Stainless steel barrels will outlast the more common chrome molybdenum tubes. The former type can't be blued by the ordinary commercial process, though, so if you're bound to have a blue barrel, be prepared to sacrifice some barrel life or spend several extra dollars having the thing plated.

A top-notch custom barrel blank sells for about $55 to $60. Installation charges vary, but the minimum is probably around $25.

When the old gun ceases to shoot, don't be too quick to panic, even if all indications point to the barrel as the source of the trouble. Sometimes the tube is "eroded" only about an inch or so in front of the throat - just enough to spoil accuracy. When this is the case, a gunsmith can often chop off the worn part, rechamber, and add another 1000 rounds to your barrel's useful life.

An even less serious cause of poor accuracy is damage to the muzzle's crown. Most crowns are recessed, but if the rifle is carried muzzle-downward in a car over a period of time, small gravel on the floorboard can do sufficient damage to affect accuracy. Often the damage is all but invisible. Here the solution is simple. The barrel can be recrowned, usually without even removing it from the action. The procedure is fast, inexpensive, and most important, effective.

Once you get your barreled action bolted back in the stock, a few last minute adjustments can pay added dividends in terms of accuracy.

If your action is of the flat-bottomed variety as mentioned before, backing off the rear tang screw one-quarter to one-half a turn will often shrink groups substantially. This writer's custom .25/06 (FN Mauser action) would consistently shoot three-shot groups of just under an inch at 100 yards with all screws in the action tight. But loosening the rear tang screw just a dab tightened up successive three-shot groups to under one-half an inch - a payoff well worth the effort. Of course, this operation causes the gun to group higher, and the change must be compensated for by readjusting the sights.

Now after you've finished tuning your rifle, whether it's a .300 magnum or a .222, and have worked up a load that seems to outperform all others, your gun ought to shoot with any other rifle in its

314

class - if your equipment is in good shape and if you've done a good job. But don't expect your big bore magnum to shoot like a heavy barreled varminter, because it just won't happen. Don't be too surprised when you discover your pet varminter can't compete with your buddy's benchrest rifle, either.

But remember - even though your rifle won't ream them all in the same hole, it will still shoot more accurately than you can hold it in most cases.

So with that idea in mind, it wouldn't do any harm to try to upgrade your own ability by putting in a few off-season practice sessions at the range. You'd be surprised how much you can improve with a minimum of practice, and if you're any kind of shooter at all, the idea ought to appeal to you.

And come next hunting season, with your gun performing like a champ and your own ability better than ever, you're bound to spot an even better buck than the one you saw last year - and this time you won't miss!

 - *Jim Gilmore, Reprinted by special permission of* GUNS & AMMO *Magazine, November 1967*

WORKING OVER TRIGGER PULL ON .45 ACP

When working over the trigger pull on the .45 ACP, mount the hammer and sear with their respective pins on the outside (left) of

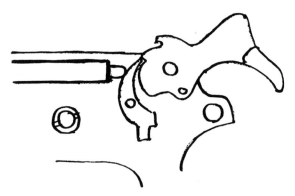

the frame and you get a clear picture of what is happening inside. The safety plunger and spring act as a sear spring. The sketch gives you an idea of what I mean. (Was too lazy to take a gun apart to sketch to exact scale, so is just freehand!)

Now, you can go ahead with your job and be sure of what you are doing.

 - *M. C. Ray, Cleveland, Ohio*

STIPPLING PISTOL GRIP FRAME ON .45 AUTO

In giving the .45 Auto an accuracy job, most people want the front of the frame roughed up to prevent slipping or for a better grip. There are several ways of doing this. I've settled on the following: Take a prick punch ground to a 45 degree point, about an 8-oz. hammer, and start tapping. Takes about an hour, looks good, gives rough finish and no one kicks at the price.

- *Melchor Enterprises, Inc., Norfolk, Virginia*

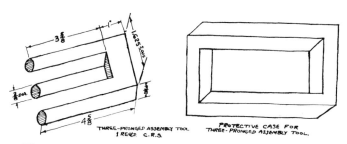

THREE-PRONGED ASSEMBLY TOOL
1 REQD. C.R.S

PROTECTIVE CASE FOR
THREE-PRONGED ASSEMBLY TOOL.

- *Thanks to M. C. Ray, Cleveland, Ohio*

ENFIELD EARS

Every few days - or weeks - we get letters from customers wanting to know how to take off the ears from an Enfield action when you do not have a milling machine nor access to one. Now, I don't know how the rest of you do it, but when I was gunsmithing, there wasn't a mill within 50 miles - and even when there was one, there were no form cutters for that special job. So, I turned on my bench grinder, had a bucket of water handy to dunk the heated work in, and started grinding. After doing a couple, one gets so they know just about how much to grind off and where. Matter of fact, I believe you can do the job about as fast that way as you could loading up in the car, driving to some machine shop and sitting around on your hands waiting for a machinist to get around to doing the job for you. Only place you can have trouble is getting it flat or round - as you might choose - to fit scope mounts. So, I always had the mounts to be used on hand and checked against them as I went...

- *Bob B.*

ENFIELD MAGAZINE BOXES

I noticed in the Newsletter someone wondering about the ends in Enfield Magazine Boxes. I take the ends out and turn them around and silver solder them back in for 300 - 375 and 458's. Works good.

- *Parmele's Gun Shop, Little Falls, Minnesota*

INSTALLING BLADE-TYPE SAFETY/BOLT LOCK

The blue print along side gives the exact factory specs for slot-

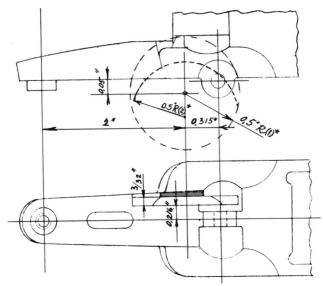

ting the receiver for a trigger/safety combination with a blade-type
bolt lock when installing the trigger/safety on the old FN's or 98's.

- *Firearms International, Washington, D.C.*

ITHACA PARTS SUPPLY

For any Ithaca Single Barrel Trap Gun having a serial number
UNDER 400,000, we no longer can furnish any parts or any service.
The changeover in design to the current model Ithaca Single Barrel
Trap Gun was made way back in year 1922. For the current guns, all
of which have a serial number OVER 400,000 we can still furnish all
parts and all service. For the former Ithaca Double Barrel Shotguns,
we no longer can furnish any parts or any service for those having
numbers UNDER 400,000. For those having numbers OVER 400,000,
we have finally had to discontinue SERVICE of any kind in our plant,
but we can still furnish some (but not all) parts...

- *Sheldon M. Smith, President of Ithaca*

ADVICE TO BIG GAME HUNTERS

If you are planning on going to Africa after Big Game, note the
following advice: "The best and only way to stop a charging elephant
is to take away his credit card."

- *Cameron's Guns, Corinne, Utah*

EXTRACTOR PROBLEMS ON ITHACA Mod 49 Saddle Gun

Often this gun will not extract the 22 short cases although it works fine on 22 long and 22 long rifle. It does not work because there is not enough of a bend in the extractor to make contact with the 22 short rim. A slight adjustment to the extractor will correct this problem, and it can be done without removing the extractor.

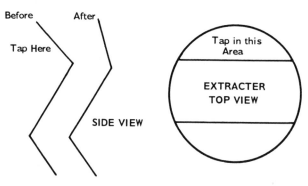

Merely use a flat face object and tap the top 1/3'd of the extractor face. After each tap or two, try the shell. Keep tapping and trying until the adjustment is correct and it extracts properly. If you were to look at a side view of the extractor, you are actually bending the top dog-leg back, making a wider angle between it and the center "leg".

- *George Clearwater, White Plains, New York*

FRONT SWIVELS FOR ITHACA 49

I finally found a way to do it. Makes a nice looking job too. It takes two butt stock screws, one in the butt and the front one goes in the front barrel band. Just remove the barrel band screw, then counterbore the screw hole just large enough and deep enough to take the smooth part of the butt stock screw. Then drill a smaller hole in the wood for the screw!

- *Westphal's Gun Shop, Austin, Minnesota*

INLETTING TRICK FOR THE L. C. SMITH

I've stocked a lot of Smith's in my time, and of course the first one was the roughest. After sweating out a few, I finally came up with a way to make the final fitting easier. As you know, when the trigger plate is fitted and installed, a small screw has to be screwed through the trigger plate into the bottom of the connector from the top lever. The bottom of this connector is turned exactly to fit the hole in the trigger plate, and the trigger plate is counterbored to accept the screw. And the whole thing is under considerable side pressure from the top lever spring which is located in a slot on the bottom of the receiver. Everytime I want to check the fit on the trigger plate, I have to fight that cussed connector to get it lined up and seated in its hole before I can check anything.

So, to overcome all this, I drill a #31 hole through the inside webbing in the bottom of the receiver just back of the cocking cam on the left side. The hole comes out at a slight angle because of the contours of the receiver, but still is straight enough to let a 6-48 screw get a good purchase against the spring on the other side of the action. After tapping, I put in a 1/2" long 6-48 and run it in until it pushes the spring legs together (this works easier if you can find an allen head screw). From then on, I can do all the fitting of the lock plates, trigger plate and so on with complete ease because the trigger plate literally falls into place whenever I assemble and reassemble.

- *R. A. Jerrue, Abingdon, Virginia*

MARLIN 336 JAMMING

I got 2 Marlin 336's in in one month - 30 cal. Both with same trouble, they couldn't digest the shells from the magazine. The shell in the carrier would stick about half way into the carrier. It would start up and there she jammed. I checked the carrier and everything I could think of, tore my hair, got my fingernails full of scalp and dandruff and still had the jam. This on the first gun...polished everything up but still jammed - not every time, but often enough so the rifle was no good.

When the second one came in, I told myself, "This is it. I'm going to find it or bust a gut." I finally did! So "D" simple I am ashamed to tell: The magazine tube was about 1/16" short and did not seat against the shoulder in the receiver so every now and then the shell rim would drop into the space left between the magazine tube and receiver shoulders. Thus, the shell ahead of the one in the carrier would not shove the one on deck clear back into the carrier, which would start to rise - and there was the job.

I ground a 21/32" drill to about 30 degrees each side and turned it in the receiver recess to bevel the edge. Everything works OK now!

- *Don Houston, Madera, California*

PARKER SHOTGUN DATA

From Jim Baker who's been collecting Parkers for over 40 years and who has compiled data information on the guns. He's given us permission to include the following interesting information on the Parkers: 8 and 10 gauge, Heavy, Frame #3, Action Width 1-7/8", Barrel Width 2-1/2". Light 10 and Heavy 12, Frame #2, Action Width 1-25/32", Barrel Width 2-5/16". Light 12 and Heavy 16, Frame #1-1/2,

Action Width 1-3/4", Barrel Width 2-1/4". Light 16, Frame #1, Action Width 1-23/32", Barrel Width, 2-3/16". Light 20, Frame #0, Action Width 1-21/32", Barrel Width 2-1/32".

- *Jim Baker, Decatur, Illinois*

CUSTOM AUTOGRAPH

Mr. and Mrs. R. D. Harris stopped by the other day to pick up a copy of The Encyclopedia. Have been doing business with "R. D." for Lo! these many years and I suspect the only reason they didn't order the book by mail is that Fleta (who reads this thing and knows her husband) wanted to be positive I put in the autograph just the way she wanted it - and that I did - "From one durned fool to another"...

- *R. D. and Fleta Harris, Mansfield, Missouri*

RECOIL WASHER IN REMINGTON AUTOS

J. Bulwan uses break-lining to replace the recoil washer in the old style Remington autos. Shapes it to size, drills and counterbores for 6x48 screw, drills and threads rear of receiver and screws in place. Smooths down end of screw, blackens with Oxpho and swears it'll last forever.

- *J. W. Bulwan, Alliance Nebraska*

REMINGTON 11/48 SHELL HOLDER "HOLDER"

Ralph Walker has come up with more unusual jigs, fixtures, work holders, short-cuts and ideas than you'll find in a lot of books. One of the darndest guys I've ever corresponded with. Next page is an outline of a piece of bent wire...wire to measure about 3/32" o.d. and should be bent to fit into the outline. Here is what it is for:

"If you have ever put a Remington 11-48 back together you will have enjoyed (?) cussin the little can-cutter-shell holder that is on the right side of the receiver (belly-up). This thing must be held in place whilst inserting, or trying to insert, the trigger group. It won't stay in place. Much cussin results.

"This Whia-Gizzmo Mark II does the job. Here's how...With the receiver belly-up, insert the shell holder in place. Now insert the end of gizzmo thru the operating handle slot part of the receiver, end pointed toward the muzzle...It goes under the two arms that connect the breech block with the spring. Now, twist it upwards, letting the little tit press the shell holder back in place with the back of the wire against the arm. Don't worry about lining the hole in the shell holder with the receiver hole. Now insert the **back** of the trigger group in the receiver and press down, easing the forward end down slowly and when it touches the gizzmo, rotate the gizzmo toward the muzzle and out. It is in place - WALLA! Now insert the big pin and seat. Next, insert

Ralph Walker's "Whia-Gizzmo Mark II" for assemblying Remington 11/48's. Drawing is to actual size, so to make holder, simply bend wire to fit within outlines of drawing.

the small forward pin from the OPERATING HANDLE SIDE and push it as far as it will go. Insert a nailset or pin punch on the other side and push the shell holder in line for the small pin to go thru... It works like a breeze - I use it constantly."

- Ralph Walker, Walker Arms Co., Selma, Alabama

REMINGTON 11/48 SHELL LATCH PIN

This pin is hollow and is threaded. The Remington company sells a puller for this pin for a cost of 92¢ each. In case the pin is not rusted in the socket it will come out fairly easy; in case it is rusty then it don't come so nice.

- W. A. Smith, Huntington, West Virginia

FITTING BARRELS TO THE REMINGTON 40X

It is standard practice for the factory to face the breech of the barrel from the chamber out to the periphery of the barrel extension with a 2 degree slope instead of squared off as most gunsmiths try to fit it. In other words, the breech of the barrel should resemble a shallow cone with an included angle of 176 degrees. This is sufficient clearance for even a maximum bolt to clear and not gall the face of the breech. And the slight clearance allows space for the usual firing residue to accumulate.

The chamber mouth is radiused .003" to promote smooth feeding and to reduce damage to the chamber while cleaning the barrel.

If the breech is faced slightly to increase head-space, as a rule only a thousandth or two is required. This leaves only a small bright ring around the chamber mouth due to the 2 degree clearance provided. Radius of the chamber mouth should then be rechecked to be sure it is adequate.

- Dan Carroll, at an NRA show

REMINGTON 721 TRIGGER GUARD MODIFICATION

Temple Lide modifies the Remington 721 for beauty and practicality like this: Make a saw cut across the Remington floor plate a quarter inch (plus) back of the middle retaining screw hole. Take either the Mauser or Springfield trigger guard assembly, make a saw cut parallel to the top of the guard and into the magazine well; another cut at the forward part of the floor plate catch well and thru the first cut. Install into the hole for the floor plate catch a bushing to accommodate the Remington middle floor plate retaining screw. Pin in this bushing in line with screw hole in receiver. Use the Remington floor plate without the trigger guard as a floor plate. The new trigger guard properly inletted will really dress up the 721.

- Temple Lide, Texas City, Texas

REMOVING THE RUGER No. 1 STOCK BOLT

Had reason to remove the stock bolt from my new Ruger No. 1 the other day, and as could not tell for sure what to do or how it was held together, dropped Ruger a line and they told me the following.

The stock is secured by a 7/16" Hex-head through bolt. This may be removed by using a THIN wall 7/16" socket wrench which you should be able to obtain locally.

- *Dr. S. D. Poore, Villisca, Iowa*

SAVAGE 94 FIRING PIN HOLE

G. Miller advised: "Savage now makes a new over size firing pin (for the Stevens M94) and on the older models it is necessary to ream out the hole. They recommend reaming from the face of the breech."

E. M. Start, Savage Arms writes..."The hole size is 1/8", which is done with a standard drill."

- *G. Miller, Wilmington, North Carolina*
- *E. M. Start, Chief Engineer, Savage Arms Company*

SAVAGE 99

Don't ask me why it does it, but Acraglassing the fore-arm on a Savage 99 will transform it into an accurate shooting rifle!!!

- *Patrick O'Neill, Bellerose, New York*

SAVAGE BARREL-STOP REPAIR

Had an old Savage automatic come in the shop a while back that had the barrel stop in the fore-end so worn, battered and oil-soaked that the barrel extension stuck out of the receiver a good 3/8". I made a coffer dam of aluminum sheet to just fit inside the fore-end, located it a bit more than needed to the rear and using your Acraglas, ran a ring to replace the missing wood. Then, by keeping an eye on the curing time, I fitted the whole thing, before the glass got so hard the chisels would not touch it. This stunt worked so well I've done it to some new ones I've sold, at the buyer's request (and my suggestion) to prevent the above trouble...

- *Bill DeMott, Lebanon, New Jersey*

ASSEMBLING STEVENS M-311

Had a problem getting the hammer spring compressed, the hammer in position and the hammer pin through the receiver and the hammer without rupturing myself. The hammer is an odd-ball shape, so no holding jig is possible. And the spring is stronger than a mule.

Tried to grind a screwdriver to fit back of the hammer to press it in - as suggested in one of the books. Results were skinned up knuckles - cussing and screwdriver thrown across the shop with a proper parting discussion of its ancestry.

So, get everything in line with the receiver held in a vise. Take an extra pin of the same make and grind the forward 1/3 'rd of the pin to an ice pick sort of taper and point, making a slave pin. Press the hammer inward with the left thumb. About 1/4 of the hole in the hammer is now visible through the hole in the receiver. Insert the slave pin and tap with a hammer lightly. The taper will pull the hammer forward into correct alignment with the receiver pin hole. Insert the other hammer and push in with thumb. Tap slave pin until point enters hammer hole and holds it. Now you can place the regular pin against the end of the slave pin and give a quick tap. It goes through the receiver hole and follows the slave pin right on through the hammers and through the opposite side - right where it is supposed to. And the slave pin drops away. Works pretty neat!

- *Ralph Walker, Selma, Alabama*

INSERTING MAIN SPRINGS ON STEVENS DOUBLES

Take a regular screwdriver with about a 6" blade and file the notches as per the drawing above. The "V" notch in the end holds the spring in place while the "U" notch on the top of the blade permits inserting the taper pin while still holding the spring. Works real slick!

- *Ben Newman, Agency, Iowa*

SMITH AND WESSON MAGNUM REVOLVER CONVERSIONS

Since releasing the new Smith & Wesson 22 Magnum Revolver, we have had many inquiries relative to the conversion of existing guns to this caliber. It has long been our policy to reply negatively to inquiries of this type since each gun is specially designed to handle some particular cartridge, and we have never been in favor of converting a weapon for use with a cartridge for which it had not been originally designed.

This applies even more emphatically in the case of our various Magnum revolvers where we not only advise against conversions to the Magnum calibers but support this by refusing to sell the major components of all Magnum revolvers for such use. The fact should also be considered that a major conversion of this type usually results in prohibitive cost, sometimes even equaling or exceeding the price of a new revolver, and it should be here noted that our new 22 Magnum has dual firing pins to take care of ignition requirements of both rimfire and center-fire cartridges. Any attempt to convert existing revolvers to this system would require considerable work in this area, with the ever present possibility of weakening the frame of the gun.

The new 22 Remington Jet Center-Fire Magnum cartridge is a high-performance load involving great bullet speed and high chamber pressure. To handle these a revolver must be constructed of especially prepared and treated components and built to very precise specifications. The mechanical adaptation of existing revolvers to this new Magnum caliber should not, for these obvious reasons, be undertaken. If this information is transmitted to your readers it would constitute a definite public service and it might prevent some thoughtless person from experimenting along lines that could be costly in many ways.

- *F. H. Miller, Sales Manager, Smith & Wesson*

SMITH AND WESSON REBOUND SLIDE SPRING INSTALLER

If you're finally tired of jabbing a screwdriver into your hand when you try to install the rebound slide springs in the S&W's, the little jig pictured will stop it once and for all.

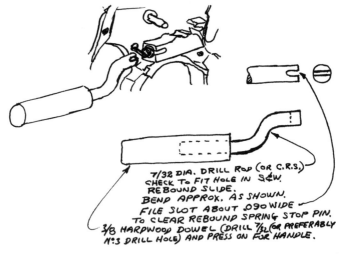

7/32 DIA. DRILL ROD (OR C.R.S.)
CHECK TO FIT HOLE IN S&W.
REBOUND SLIDE.
BEND APPROX. AS SHOWN.
FILE SLOT ABOUT .090 WIDE
TO CLEAR REBOUND SPRING STOP PIN.
3/8 HARDWOOD DOWEL (DRILL 7/32 OR PREFERABLY
N°3 DRILL HOLE) AND PRESS ON FOR HANDLE.

I used 7/32" diameter drill rod. But be sure to check that it does go through the hole in the rebound slide. Bend approximately as shown. Slot is about .090 wide to clear rebound spring stop pin. Handle is 3/8" hardwood dowel, drilled with #3 drill, and pressed firmly on bent drill rod.

- *M. C. Ray, Cleveland, Ohio*

.303 SMLE FLOORPLATE CONVERSION

A little trick that I have been using to make those numerous .303 SMLE's look better is to cut off the magazine flush with the trigger guard, file a P17 or P14 floorplate to fit the contour of the guard and then cut a notch in the present magazine release to hold the new floor plate in. Sometimes this requires straightening the magazine release and then recurving it further down, as the notch sometimes hits where the release begins to curve.

- *Robert R. Lergen, Navy Arms Co., Ridgefield, New Jersey*

NOMENCLATURE:

Rose, the farmer's daughter back from college, became upset when her father said he was going to spread manure on the North 40. "You should tell him to use the word fertilizer," said Rose to her Mother. "Fertilizer?" said the mother, "Why, Dear, I've been 20 years getting him to call it manure."

- *Fred Moulton,* The American Rifleman

STRENGTH OF THE TEXAS MAGNUM

One of the new Texas Magnum Actions was fitted with a barrel and chambered for the 7 m/m Weatherby Magnum. Only thing wrong was that when it was fired, the cleaning rod had been left in the barrel. The action remained intact, gas vented out the bottom through the magazine like it was supposed to, and the shooter was not harmed. They figure that there must have been in excess of 180,000 PSI - and that's a lot of push!!! Needless to say, the gunsmith is mighty, mighty happy, and has placed additional orders for the Texas Magnum!

- *Reported to Bob B. - by an Embarrassed Gunmaker*

WINCHESTER .22 PUMP TRIGGER-RETURN SPRING

Winchester .22 pump trigger-return spring can quickly be made from the rear sight leaf spring of a Jap military rifle. Hole and shape fit almost perfectly and takes a minimum of grinding to get the right width.

- *John R. Wever, Grand Rapids, Michigan*

WINCHESTER EJECTOR BUSHINGS

Was staring at the wall of my shop the other night and saw a bike chain hanging there doing nuttin'. So, I wondered if one of the rollers was anywhere near the size of the Win. 86 ejector bushing. Sure enough, they are and also harder than hell. So, of course, a smaller chain roller would serve for the 92 - 54 and 65!

- *Hazen Trueworthy, Lincoln Center, Maine*

WINCHESTER MODEL 11 RECOIL SPRING

First, I took out the issue recoil spring and threw it out the back door. Then I installed a Remington recoil spring and friction piece, cutting off the recoil tube to match. Next, one of the main curses of this gun being that the bolt follows the barrel so closely during ejection as to sometimes catch the spent shell, I worked the mechanism over so the bolt is held till the barrel is within 1/8" of home position. This gives the spent shell more chance for ejection and compensates for the slower forward movement of the new friction ring.

- *Carol W. Vennink, Manilla, Iowa*

WINCHESTER MODEL 12 FIRING PIN FOR 20 GAUGE

If you find yourself out of firing pins to fit the 20 gauge, but have some around to fit the 12 gauge - you're in luck! All you have to do is cut the back end off the 12 ga. firing pin a bit - to fit of course - and will work perfectly in the 20 ga. Also saves keeping a stock of both of them around the shop!

- *Benny Newman, Agency, Iowa*

FIRING PIN SPRINGS FOR WINCHESTER MODEL 37

Couldn't get the springs for this single barrel from Winchester. They tell me they are out and are not going to be making any more of them. So, I tried the extractor spring out of a 1200 or 1400 Winchester, and it worked just jim-dandy!

- *Jerry Stevens, St. Louis, Missouri*

WINCHESTER 62A EXTRACTORS

I found the Win. 62A extractors are still stocked and are interchangeable with the 90 and '06 rifles...

- *Charles L. Kovarik, Edwardsville, Illinois*

SLIDING TANG SAFETY FOR MODEL 70's, Japs, etc.

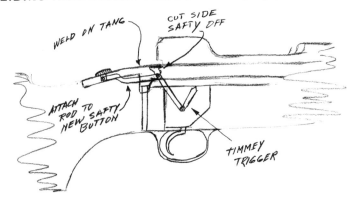

I've made up a bunch of these over the years and they work real well. Works real well with any trigger that has a side-type safety.

- Jim Thomas, Hortonville, Wisconsin

SAFETIES FOR PRE WAR 70's

I note in your Newsletter that someone is looking for a safety for a pre-war 70. It is no great job to fit Winchester's late safety for this gun. I have done it several times with good results.

- Pat Patton, Auburn, California

A WINNING MODEL 70 WINCHESTER

Acraglassed Ammon (Butch) Bell's Van Ord Model 70 Winchester - and with it "Butch" then won the National Matches in 1957 and 1959!

- Russell L. Ricker, Jr., Hummelstown, Pennsylvania

WINCHESTER MODELS 76 & 73 LOADING LEVER SCREWS

Weaver 6 x 48 oval head screws are excellent for the loading levers on Winchester Models 76 & 73.

- Norm Talbert, Sandy Springs, Georgia

WINCHESTER 88 LEFT-HAND SAFETY

I think I have found some very interesting information that you might find useful. In studying the diagrams in your Encyclopedia it dawned on me that the original design was such that the safety was reversible. There is no note to this effect in the manual and I understand that Winchester does not consider favorable left-hand safeties on their guns because of accident potential. However, with the gun cocked, the safety is easily removable, being careful not to lose the pin, and insert from the other side. The entire operation takes less than three minutes.

- Colonel Richard A. Legg, USAF

BLUE-PRINTS FOLLOWING -

The following pages of blue print reproductions were taken from original drawings made by M. C. Ray, Cleveland, Ohio, during the 40's. In order to include them in the book, we have had to reduce their size by about 37% of original size. Of course, we can assume no responsibility for damage to personal property or persons which may directly or indirectly result from the reader or any other person following the prints.

- Bob Brownell

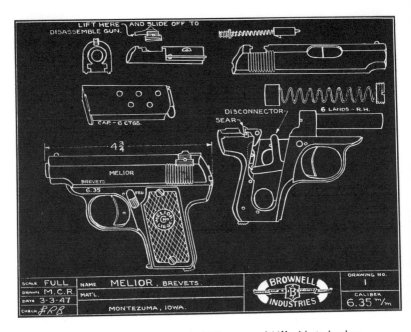

SCALE: About 37% of original which measured 11'' wide to borders.

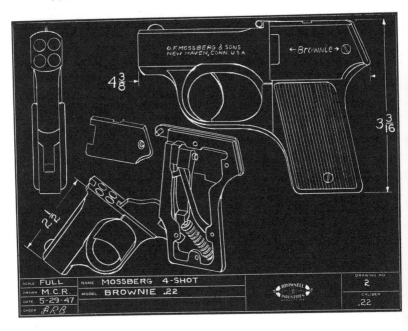

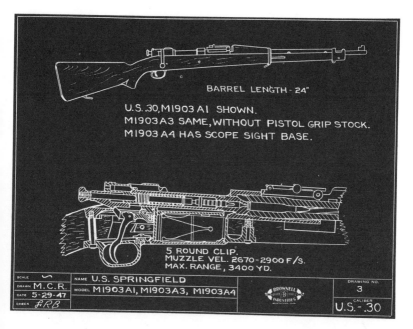

BARREL LENGTH - 24"

U.S. .30, M1903A1 SHOWN.
M1903A3 SAME, WITHOUT PISTOL GRIP STOCK.
M1903A4 HAS SCOPE SIGHT BASE.

5 ROUND CLIP.
MUZZLE VEL. 2670-2900 F/S.
MAX. RANGE, 3400 YD.

SCALE	⌣	NAME U.S. SPRINGFIELD		DRAWING NO.
DRAWN	M.C.R.	MODEL M1903A1, M1903A3, M1903A4	BROWNELL INDUSTRIES	3
DATE	5-29-47			CALIBER
CHECK	J.R.B.			U.S. - .30

SCALE: About 37% of original which measured 11" wide to borders.

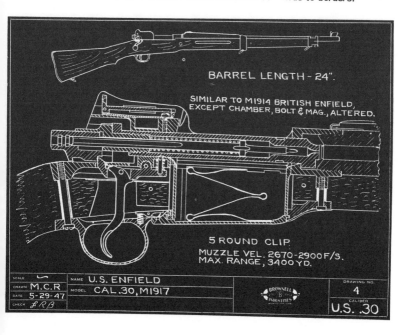

BARREL LENGTH - 24".

SIMILAR TO M1914 BRITISH ENFIELD,
EXCEPT CHAMBER, BOLT & MAG., ALTERED.

5 ROUND CLIP
MUZZLE VEL. 2670-2900 F/S.
MAX. RANGE, 3400 YD.

SCALE	⌣	NAME U.S. ENFIELD		DRAWING NO.
DRAWN	M.C.R	MODEL CAL. .30, M1917	BROWNELL INDUSTRIES	4
DATE	5-29-47			CALIBER
CHECK	J.R.B			U.S. .30

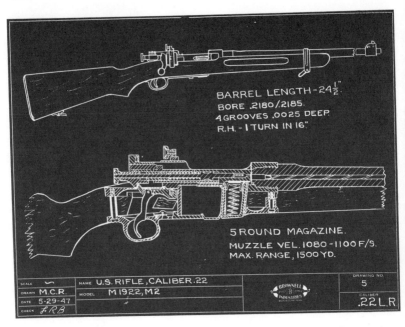

BARREL LENGTH - 24½".
BORE .2180/.2185.
4 GROOVES .0025 DEEP.
R.H. - 1 TURN IN 16".

5 ROUND MAGAZINE.
MUZZLE VEL. 1080-1100 F/S.
MAX. RANGE, 1500 YD.

SCALE	NAME U.S. RIFLE, CALIBER .22	DRAWING NO. 5
DRAWN M.C.R.	MODEL M1922, M2	
DATE 5-29-47		CALIBER .22 L.R.
CHECK FRB		

BROWNELL INDUSTRIES

SCALE: About 37% of original which measured 11" wide to borders.

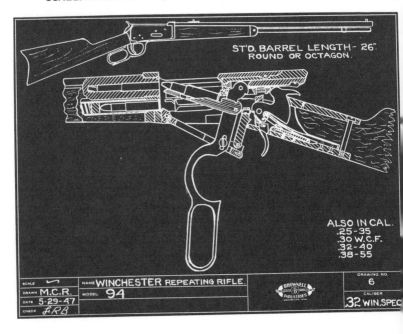

ST'D. BARREL LENGTH - 26".
ROUND OR OCTAGON.

ALSO IN CAL.
.25-35
.30 W.C.F.
.32-40
.38-55

SCALE	NAME WINCHESTER REPEATING RIFLE.	DRAWING NO. 6
DRAWN M.C.R.	MODEL 94	
DATE 5-29-47		CALIBER 32 WIN. SPEC.
CHECK FRB		

BROWNELL INDUSTRIES

TO DISMOUNT -
PULL BACK SLIDE AND TURN
SLIDE LOCK LEVER AS SHOWN.

SCALE	FULL	NAME	WALTHER H.P.		DRAWING NO.
DRN	M.C.R.	MODEL	P.38		7
DATE	5-29-47				CALIBER
CHECK			BROWNELL INDUSTRIES		9 m/m LUGER

SCALE: About 37% of original which measured 11'' wide to borders.

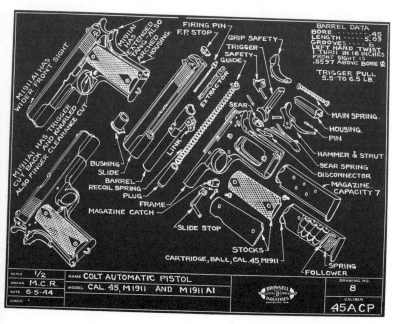

M1911A1 HAS WIDER FRONT SIGHT.

M1911A1 HAS TRIGGER CUT BACK AND KNURLED ALSO FINGER CLEARANCE CUT

M1911A1 HAS EXTENDED TANG. ALSO ARCHED HOUSING.

FIRING PIN
F.P. STOP

GRIP SAFETY

TRIGGER

SAFETY
GUIDE

EXTRACTOR

SEAR

LINK

BUSHING
SLIDE
BARREL
RECOIL SPRING
PLUG
FRAME
MAGAZINE CATCH

SLIDE STOP

STOCKS

CARTRIDGE, BALL, CAL .45 M1911

BARREL DATA
BORE ------.45
LENGTH ---5.03
GROOVES ------6
LEFT HAND TWIST
1 TURN IN 16 INCHES
FRONT SIGHT IS
.5597 ABOVE BORE ℄

TRIGGER PULL
5.5 TO 6.5 LB.

MAIN SPRING.

HOUSING.
PIN

HAMMER & STRUT

SEAR SPRING

DISCONNECTOR

MAGAZINE.
CAPACITY 7

SPRING
FOLLOWER

SCALE	1/2	NAME	COLT AUTOMATIC PISTOL		DRAWING NO.
DRAWN	M.C.R.	MODEL	CAL .45, M1911 AND M1911A1		8
DATE	6-5-44				CALIBER
CHECK			BROWNELL INDUSTRIES		45ACP

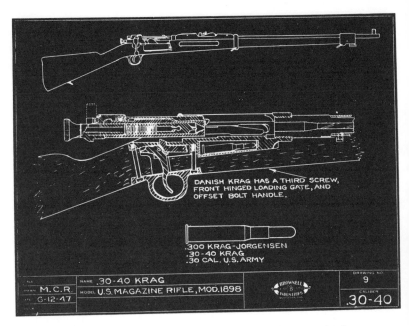

DANISH KRAG HAS A THIRD SCREW, FRONT HINGED LOADING GATE, AND OFFSET BOLT HANDLE.

.300 KRAG-JORGENSEN
.30-40 KRAG
.30 CAL. U.S. ARMY

SCALE	NAME .30-40 KRAG	DRAWING NO. 9
DRAWN M.C.R.	MODEL U.S. MAGAZINE RIFLE, MOD.1898	BROWNELL INDUSTRIES
DATE 6-12-47		CALIBER .30-40

SCALE: About 37% of original which measured 11" wide to borders.

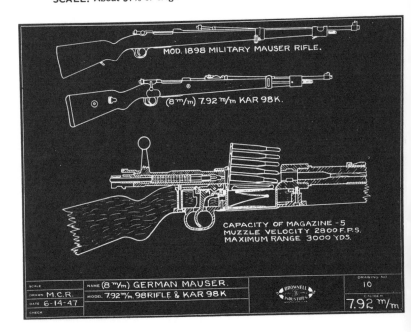

MOD. 1898 MILITARY MAUSER RIFLE.

(8 ᵐ/ₘ) 7.92 ᵐ/ₘ KAR 98K.

CAPACITY OF MAGAZINE -5
MUZZLE VELOCITY 2800 F.P.S.
MAXIMUM RANGE 3000 YDS.

SCALE	NAME (8 ᵐ/ₘ) GERMAN MAUSER.	DRAWING NO. 10
DRAWN M.C.R.	MODEL 7.92ᵐ/ₘ. 98 RIFLE & KAR 98K	BROWNELL INDUSTRIES
DATE 6-14-47		CALIBER 7.92 ᵐ/ₘ
CHECK		

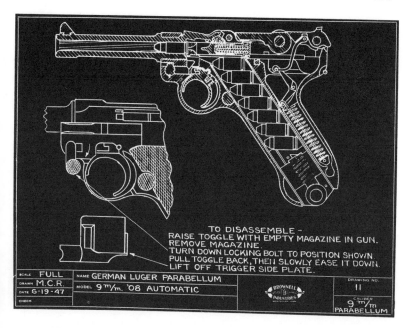

TO DISASSEMBLE -
RAISE TOGGLE WITH EMPTY MAGAZINE IN GUN.
REMOVE MAGAZINE.
TURN DOWN LOCKING BOLT TO POSITION SHOWN.
PULL TOGGLE BACK, THEN SLOWLY EASE IT DOWN.
LIFT OFF TRIGGER SIDE PLATE.

SCALE	FULL	NAME	GERMAN LUGER PARABELLUM		DRAWING NO. 11
DRAWN	M.C.R.	MODEL	9 m/m. '08 AUTOMATIC	BROWNELL INDUSTRIES	
DATE	6-19-47				CALIBER 9 m/m PARABELLUM
CHECK					

SCALE: About 37% of original which measured 11'' wide to borders.

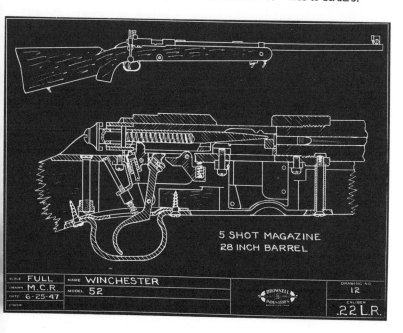

5 SHOT MAGAZINE
28 INCH BARREL

SCALE	FULL	NAME	WINCHESTER		DRAWING NO. 12
DRAWN	M.C.R.	MODEL	52	BROWNELL INDUSTRIES	
DATE	6-25-47				CALIBER .22 L.R.
CHECK					

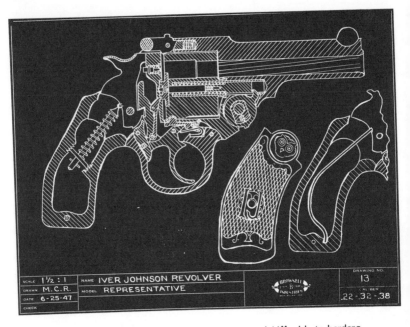

SCALE 1½ : 1	NAME IVER JOHNSON REVOLVER		DRAWING NO. 13
DRAWN M.C.R.	MODEL REPRESENTATIVE	BROWNELL INDUSTRIES	
DATE 6-25-47			CALIBER .22 -.32 -.38
CHECK			

SCALE: About 37% of original which measured 11" wide to borders.

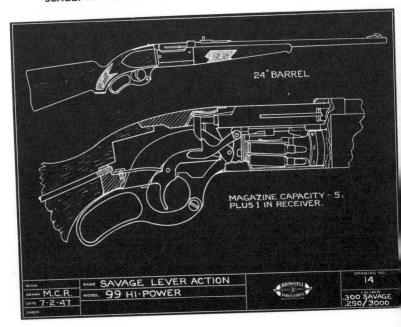

24" BARREL

MAGAZINE CAPACITY - 5, PLUS 1 IN RECEIVER.

SCALE	NAME SAVAGE LEVER ACTION		DRAWING NO. 14
DRAWN M.C.R.	MODEL 99 HI-POWER	BROWNELL INDUSTRIES	
DATE 7-2-47			CALIBER .300 SAVAGE .250/3000
CHECK			

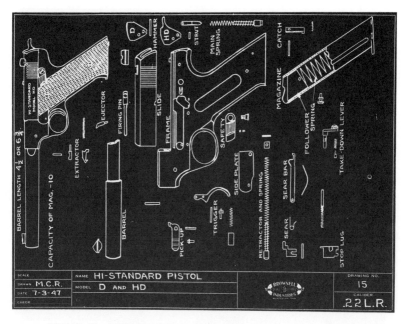

SCALE: About 37% of original which measured 11'' wide to borders.

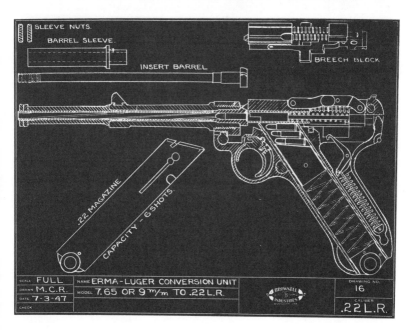

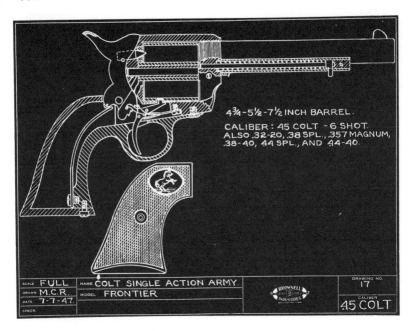

SCALE: About 37% of original which measured 11" wide to borders.

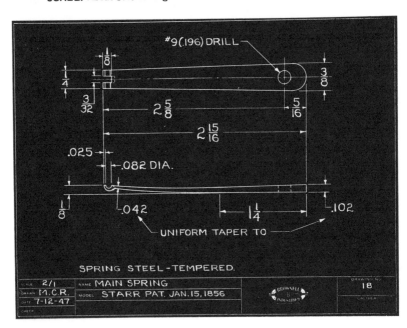

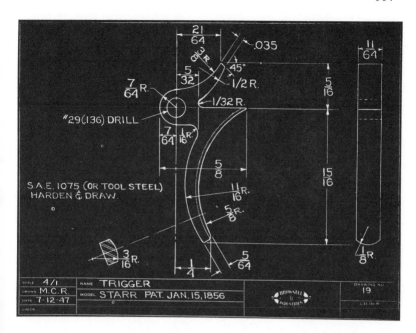

SCALE: About 37% of original which measured 11" wide to borders.

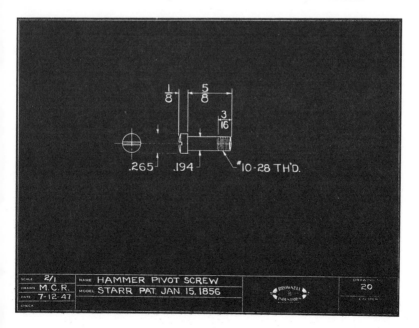

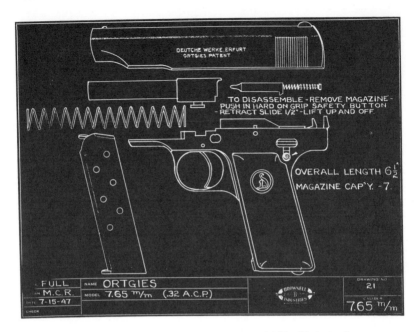

SCALE: About 37% of original which measured 11" wide to borders.

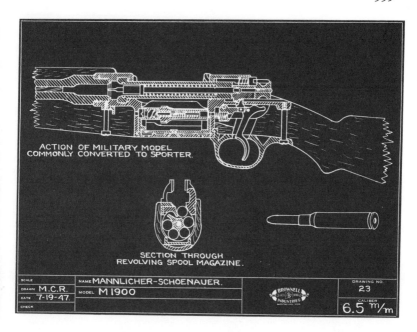

ACTION OF MILITARY MODEL
COMMONLY CONVERTED TO SPORTER.

SECTION THROUGH
REVOLVING SPOOL MAGAZINE.

SCALE	NAME MANNLICHER-SCHOENAUER.	DRAWING NO. 23
DRAWN M.C.R.	MODEL M 1900	
DATE 7-19-47.	BROWNELL INDUSTRIES	CALIBER 6.5 m/m
CHECK		

SCALE: About 37% of original which measured 11" wide to borders.

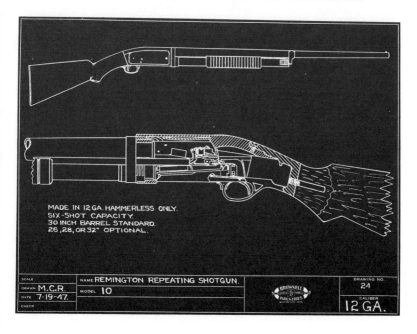

MADE IN 12 GA. HAMMERLESS ONLY.
SIX-SHOT CAPACITY.
30 INCH BARREL STANDARD.
26, 28, OR 32" OPTIONAL.

SCALE	NAME REMINGTON REPEATING SHOTGUN.	DRAWING NO. 24
DRAWN M.C.R.	MODEL 10	
DATE 7-19-47.	BROWNELL INDUSTRIES	CALIBER 12 GA.
CHECK		

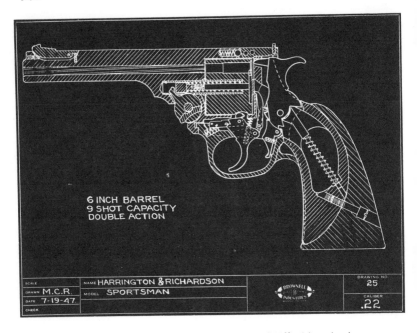

6 INCH BARREL
9 SHOT CAPACITY
DOUBLE ACTION

SCALE	NAME HARRINGTON & RICHARDSON		DRAWING NO. 25
DRAWN M.C.R.	MODEL SPORTSMAN	BROWNELL INDUSTRIES	CALIBER
DATE 7-19-47			.22
CHECK			

SCALE: About 37% of original which measured 11." wide to borders.

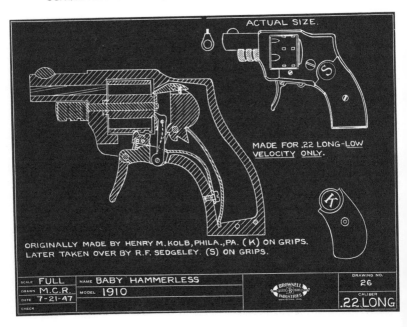

ACTUAL SIZE.

MADE FOR .22 LONG-LOW VELOCITY ONLY.

ORIGINALLY MADE BY HENRY M. KOLB, PHILA., PA. (K) ON GRIPS.
LATER TAKEN OVER BY R.F. SEDGELEY. (S) ON GRIPS.

SCALE FULL	NAME BABY HAMMERLESS		DRAWING NO. 26
DRAWN M.C.R.	MODEL 1910	BROWNELL INDUSTRIES	CALIBER
DATE 7-21-47			.22 LONG
CHECK			

TO DISASSEMBLE –
PRESS IN SMALL DETENT
PIN AND LOOSEN THIS SCREW
THEN LIFT OFF SIDE PLATE.

CAPACITY OF MAGAZINE
- 8 ROUNDS.

THIS EMBLEM
APPEARS ON GRIPS
OF NAVAL MODEL.
ARMY 1910 MODEL
HAS PLAIN GRIPS.

NOTE – USE 9 ᵐ/ₘ GLISENTI AMMO ONLY. THIS GUN WILL CHAMBER
9 ᵐ/ₘ LUGER AMMO BUT WOULD BE DANGEROUS TO FIRE.

SCALE FULL	NAME GLISENTI, ITALIAN SERVICE	BROWNELL INDUSTRIES	DRAWING NO. 27
DRAWN M.C.R.	MODEL NAVAL, ALSO ARMY 1910		CALIBER
DATE 7-23-47			9 ᵐ/ₘ GLISENTI
CHECK			

SCALE: About 37% of original which measured 11" wide to borders.

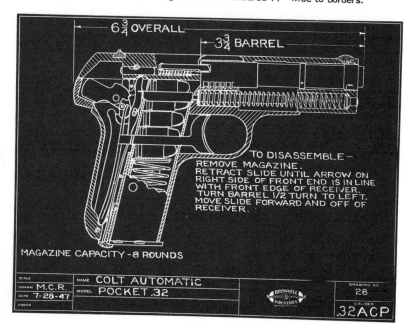

6¾ OVERALL

3¾ BARREL

TO DISASSEMBLE –
REMOVE MAGAZINE.
RETRACT SLIDE UNTIL ARROW ON
RIGHT SIDE OF FRONT END IS IN LINE
WITH FRONT EDGE OF RECEIVER.
TURN BARREL 1/2 TURN TO LEFT.
MOVE SLIDE FORWARD AND OFF OF
RECEIVER.

MAGAZINE CAPACITY - 8 ROUNDS

SCALE	NAME COLT AUTOMATIC	BROWNELL INDUSTRIES	DRAWING NO. 28
DRAWN M.C.R.	MODEL POCKET .32		
DATE 7-28-47			CALIBER
CHECK			.32 ACP

.22 LONG RIFLE CTG.

SMITH & WESSON

LENGTH OF BARREL 10". TAPER BORED.
OVER-ALL LENGTH 11⅛.
THIS GUN IS SAFE FOR HIGH-SPEED AMMO.
PULL HAMMER TO HALF-COCK.
PRESS THUMB PIECE ON LEFT SIDE OF FRAME,
SWING BREECH END OF BARREL TO THE RIGHT.

SCALE FULL	NAME SMITH & WESSON		DRAWING NO. 29
DRAWN M.C.R.	MODEL STRAIGHT-LINE, SINGLE SHOT	BROWNELL INDUSTRIES	CALIBER
DATE 7-31-47			.22
CHECK			

SCALE: About 37% of original which measured 11" wide to borders.

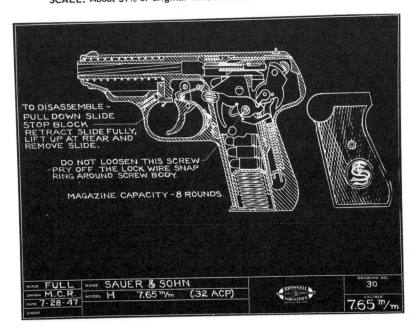

TO DISASSEMBLE -
PULL DOWN SLIDE
STOP BLOCK
RETRACT SLIDE FULLY,
LIFT UP AT REAR AND
REMOVE SLIDE.

DO NOT LOOSEN THIS SCREW -
-PRY OFF THE LOCK WIRE SNAP
RING AROUND SCREW BODY.

MAGAZINE CAPACITY - 8 ROUNDS.

SCALE FULL	NAME SAUER & SOHN		DRAWING NO. 30
DRAWN M.C.R.	MODEL H 7.65 ᵐ/ₘ (.32 ACP)	BROWNELL INDUSTRIES	CALIBER
DATE 7-28-47			7.65 ᵐ/ₘ
CHECK			

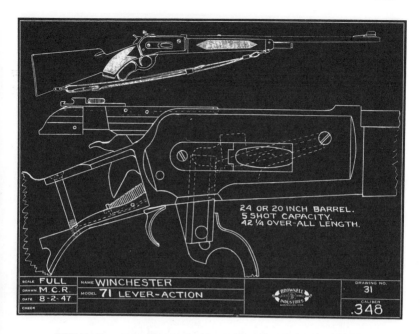

24 OR 20 INCH BARREL.
5 SHOT CAPACITY.
42 ¼ OVER-ALL LENGTH.

SCALE FULL	NAME WINCHESTER		DRAWING NO. 31
DRAWN M.C.R.	MODEL 71 LEVER-ACTION	BROWNELL INDUSTRIES	
DATE 8-2-47			CALIBER .348
CHECK			

SCALE: About 37% of original which measured 11" wide to borders.

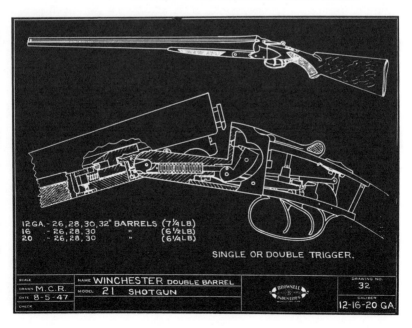

12 GA. - 26, 28, 30, 32" BARRELS (7¼ LB.)
16   - 26, 28, 30   "   (6½ LB.)
20   - 26, 28, 30   "   (6¼ LB.)

SINGLE OR DOUBLE TRIGGER.

SCALE	NAME WINCHESTER DOUBLE BARREL		DRAWING NO. 32
DRAWN M.C.R.	MODEL 21 SHOTGUN	BROWNELL INDUSTRIES	
DATE 8-5-47			CALIBER 12-16-20 GA.
CHECK			

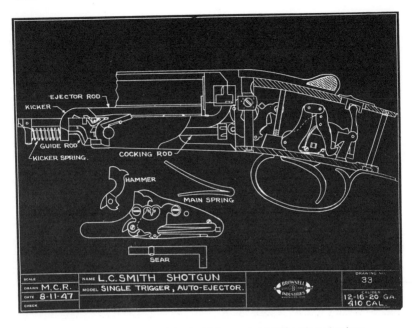

SCALE: About 37% of original which measured 11" wide to borders.

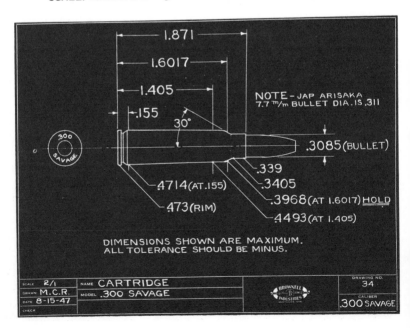

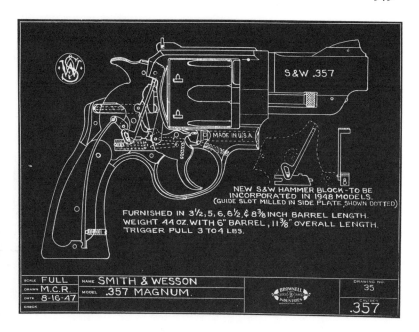

S&W .357

MADE IN U.S.A.

NEW S&W HAMMER BLOCK-TO BE
INCORPORATED IN 1948 MODELS.
(GUIDE SLOT MILLED IN SIDE PLATE SHOWN DOTTED)
FURNISHED IN 3½, 5, 6, 6½, & 8⅜ INCH BARREL LENGTH.
WEIGHT 44 OZ. WITH 6" BARREL, 11⅜" OVERALL LENGTH.
TRIGGER PULL 3 TO 4 LBS.

SCALE FULL	NAME SMITH & WESSON		DRAWING NO. 35
DRAWN M.C.R.	MODEL .357 MAGNUM.	BROWNELL B INDUSTRIES	
DATE 8-16-47			CALIBER
CHECK			.357

SCALE: About 37% of original which measured 11" wide to borders.

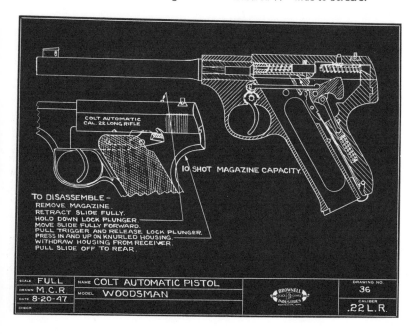

COLT AUTOMATIC
CAL. 22 LONG RIFLE

10 SHOT MAGAZINE CAPACITY

TO DISASSEMBLE—
REMOVE MAGAZINE.
RETRACT SLIDE FULLY.
HOLD DOWN LOCK PLUNGER.
MOVE SLIDE FULLY FORWARD.
PULL TRIGGER AND RELEASE LOCK PLUNGER.
PRESS IN AND UP ON KNURLED HOUSING.
WITHDRAW HOUSING FROM RECEIVER.
PULL SLIDE OFF TO REAR.

SCALE FULL	NAME COLT AUTOMATIC PISTOL		DRAWING NO. 36
DRAWN M.C.R.	MODEL WOODSMAN	BROWNELL B INDUSTRIES	
DATE 8-20-47			CALIBER
CHECK			.22 L.R.

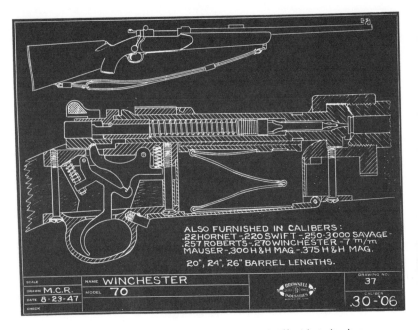

ALSO FURNISHED IN CALIBERS:
.22 HORNET - 220 SWIFT - 250-3000 SAVAGE - .257 ROBERTS - .270 WINCHESTER - 7 m/m MAUSER - 300 H & H MAG. - .375 H & H MAG.

20", 24", 26" BARREL LENGTHS.

SCALE	NAME WINCHESTER		DRAWING NO. 37
DRAWN M.C.R.	MODEL 70	BROWNELL INDUSTRIES	CALIBER
DATE 8-23-47			.30-'06
CHECK			

SCALE: About 37% of original which measured 11'' wide to borders.

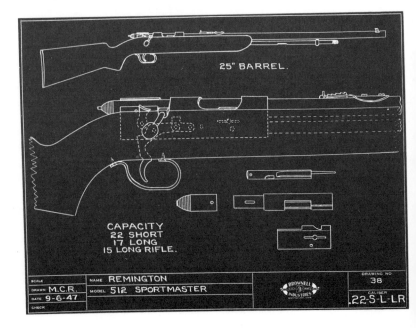

25" BARREL.

CAPACITY
22 SHORT
17 LONG
15 LONG RIFLE.

SCALE	NAME REMINGTON		DRAWING NO. 38
DRAWN M.C.R.	MODEL 512 SPORTMASTER	BROWNELL INDUSTRIES	CALIBER
DATE 9-6-47			.22-S-L-LR
CHECK			

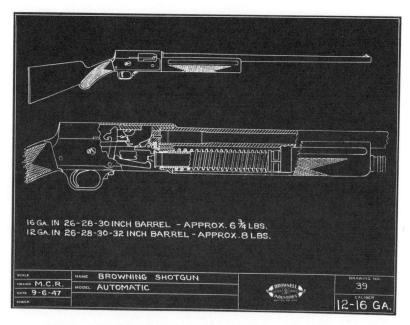

16 GA. IN 26-28-30 INCH BARREL - APPROX. 6¾ LBS.
12 GA. IN 26-28-30-32 INCH BARREL - APPROX. 8 LBS.

SCALE	NAME BROWNING SHOTGUN	BROWNELL INDUSTRIES	DRAWING NO. 39
DRAWN M.C.R.	MODEL AUTOMATIC		
DATE 9-6-47			CALIBER
CHECK			12-16 GA.

SCALE: About 37% of original which measured 11" wide to borders.

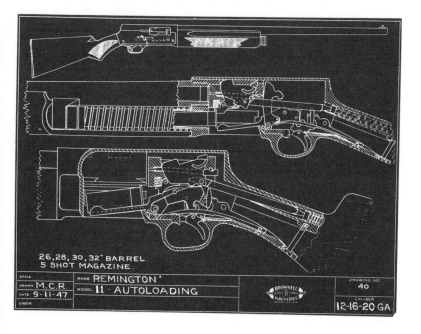

26, 28, 30, 32" BARREL.
5 SHOT MAGAZINE.

SCALE	NAME REMINGTON'	BROWNELL INDUSTRIES	DRAWING NO. 40
DRAWN M.C.R.	MODEL 11 - AUTOLOADING		
DATE 9-11-47			CALIBER
CHECK			12-16-20 GA.

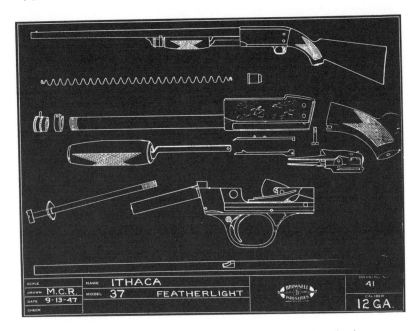

SCALE	NAME	ITHACA		DRAWING NO. 41
DRAWN M.C.R.	MODEL 37	FEATHERLIGHT	BROWNELL INDUSTRIES	CALIBER
DATE 9-13-47				12 GA.
CHECK				

SCALE: About 37% of original which measured 11" wide to borders.

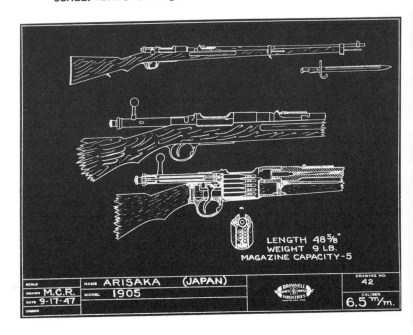

LENGTH 48⅝"
WEIGHT 9 LB.
MAGAZINE CAPACITY-5

SCALE	NAME	ARISAKA (JAPAN)		DRAWING NO. 42
DRAWN M.C.R.	MODEL 1905		BROWNELL INDUSTRIES	CALIBER
DATE 9-17-47				6.5 m/m.
CHECK				

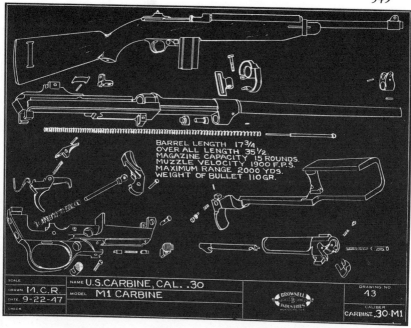

BARREL LENGTH 17¾
OVER ALL LENGTH 35½.
MAGAZINE CAPACITY 15 ROUNDS.
MUZZLE VELOCITY 1900 F.P.S.
MAXIMUM RANGE 2000 YDS.
WEIGHT OF BULLET 110 GR.

SCALE		NAME U.S.CARBINE, CAL. .30		DRAWING NO.
DRAWN M.C.R.		MODEL M1 CARBINE	BROWNELL INDUSTRIES	43
DATE 9-22-47				CALIBER
CHECK				CARBINE .30-M1

SCALE: About 37% of original which measured 11" wide to borders.

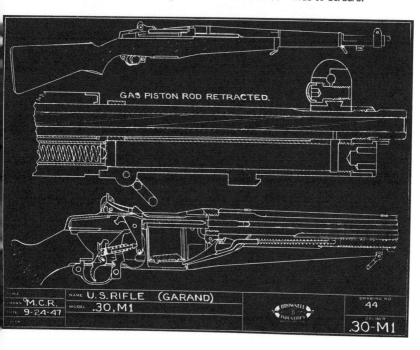

GAS PISTON ROD RETRACTED.

SCALE		NAME U.S. RIFLE (GARAND)		DRAWING NO.
DRAWN M.C.R.		MODEL .30, M1	BROWNELL INDUSTRIES	44
DATE 9-24-47				CALIBER
CHECK				.30-M1

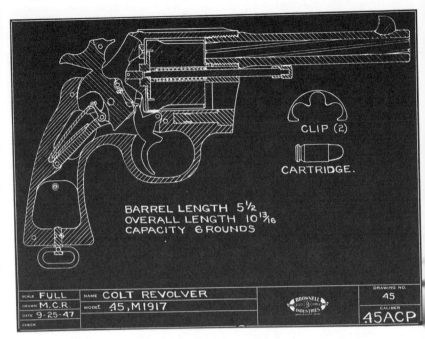

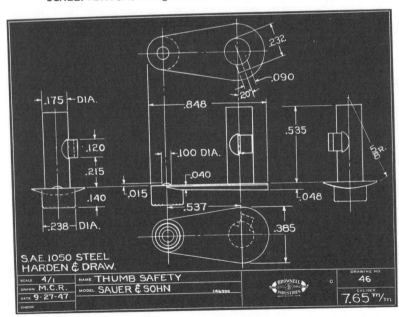

SCALE: About 37% of original which measured 11'' wide to borders.

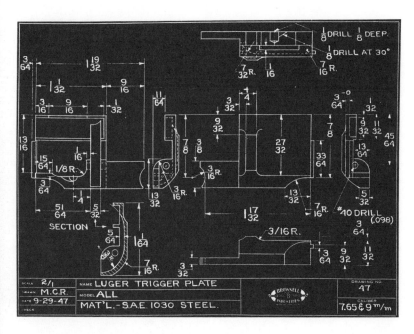

SCALE: About 37% of original which measured 11" wide to borders.

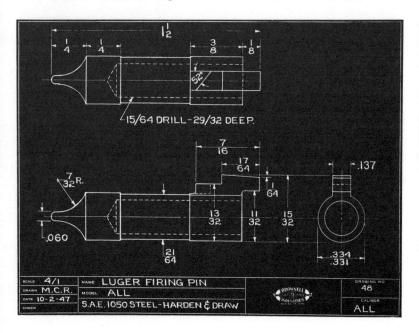

352

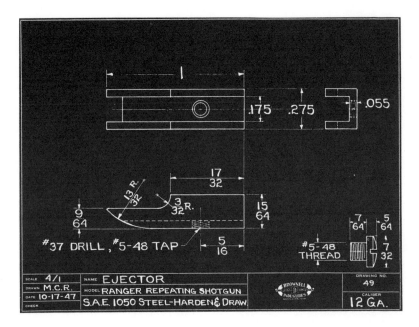

SCALE: About 37% of original which measured 11" wide to borders.

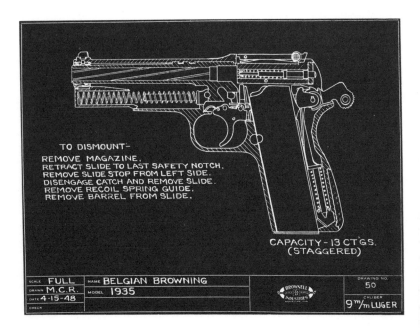

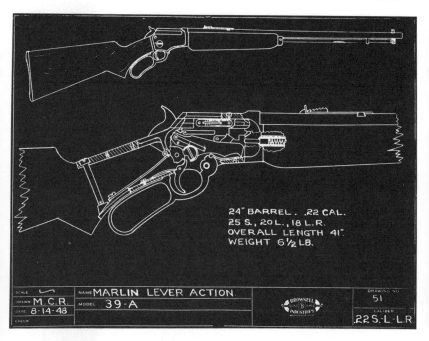

24" BARREL. .22 CAL.
25 S., 20 L., 18 L.R.
OVERALL LENGTH 41".
WEIGHT 6½ LB.

SCALE	NAME MARLIN LEVER ACTION.		DRAWING NO. 51
DRAWN M.C.R.	MODEL 39-A	BROWNELL INDUSTRIES	
DATE 8-14-48			CALIBER .22 S.-L-L.R.
CHECK			

SCALE: About 37% of original which measured 11" wide to borders.

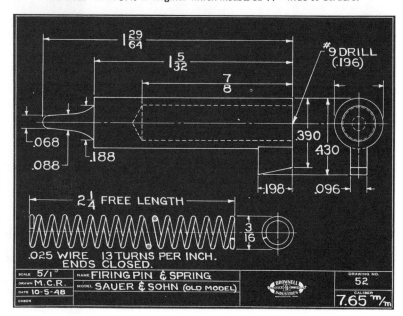

#9 DRILL (.196)

1 29/64

1 5/32

7/8

.390
430

.068
.088
.188
.198
.096

2 1/4 FREE LENGTH

3/16

.025 WIRE   13 TURNS PER INCH.
ENDS CLOSED.

SCALE 5/1	NAME FIRING PIN & SPRING		DRAWING NO. 52
DRAWN M.C.R.	MODEL SAUER & SOHN (OLD MODEL)	BROWNELL INDUSTRIES	
DATE 10-5-48			CALIBER 7.65 m/m
CHECK			

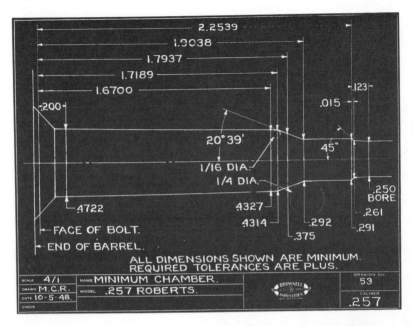

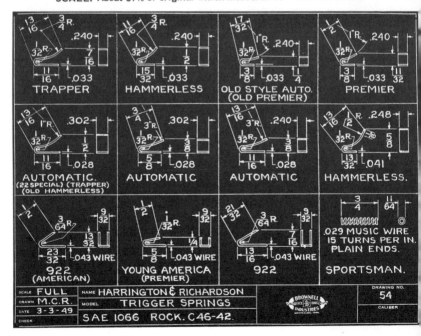

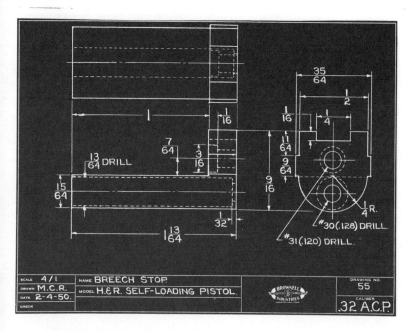

SCALE: About 37% of original which measured 11" wide to borders.

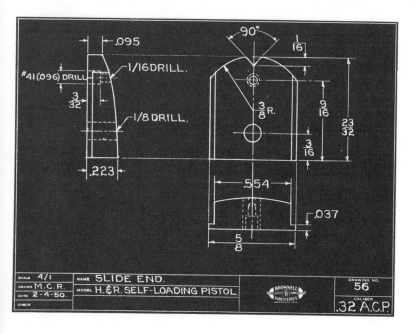

356

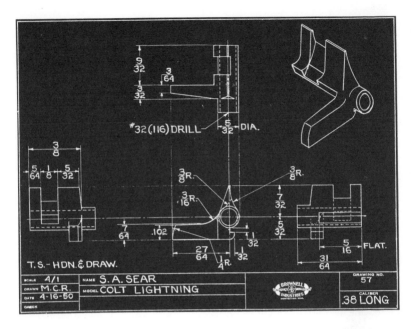

SCALE: About 37% of original which measured 11″ wide to borders.

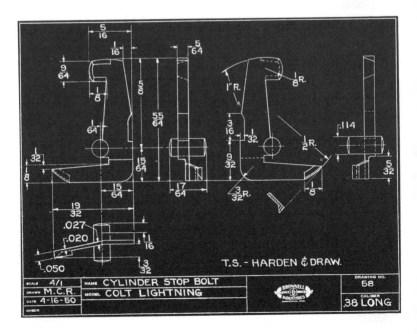

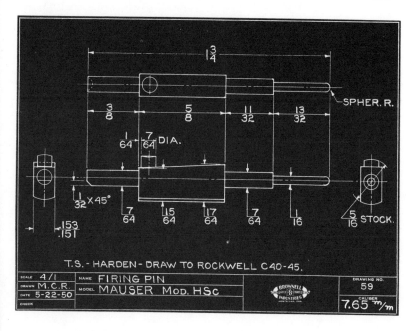

T.S. - HARDEN - DRAW TO ROCKWELL C40-45.

SCALE 4/1	NAME FIRING PIN		DRAWING NO. 59
DRAWN M.C.R.	MODEL MAUSER MOD. HSC	BROWNELL INDUSTRIES	
DATE 5-22-50			CALIBER 7.65 m/m
CHECK			

SCALE: About 37% of original which measured 11" wide to borders.

CHAPTER 10

SHOP TOOLS & TECHNIQUES

SPECIAL BOLTS

In view of the difficulties encountered in the Assembly area, the bolts shown below are suggested for use to eliminate some of the Assembly Problems.

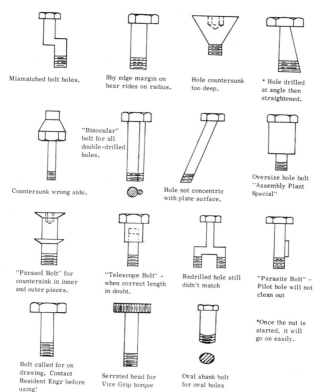

Mismatched bolt holes.

Shy edge margin on hear rides on radius.

Hole countersunk too deep.

* Hole drilled at angle then straightened.

"Binocular" bolt for all double-drilled holes.

Countersunk wrong side.

Hole not concentric with plate surface.

Oversize hole bolt "Assembly Plant Special"

"Parasol Bolt" for countersink in inner and outer pieces.

"Telescope Bolt" – when correct length in doubt.

Redrilled hole still didn't match

"Parasite Bolt" – Pilot hole will not clean out

Bolt called for on drawing. Contact Resident Engr before using!

Serrated head for Vice Grip torque

Oval shank bolt for oval holes

*Once the nut is started, it will go on easily.

- Thanks to M. C. Ray, Cleveland, Ohio

CHISEL SHARPENING & CARE

(EDITOR'S NOTE: - It is doubtful if anyone in the country is better acquainted with the problems of caring for chisels and gouges than Zene "Buck" Denman. He is a professional model and pattern maker for one of America's largest aircraft manufacturers. In his work tools have to be RIGHT and, to put it in his own words, "There is so much to know about chisels & gouges that I could write a book!" The following article and accompanying sketches will get you off on the right foot in caring for chisels and gouges. Proper sharpening has long been a bug-a-boo in the trade - and a poorly sharpened chisel is just no chisel at all!)

There are many chisels and gouges for sale on the market, both American and foreign made; some are tools of good quality, many are not. Usually, but not always, the prices you pay for tools are indicative of their worth. Any reputable dealer or manufacturer will guarantee his tools if they have not been abused.

The manufacturer of chisels and gouges is in a very unique, and sometimes dubious position in that the worth of his product is entirely in the ability of the user to properly sharpen the tools, evaluate the the cause should the tool fail to hold an edge, and proceed to change the cutting edge of some tool so that it will do its job in a satisfactory manner.

We shall, in this article, release the necessary information that will enable the user to do his part in the sharpening of chisels and gouges. It is customary in the United States to call flat tools chisels and radius tools gouges. These are the terms we will use to designate the difference in carving tools in this article.

Let us assume you have a good set of tools that, if properly sharpened for the wood you are working, will hold an edge. Since we have to start from some degree of angle, we will start with 10 degrees. This is the angle to sharpen the tool too, and we can use it as a reference angle should we find that it is not the proper angle for this particular wood or tool.

Depending on the hardness and the percentage of silicate in the wood, some tools will do the job with an angle of slightly less than 10 degrees; others will need a great deal larger angle, as much as 20 degrees in some cases. Using a bench or pedestal grinder with a 6" or larger wheel of good quality and grit, rough grind the 10 degree angle on the working edge of the tool, using a light to moderate pressure. Let the wheel do the work and save your strength. A grinding wheel well dressed with a star dresser will have sharp grits to do the grinding. Too much pressure does many things detrimental to our best interests. The excessive heat generated changes the hardness of the tool, dulls and glazes the wheel and slows the sharpening process.

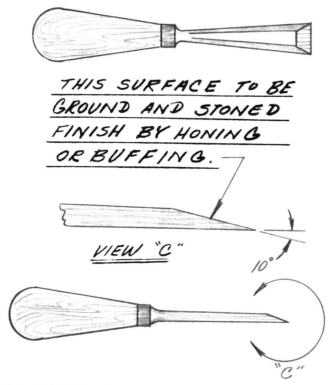

THIS SURFACE TO BE GROUND AND STONED FINISH BY HONING OR BUFFING.

VIEW "C"

10°

"C"

Grind this tool as sharp as possible. Now, using the rough side of your oil stone, remove any hollow grinding produced by the wheel. When this has been accomplished you will have removed the bulk of the grinding wheel marks; keep stoning until they have all been removed. Now, using a 6" to 8" cloth buffing wheel (and gray or fine buffing compound) at a spindle speed of 1500 rpm, buff the edges shown in the sketches. Use care in buffing in order to keep the edge we have stoned as flat as possible. A word of caution is in order at this time. Never, ever, under any circumstances, buff the tool with the cutting edge of the tool facing against direction of rotation.

The buffing wheel may be used in a bench or pedestal-type grinder. However, I prefer to use it in a drill press which gives me the advantages of a wider variation of surface speed, better control of the tool during buffing, and better visibility of the edge I am working on.

Gouges of the paring type, inside grind sharpened, are buffed one side only; however, on my personal tools I buff both surfaces, using care not to roll over or radius the cutting edge of the tool. Gouges with the outside grind sharpened are buffed or honed both outside and

362

inside with emphasis on, or the bulk of the buffing or honing being done on, the outside bevel. After buffing with the gray compound, change the cloth buffing wheel for another of the same type, and using red jeweler's rouge finish the buffing process. This method produces tools with as keen an edge as is possible to produce.

"V" CHISELS

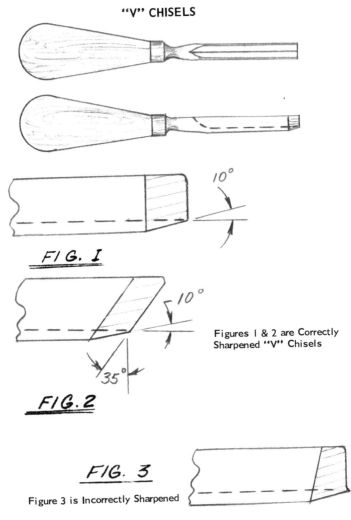

$10°$

FIG. I

$10°$

Figures I & 2 are Correctly Sharpened "V" Chisels

$35°$

FIG. 2

FIG. 3

Figure 3 is Incorrectly Sharpened

Due to the fact that the wheel is actually vibrating and beating on the chisels, the molecular structure of the tool is changed, particularly on the surface holding the edge. The molecules are in a state of being compressed by the action of the wheel, and this is in itself beneficial. The surface of the tool holding the cutting edge has a finer polish, and the sharpening process is much faster and easier to obtain than with the conventional method of rough grinding, rough stoning, smooth stoning and final honing with a slip stone or leather strap as is sometimes used. Like any other trick of the trade, this process will not be the easiest to master, but diligence and patience will pay off in big dividends.

When using the tools, stop about every twenty or thirty minutes, turn on the grinder or drill press, and using the wheel impregnated with red jeweler's rouge, slightly buff the edge. Do not wait until the tool is dull to do this as once a tool is dull we should resharpen on the rough oil stone and repeat the buffing operation as in sharpening a new tool. I have tools that have been in use a good many years that have never, since the original sharpening, had a stone touched to them.

GOUGE — Outside Ground

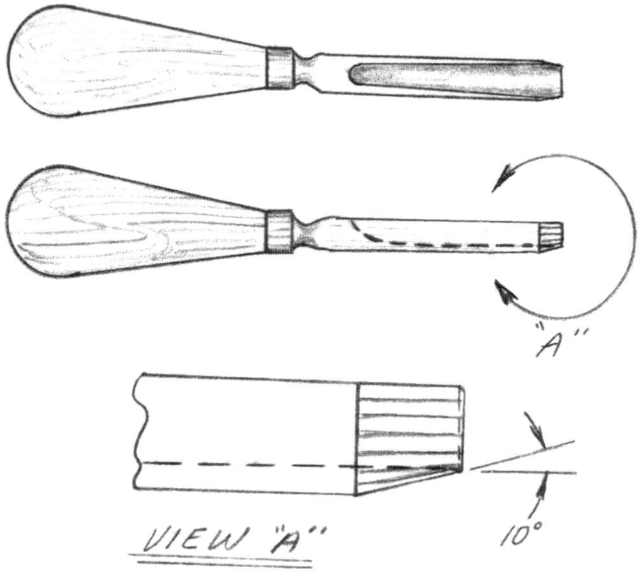

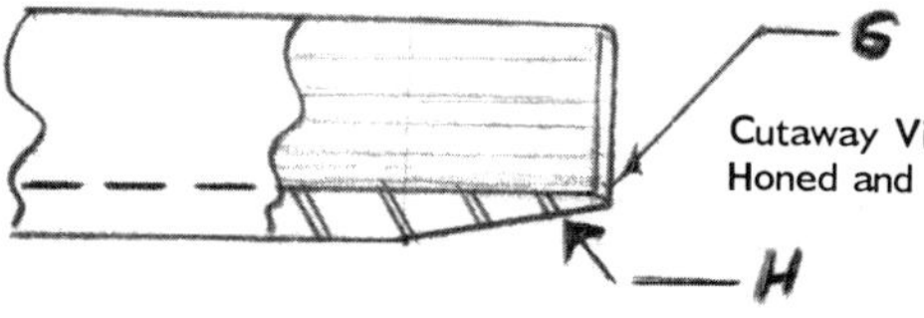

VIEW "A"

10°

Cutaway View to Clarify Surfaces to be Honed and Buffed in Sharpening Gouges

G

H

GOUGE — Inside Ground

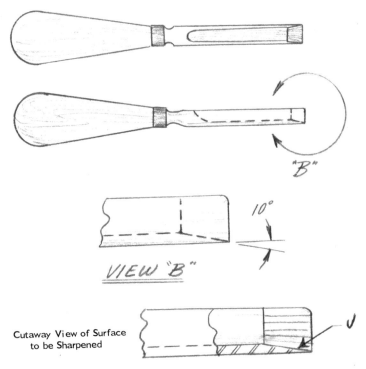

VIEW "B"

10°

Cutaway View of Surface
to be Sharpened

On occasion, until you have the knack to properly buff the cutting edges of the tool, you will radius or roll over the cutting edge of the chisel, and although it feels and appears sharp it will not perform for you as it should. This necessitates restoning with the rough stone to maintain a straight surface on the chisel, followed by the smooth stone and honing or buffing to complete the sharpening operation.

You will have disappointments in sharpening tools so be prepared to accept them and determine the cause of the tool's failure. Some pertinent facts to remember are:

The quality of the steel, its heat treatment or temper, and the hardness of the wood determine the degree of angle of the cutting edge of the tool.

Due to variations in the thickness of the body or blade of various makes of tools, the degree of angle and not the length of the ground portion is the determining factor.

Patience and the willingness to devote the time to properly sharpen chisels are necessary.

GOUGE – Outside Ground & Sharpened

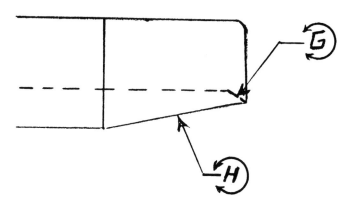

(G) Arrow points to surface to be honed or buffed. This is a secondary surface but is necessary to keep the cutting edge of the tool from breaking or chipping when coming out of the cut. It also facilitates coming out of the cut. Surface radius is exaggerated for clarity.

(H) Primary surface of the gouge and to be kept as STRAIGHT as possible. This is the surface that is the cutting edge.

Buy the best oilstones, grinding wheels, buffing wheels, and compounds obtainable; the same is true for tools. Better to have three or four good tools than a dozen poor ones; the cost is the same. The time saved with good tools soon pays for them many times over.

After the sharpening process has been mastered, you will be able to sharpen tools that can be used in all types of woods of various hardnesses...a "universal tool", so to speak, that will do a better-than-average job in any wood you may choose to use it on. Take good care of your tools, too. If you cannot hang them up or case them, at least put them in a wooden box to protect the cutting edge you worked so hard to achieve. Don't just carelessly throw them on the bench.

Good stones are also expensive, and your oil stones will do best if placed in a container and completely covered with oil. In using your oil stones keep them well oiled; this keeps them from glazing over and enables the sharp grits to do their job of cutting.

Follow the sketches as closely as possible; the corners of your gouges and veining tools should be radiused to keep them from digging-in in use. About a 1/16 radius or less is desirable. Flat chisels should not have a radius at the corners, although in use they will gradually accumulate a small radius. This will not do too much harm and will not affect their efficiency to a great extent.

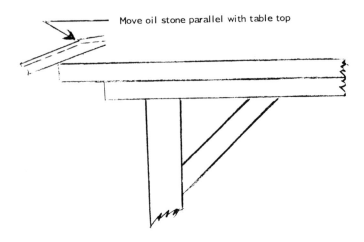

Move oil stone parallel with table top

Above shows a method for holding outside-ground gouges for rough stoning. Hold the gouge at the proper angle for stoning at edge of table as illustrated, then run stone parallel to top of the table. This is very unorthodox, but effective and fast. You can also see what is being accomplished as you stone the edge of the tool. Line shown by the arrow should be straight and parallel to the cutting edge.

There are very few hobbies that give the satisfaction that the handwork in wood will give you. There is equal satisfaction in knowing how to properly sharpen the chisels that give you the means to pursue and obtain this pleasure.

- *Zene Denman, Hawthorne, California*

SHARPENING WOODCUTTING TOOLS

John Westrom sent along the following:

"Wood carver August Crabtree, whose wood carvings are valued at $100,000, has his own unique method for producing a tool edge so keen that he can shave with it.

"His power grinder is a plywood disc mounted on a 1/4-horse-power motor shaft. He cements thin, replaceable abrasive discs (available at most hardware stores) to the plywood and does his grinding against the face of the disc. If a tool is badly dulled or nicked, Crabtree begins re-sharpening on the power grinder, moving the blade gently from side to side during the process. He grinds the long bevel on the back of the chisel at an angle of 35 degrees if he plans to use the tool with a mallet, 18 degrees if for hand work. He forms the cutting edge by grinding a steeper bevel (whetting angle) at 38 degrees at the edge of the blade for mallet work, 24 degrees for hand work. If much metal is to be ground away, the tool is frequently dipped in water to prevent overheating. For average work with or without a mallet you can use the single set of angles suggested by Stanley Tools: 25-30 degrees for the bevel, 30-35 degrees for the whetting angle. When power grinding is completed, Crabtree dresses the blade on a flat, fine Carborundum stone.

"To prevent rocking, Crabtree holds the tool with both hands. Resting the surface of the short whetting angle bevel flat on the stone, with the flat side of the chisel away from him, he draws the blade toward him across the stone with a downward pressure. Light motor oil, diluted with an equal amount of kerosene, lubricates the stone.

"A length of razor strop, cemented to the top of a flat board, provides the final touch. With this, Crabtree follows the same procedure as with the stone, but he omits the lubricant. He keeps the keen edge on his tools by touching them up on the stone and strop before they become dull, and seldom does he have to use his power grinder for anything but changing bevels or adapting tools for special work."

John says the above method works like a charm - has been using it for years and thought you-all would be glad to get it.

- *John Westrom, Des Moines, Iowa*

KNIFE SHARPENING

Those fine metal checkering files are the answer for sharpening carving knives. File serrations at an angle and you'll have about the best meat carving knife you ever saw.

- *Jack Knode, Savage Arms Co.*

BANDSANDER SHARPENING

That BANDSANDER is the best piece of equipment for the money that I have in the shop. Besides the gun work, I sharpen saws and other edged tools. Setting the table at a 10° or 15° angle it is just the thing for cutting the heel of teeth on combination blades and for scissors it is just right. I can do them in half the time and better.

- *Mar's Gun Shop, Brookings, South Dakota*

FOR YOUR ARCHERY CUSTOMERS

Those little sharpening steels that you sell work slick as can be for sharpening arrow heads in the field. With a nylon thong and snap they will hook onto the belt and can't get lost.

- *Vernon M. Herr, Madison, Wisconsin*

BEAUTIFUL WOMEN

I believe you can tell a man's profession by the trend of his conversation when introduced to a beautiful woman. A lawyer would start discussing her will. A banker would inquire into her reserves. A bookkeeper would be most interested in the form. But a gunsmith would stay strictly to business and only show interest in her action!

- *Bob B.*

TOOL SHARPENING

It is very seldom, in fact almost an impossibility, to find good instructive information on the proper sharpening of wood carving chisels and gouges. Probably one reason for this is that most authors realize it is very difficult to get any two professional men out of a group to agree on this subject. As a general rule, about all that is said is that the bevel should be longer than is used by the carpenter, about twice as long and very little more. Without exception we seem to do better and faster work with a long bevel.

There is one most important point for the beginner to keep in mind in regards to the bevel angle: it is determined by the hardness of the wood he is going to work on. The gun lover is not content with just any piece of wood available but is in constant search for beautiful woods, and the more figure and contrasts in it the better. These beautiful woods are hard. Even in plain walnut you will occasionally run into a piece that works about like Ligma Vita or desert ironwood. The woodcarver is usually shrewd enough to by-pass these woods but not the gunstocker. He is, as a general rule, just as eager to see that stock when it is finished as is the customer, and the self-satisfaction and praise of the customer is usually the biggest part of his remuneration for the job.

But let's get down to work. You can start, if you wish, by grinding just as long an angle as you wish. Then thoroughly sharpen your tool by removing the hollow grind with the rough side of your India whetstone; removing all the scratches with the fine side of the stone. Keep the stone flooded with oil. The finer the oil the better. Many use kerosene in the place of oil. With a HARD Arkansas stone remove the rest of the fine scratches until you have all the minute scratches eliminated and have a tool with razor sharp edges with no burrs or saw edge on it. Took a long time, didn't it? And the hell of it is, if you are like most of us when we started out, the first couple of whacks at that hard wood are going to ruin the edge of your chisel. More than likely it will curl up on you and you will start cussing the tool, and the manufacturer and tell the wife to go away and leave you alone. An hour and a half to sharpen it and then you find out it is not worth a tinker's dam.

Many good cabinet makers, gunsmiths and others run right back to the grinder and sharpen the tool with the same angle that just got thru breaking down with them. That is where the mistake begins. One of the chisel manufacturers set up a test program in which he purposely broke down the cutting edge of a tool in order to find out just how critical the bevel angle is. In his test, he started with one tool ground to too long a bevel angle and changed the degree of angle by only 1-1/2 degrees at each resharpening. It took eight complete re-sharpenings before the tool would hold an edge in the piece of maple being used as a test block...which would seem to prove conclusively that as little as 1-1/2 degrees difference in the bevel angle will give you a tool that breaks down and one that will hold an edge.

There is another method of sharpening tools that is known by but few men, altho it has been used for sharpening other instruments of another profession for a good many years. First you establish the approximate bevel you want. This comes with experience, using a coarse grit grinding wheel of around 50 or 60 grit size. Grind your tool as sharp as you can get it on the grinder, being very careful not to draw the temper. Next remove the hollow grind with your medium stone and sharpen as sharp as you can get it. With a cloth buffing wheel and around 555 Polish-O-Ray buff the edges, being careful not to hold the tool at any time so that it can be caught by the buffing wheel.

You are due for a surprise if you have not previously used this method for it really sharpens chisels. It takes practice and at first the corners of your gouges will need retouching on a stone, but once you have mastered it, you will find you can put an edge on your tools faster and better. Any metal trades mechanic realizes that when you work metal you toughen it and altho the good gained by this is minute, it is still beneficial.

Some cardinal points for the beginner to remember and a refreshment for some professional men are as follows:

1. The deciding factor of the bevel to which a tool is sharpened is the hardness of the wood in which it will be used.

2. A tool that is not razor sharp to begin with loses its sharpness many times faster than one that is.

3. Learn to tell when a tool starts to dull and either buff or hone or strop the edge immediately.

4. An occasional light buffing around 30 seconds running at moderate speed, keeps them sharp.

5. Your **outside** ground gouges should also be stoned or buffed from the inside very slightly. This removes wire edge and also keeps the edge from breaking down when coming out of a heavy cut.

6. Corners of both inside and outside ground gouges should be rounded slightly to keep them from digging in.

7. It is not suggested that the angle of the cutting edge be changed for each stock of different hardness. It is better to use wood that is going to be harder than you work with the majority of the time

to test your tools on when first sharpening them. A tool with a keen edge and properly sharpened is much faster and requires less resharpening than one that is of too long a grind and keeps breaking down.

There are many different methods of sharpening. The Swiss woodcarver does it a little differently from the German woodcarver, etc. The foregoing, however, gives you an excellent start in the right direction, and as you gain experience you will develop your own fine techniques.

- *Bob B. from Catalog No. 2*

SHARPENING WITH CUTOFF WHEEL

I use a cutoff wheel for sharpening tools. It is evidently an impregnated affair. The ones I use are 1/8" thick and they never seem to wear out but are easily broken. They can also be used for cutting hard steel. A few licks on an oil stone after using one of these will give a real shaving edge.

- *Pat Patton, Auburn, California*

CHANGING THERMOMETERS

This doctor buys a bunch of stuff in the local drugstore and when he reaches into his pocket he pulls out a rectal thermometer. He stares at it unbelievingly for a moment, looks at the druggist and says, "You know what? Some poor ass has got my pen!"

- *Burt Munhall, Federal Cartridge Co.*

HOW TO SHARPEN OUTDOOR/POCKET KNIVES

A good knife can be made to "hold its edge" by using the simple methods of the master cutlers. For materials you will need a medium-fine toolmaker's file, a pair of high-grade combination oil stones - a small stone for carrying and field use; a large stone not less than 2" x 6" for home or base camp use, and some very light oil to keep the stone cutting grits clean and well lubricated when honing.

The steps in sharpening are as follows: (Note - when resharpening, always try to create a small but noticeable edge bevel to support the cutting edge.)

1. For badly worn or damaged edges, use a good quality medium-fine toolmaker's file to remove the blade-edge nicks or badly turned edges. File (pushing only) to produce a small but definite supporting bevel to the working edge.

2. After filing, use the medium-course side of the stone. Place the stone on a flat, firm surface. Lay the main blade surface lightly upon the stone. Raise the back edge of the blade off the stone to a 20-22-1/2 degree angle and think in terms of "slicing" a thin layer from the top of the stone. Draw the blade across the stone with firm pressure and in

one direction only for a count of 10 strokes. Turn the blade over, raise the back edge off the stone to the same angle and repeat "slicing" strokes in the opposite direction for a count of 10 strokes to make a balanced edge.

3.   Finish with a half-dozen lighter pressure strokes, alternating one stroke to a side of the blade.

4.   Turn the stone over to the fine-grain side, apply a little light oil to the stone and repeat steps 2 and 3. If the edge needs rehoning only, do not use the coarse side of the stone, but touch it up on the fine-grained side only.

5.   If the edge is still not satisfactory, keep in mind that hard tempered blades require extra grinding or honing time. Simply repeat operations 2 to 4 until the blade tests to your satisfaction.

A simple check for "oversharpening" of the blade are file or sharpening stone scratches still left on the blade surface. These must all be worked out.

If you can slice a layer from a thin piece of paper held over a finger, or slice the ink printing from a piece of newspaper and still show a good edge-supporting bevel, your blade's cutting edge will stand up to much harder and longer cutting than if you have finished it to a too-thin and weak so-called "razor edge".

Some of the most common mistakes made in knife blade sharpening are "oversharpening" to a too-thin "razor edge", using poor quality sharpening stones and oils; using careless or wrong sharpening methods; and using the knife improperly, either as a screwdriver or for scraping, prying, digging or chopping.

- *Dean Russell, Russell Belt Knife Inventor, Ontario, Canada*

SILVER SOLDER HEALTH WARNING

From the U.S. Department of Health - reports two recent poisoning deaths traced to improper use of silver solder containing cadmium. When using this type of material, such as Silvaloy, the warning labels should be carefully read and followed - working area should be properly ventilated, preferably with specific exhaust systems - workers must avoid breathing emitted fumes. The Health Department stressed that all workers should tell their physicians what their jobs are and what types of materials they handle. Occupationally-caused illnesses and diseases can be easily overlooked if physicians do not have this vital information. End of Department of Health Bulletin.

The amount of silver-soldering the average gunsmith does at a time, such as sweating on an occasional ramp or rear sight, should pose no serious health hazard so long as normal health precautions are taken. BUT, remember it is your life and health you could be saving, so take the above information seriously: have some ventilation and

don't breathe the fumes.
- *Bob B.*

PREVENTING SOLDER SPREADING

I don't know why I never could remember to pass on this bit but used it years ago with good success: When sweating on ramps with either silver solder or lead/tin solder, if you will rub in blacksmith's chalk - the kind machinists and welders use to mark their work so it won't burn off under heat, sometimes called "French Chalk" - the solders will not stick where the chalk is applied. Take it right up to your scribe lines around ramps and ribs. Sure saves a lot of work!
- *Bob B.*

'DON'T TOUCH' BEFORE SILVER SOLDERING

Back in the early 1920's my father had a Swedish cabinetmaker working for him who was truly an artist in wood. Immediately across the block from the cabinet shop was a machine shop run by a German who was an equal artist in metal. Both men were dear friends and at the same time, violent competitors, each trying to outdo the other in perfection of the finished product. Gus, the machinist, did a lot of work with special bandsaws. Whenever one of them broke, he would work for hours to get it silver soldered without success and would always end up having to take it to his Swedish friend who could mend the blade successfully. To say this upset the German and tickled the Swede is putting it mildly. My father did everything he could to get Carl, the cabinetmaker, to tell him his secret, but it wasn't until the day we moved out of that town that Carl broke down and told Dad under the strictest of promises that he would never tell Gus, the machinist. Said Carl, "That stupid Gus! When I get my Joining Tapers filed on the two blades I'm going to join, I go 'puff', 'puff'. That Gus, he wipes them off with his greasy fingers!" -- So! Keep your cotton pickin' fingers off of any area you are going to silver solder.
- *Bob B.*

WELDING WIRE

The Piano Wire in the No. 150 Kit is swell for welding small steel parts and will harden and temper. I use it to build up triggers and hammers, sear notches, etc. --
- *G. H. Bailey, Chesnee, South Carolina*

PADDED VISE JAWS

Get hold of some chunks of Celotex ceiling tile. Makes good soft jaw pads for vises. Cheap, expendable, and easy to find!
- *Willy's Gun Shop, Wadena, Iowa*

SPECIAL SHOP TOOLS

M. C. Ray (after whom our Polish-O-Ray is named) is looking for someone to make up the following items for his tool-room blue-print artist. The samples should be sent to us along with your price quotes as Ray is in Florida right now and cannot be reached.

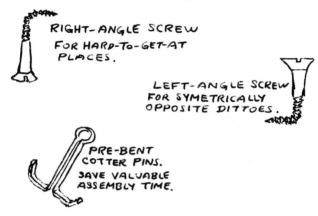

RIGHT-ANGLE SCREW FOR HARD-TO-GET-AT PLACES.

LEFT-ANGLE SCREW FOR SYMETRICALLY OPPOSITE DITTOES.

PRE-BENT COTTER PINS. SAVE VALUABLE ASSEMBLY TIME.

(A good thing Ray is in Florida or I'd clobber him myself - if I could find him...Bob B.)

- M. C. Ray, Cleveland, Ohio

PROPER STARTING PUNCH SHAPE

About 99% of the small pin punches that get busted, get that way about the second whack when trying to get a real tight pin started on its way out. One of the tool manufacturers told us that very few people knew (we didn't) that you should use a starting punch to break the pin loose and then drive it out with the pin punch. What you should do is take one of those starting punches and grind the point down to a parallel diameter slightly smaller than the pin to be removed. Use this tool to loosen the pin and then finish up with the regular pin punch - save a lot of breakage and even more bad temper exhibitions!

- Bob B.

PIN PUNCHES - FROM SPRING STOCK

Why don't you suggest your customers buy Spring Assortment No. 150 and make any size pin punch they want. This works out fine and about a million punches for three bux...

- Laurence Nauman, Douglas, Wyoming

DECAPPING-PIN PIN-PUNCHES

Cut 2" or 3" piece of cold rolled steel rod's approximately 5/16" diameter and drill a hole in one end 3/8" deep. Slip in a headless decapping pin. Makes a good, tough punch easily replaced!! Grind to smaller diameter if required.

- *George Middaugh, Bismarck, North Dakota*

"BUSTED BIFFEY BINDER"

Have about decided to put Acraglas out under another trade name: "Brownell's Busted Biffey Binder" for during the years we have had it on the market have received several letters such as this one:

"Dear Bob: - The other morning as I was shaving, I knocked a jar of face cream into the porcelain throne, putting a hole in it about the size of a grapefruit. This created an emergency requiring immediate action. So, I hurried to the shop and got my handy little Acraglas kit and plastered a piece of cardboard over the hole. Works perfectly and is likely to become a permanent fixture...Stan Baker."

And Sid Bartlett: "We weren't trying to cheat the plumber, but my son-in-law called for help one week-end when a youngster dropped something in the toilet tank, breaking out a bottom corner. We made two applications of Acraglas to the break. Presto, it was whole again..."

- *Stan Baker, Seattle, Washington*
- *Sid Bartlett, Salem, Oregon*

SHOTGUN DUMMY LOADS

Did you ever wonder what to do with left-over Acraglas? Pour it into a sized plastic shotgun shell with dead primer. Makes very good dummies for checking guns, etc!

- *R. V. Twitchell, Rozel, Kansas*

REAMER PROTECTION

Celluplastic tubes work fine for chambering reamers, mills and drills. Print information on slip of paper, roll up and slip inside with tools. My wife has snitched a couple of tubes, by the way, for knitting needles!

- *Dave McCord, Ionia, Michigan*

TOOL IDENTIFICATION

Screwdrivers are usually quite plentiful around a gun shop; so plentiful they are scattered all over and the right size for a particular screw may be on the bottom of the pile. I thought it might help keep the 30 or 40 screwdrivers in better order if they, and their racks, were color coded. If the measurements are taken in millimeters, the RMA color code may be used; brown 1, red 2, orange 3, etc. By putting my two-boy-power to work with small paint brushes and little bottles of enamel that are found in hobby shops, all the screwdrivers in sight were given a wide stripe of the proper color. I remade my racks so that there was room for 3 or 4 screwdrivers of each size, 2mm through 9mm. It is not necessary to know the color code because if the yellow is not wide enough for the screw, you automatically pick up a green or a blue. It also helps on that rare occasion when you put them back in the racks.

- *Charles Johnson, New York, New York*

HALLOWEEN TIME

This last Halloween we had a big box of apples setting on a chair beside the front door, along with a lot of candy, to give the kids when they came around trick-or-treating. Gladys was busy and I had left the shop for a few minutes and was in the kitchen when I heard some kids on the front porch and the door chimes rang. I went to the door and there were three little kids, each with a sack. The smallest kid stood right in front of me holding one of the largest paper sacks I have ever seen. When I got the door wide open he said, "Trickortreat!" I reached and got one of those big 25¢ Delicious apples and dropped it into his sack. It hit the bottom with a kind of 'Thunk'. The kid looked down into the sack, then up right at me and said, "You son-of-a-bitch, you busted my cookie."

- *George Gauthier, Pullman, Washington*

LAYOUT WASH

When you've a complicated pattern of any kind to lay out on steel, a light copper coating on the steel is easy to mark in with a scribe and gives you something easily followed. Make a solution of 4-oz. of Sulphate of copper (saturated solution); 8-oz. of water and 1-oz. of Sulphuric acid. Wipe this on the surface of the steel for a thin plating.

- *William E. Moore, Greenville, North Carolina*

OXPHO-BLUE FOR LAYOUTS

Rub Oxpho-Blue on pattern blanks before scribing. It gives a sharp distinct line with the scribe - a line that is easy to file, cut or grind to.

- *C. C. Turnipseed, Hattiesburg, Mississippi*

VISION AID

A good shop kink for guys who don't see so good anymore: Take an aluminum paint spray bomb and spray top of work bench. It surely does help!

- *Harry Horton, Mt. Morris, Illinois*

"SAFE" HAMMER

A hammer which you cannot possibly smash your fingers with.

Darned good invention, too. Needs just a bit more development over its present status. I have it to the point where if you hold the handle with both hands it works perfectly!

- *Carlos H. Mason, Bristol, Connecticut*

LEAD SHIM STOCK

My dental assistant wife saves me the lead backing from those biting X-Ray films dentists use. Average .003" thick. Very handy for shimming tools and equipment around shop. Six or seven wrapped around a screw, tapped into masonry, makes excellent anchor!

- *G. R.'s Gun Shop, Jackson, Michigan*

EMERGENCY AIR/WATER/OIL LINE REPAIR

For an on-the-spot emergency repair of an air/water/oil line, I use a strip of inner tube about 3/4" wide and wrap it around the leak much in the same manner as taping an electric connection. The secret to making this work, though, is stretching the rubber as you go along wrapping it on. Be sure to get a good tight stretch with each wrap.

Finish off the patch with any good tape to hold the rubber band in place. This won't work on high pressure lines, of course, but has certainly gotten me by many times until I could get a new piece of hose to replace the busted one.

- *John Turnbull, Toulon, Illinois*

CUTTING METAL INLAYS

Those Tyler round hacksaw blades are indispensable to anyone building muzzle loading rifles with their brass and German silver inlays. All metal inlays I use are roughed out with round blades.

- *Ted Fellowes, Seattle, Washington*

A GUNSMITH

Slim Spears says the other night his daughter told her boy friend, "My dad is a gunsmith and takes things apart just to see why they won't go." Said the boy friend: "So what?" Said the daughter: "So you'd better go..."

- *Slim Spears, Hutchinson, Kansas*

GLUING PLEXIGLAS

When you have call to join Plexiglas for any purpose and want the best, use Ethylene Dichloride. Works fast and beautifully.

- *Ron Van Ryswyk, Frostburg, Maryland*

HOMEMADE FELT BOBS

The idea is to save a little on felt bobs, etc. in polishing out the inside of trigger guards and the like. Also, this works good on flats. The idea is to split a piece of drill rod a couple of inches at one end and put a piece of old inner tube about two or three inches wide and six or eight inches long in it. Chuck up in drill or buffer chuck and hook on a piece of sand paper that is discarded after a bit of use by a body shop. You can have all you want - it's free because they throw it away - and polish away.

- *Joe Head, Mangum, Oklahoma*

LADY WITH FEET OF CLAY

She lay in the window all shiny and blue
With ivory bead sight and a middle one too.
She looked very nice from where I stood,
So I went inside to look at her good.
Thirty inch barrels - full choke and a half -
And about the price of a yearling calf.
She had a nice pull and fit just right
From the red rubber butt to the ivory front sight.
I broke her down and tried the locks -
She would do for grouse, and maybe fox.
I turned her around to look in the bore
Then set her aside and sought the door;
Altho she was nice and nearly new
In the trigger guard was a cross-cut screw!

-- *H. L. Helms*

Don't know whether any of you guys ever have read many of the poems of Robert Service or not. He's a favorite of mine - and you've heard of "Dangerous Dan McGrew" - one of his. The above poem reminds me of Service. - Bob B.

- *H. L. Helms, Quincy, Illinois*

US GUN-FIXER-UPPERS FEEL THAT A GUN-FIXER-UPPER

Is a man who, when building a part, does it by Feel, File, Form, Face, Finish, and Forge,

Puts it together with Reamer, Rivet, Roll, Rip, Rap and Rotates it for free running press fit,

And finishes it off on the end with a Slit Slanted Slot cut with a Slipfit Slanted Slot Slitter...

(Stole and re-assembled the above from a blue-print sent down by Bill Post.)

- *Bill Post, St. Paul, Minnesota*

3/16" FOREDOM COLLET

From Carlos Mason - he who is inventing that smash-proof hammer: If 3/16" capacity is needed in Foredom #5 handpiece, take a Starrett Pin Vice, cut off at shoulder, thread inside with 9/32x32 tap and you have it made.

- *Carlos Mason, Bristol, Connecticut*

STOCK BOLT SCREWDRIVER

Take that long "L" shaped auto lug wrench and hub-cap pry-off tool and grind the pry-off end of it to fit the screwdriver slot in stock bolts. It makes a really perfect tool for removing and replacing those hard to reach bolts. And with the 90 degree angle already formed in it, you can get plenty of leverage to take out the really stubborn ones - so no more blistered hands!

- *R. L. Theiss, Hearne, Texas*

TAPERING THE NYLON DRIFT

So use a pencil sharpener...

- *Wm. Billingsley, Knoxville, Iowa*

EASY WAY TO DO STIPPLING

If the metal is not too hard (Rockwell 30 or above) and I have a small flat or large convex surface to stipple, I use about a 1/4" fine-cut round pillar file (like the ones used for sharpening chain saws) and run it over the surface just like a rolling pin. Gives a very nice regular matte surface without disturbing the contours or requiring a lot of equipment. Use it with good results on custom front ramps and .45 auto slides all the time.

- *Tom Pendergast, Alexandria, Virginia*

ADJUSTABLE SPANNER WRENCHES

If you are ever in need of an adjustable spanner wrench for dis-assembling shotguns, take a heavy-duty 12" adjustable crescent wrench and square off the ends of the jaws, perpendicular to the line of the handle. Then, on one flat side of the wrench, grind off the metal except for a little nubbin at the squared-off end of each jaw. Check a couple of the pump shotguns you are going to work on, and finish file these nubbins to fit the slots in the retaining rings you want to remove.

Not only does the one wrench fit all the various gauge shotguns you have to work on, but you still have the use of the wrench!

- *Lee Crowder, Trappe, Maryland*

USED ELECTRIC MOTORS

"A kid about 10 years old walked into a pawn shop carrying an electric motor. The pawnbroker asked, 'What have you got there, Son?' And the kid replied, 'Electric motor.' 'Where did you get it?' 'At home,' was the answer. 'What did you get it off of?' he was asked. 'An iron lung' was the answer. 'What did your Dad say?' asked the pawn broker. Said the kid: 'Aghhhhhhhhhh.'"

- Curly's Gun Shop, Stroudsburg, Pennsylvania

HOW TO READ A MICROMETER

By careful observance of a few directions, the ability to read a micrometer caliper can be easily acquired. Keep in mind that a micrometer caliper is a precision instrument and should be handled carefully to preserve its accuracy.

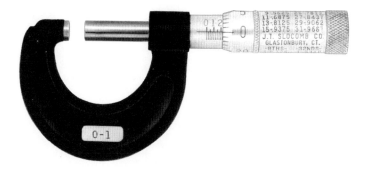

Principle of Operation

A micrometer is a measuring device which combines the double contact of slide calipers with a screw adjustment which may be read with great accuracy. It divides an inch into 1000 parts which is expressed decimally to 3 places, .000. The screw adjustment, which moves the spindle to and from the anvil, is turned by the thimble. As the pitch of the screw thread is 1/40th of an inch, it takes 40 complete revolutions of the thimble to advance or retract the spindle a distance of an inch. In other words, one revolution of the thimble is equivalent to 1/40th of an inch or .025" expressed decimally.

How To Read the Graduations on a Conventional Micrometer to Thousandths of an Inch (.000")

1. Observe the graduations on the sleeve, each graduation being .025". Every fourth graduation is marked with a whole number from 1 to 10; these numbers indicating one hundred thousandths of an inch (4x.025: is .100" decimally expressed.)

2. Observe the graduations on the bevel of the thimble. There are 25 - each graduation being 1/25th of a revolution of the thimble. As one revolution of the thimble is .025" (see paragraph 1) - each graduation is then 1/25th of .025" or .001" expressed decimally.

3. Add the two readings together to get the measurement or the distance between the anvil and the measuring end of the spindle.

EXAMPLE NO. 1

The reading is composed of
  4 large graduations or 4 x .100=.400″
  2 small graduations or 2 x .025=.050″
and 8 graduations on the thimble
       or 8 x .001=.008″
     Total Reading .458″

EXAMPLE NO. 2

The reading is composed of
  2 large graduations or 2 x .100=.200″
  3 small graduations or 3 x .025=.075″
and 14 graduations on the thimble
      14 x .001=.014″
     Total Reading .289″

EXAMPLE NO. 3

The reading is composed of
  3 large graduations or 3 x .100=.300″
  2 small graduations or 2 x .025=.050″
and 3 graduations on the thimble
      3 x .001=.003″
     Total Reading .353″

How To Read a Conventional Micrometer Caliper to Ten-Thousandths of an Inch (.0000″)

On the sleeve of a conventional micrometer graduated to read to ten-thousandths of an inch is a 3rd scale (vernier) with 11 parallel lines occupying the same space as ten lines on the thimble. Lines on the sleeve are numbered 0 to 10. The difference between the spaces on the sleeve and those on the thimble is one tenth of a space on the thimble of 1/10th of a thousandth (.0001″ expressed decimally). Read the number of the line on the sleeve that most nearly coincides with a line on the thimble and add it to the previous measurements.

How to Read the "Speedmike" Micrometer

The Slocomb SPEEDMIKE differs from the conventional micrometer caliper only in the system of reading a measurement. With the conventional micrometer, the measurement is read from graduated scales on the sleeve and the thimble. With the speedmike, the following simple procedure is used.

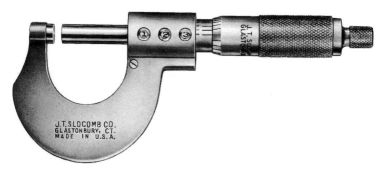

How to Read The Speedmike to Thousandth (.000") of an Inch

Measurements with the SPEEDMIKE are read directly from the numbers appearing on the three windows in the frame and are expressed in thousandths of an inch (.000").

When numbers appear partially in view, use the number which shows the greater part of itself for reading to the nearest .001". The graduations on the thimble provide for simple interpolation for reading tenths of a thousandth.

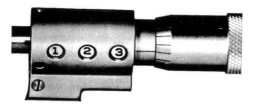

How to Read The Speedmike to Ten Thousandths (.0000") of an Inch

The pitch of the screw being 50, one revolution of the thimble is 1/50th of an inch or .020" expressed decimally. As there are 20 graduations on the bevel of the spindle, each graduation is 1/20th of a revolution (1/20 of .020") or .001" expressed decimally. Read the meaurement to thousandths. Use the vernier scale for measurements to a tenth of a thousandth of an inch.

How to Read the Shardlow "Anglometric" Micrometer

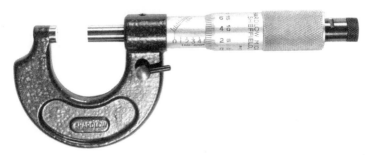

To accommodate the metric scale on the thimble of the Anglometric Micrometer, the standard inch graduations are slightly different from those usually encountered on a typical workshop micrometer.

The thimble is divided into 50 divisions each representing .0004", or .01 mm.

The English Scale on the Sleeve (engraved black) is divided into 50 divisions each representing .020".

The Metric Scale on the Sleeve (engraved red) is divided into 50 divisions each representing .5 mm.

> *- Courtesy of the J. T. Slocomb Company, South Glastonbury, Connecticut*

THE ART OF METAL ENGRAVING

"Tasteful decoration of an arm is to me recognition of faithful service by a steady friend; memories of the zest of life in the high mountains; a whiff of salt-air from the marshes." These words by Col. Charles Kirk of the USAF clearly describe the feelings of many of us.

Despite mass production of guns in America, individuality of a sort did exist even if only through variations in stock grain. But now, plastics have come along to eliminate even this. If the trend continues, "gumwood" will become a delicacy in an era of byproducts of corn cobs.

Engraving and its appreciation cannot help but raise America's standards in the world of guns. The United States has the unfortunate distinction of having perhaps fewer gun engravers than any other country in the world. This in itself would not be so bad, but if one was to choose skilled craftsmen from the individuals who hang out "GUN ENGRAVER" shingles, he would be forced to cull even a good number of these.

The lack of skilled engravers in America is a result of our high living standards, for engraving is an art which requires years of work before any degree of success is realized. Then too, there are requirements beyond the basic essentials of time and incentive. The individual who wishes to become a commercial engraver should develop his skill as a sideline, unless of course, he is financially able to practice full time. Too many so called "engravers" turn "commercial" before any degree of perfection is attained. This leads to rapid, production butchery which converts fine guns into artistically worthless iron. The American public, through ignorance for the most part, helps to perpetuate such practices by keeping these gun-gougers in business. I saw one in action at the last gun show I attended, grinning like a possum at a dung heap as he gouged guns and public alike. Even some of our gun editors are at fault by publishing photos of such work accompanied by glowing praise. The answer is to educate the public and whet its appetite to a more artistic level.

This article is aimed chiefly at those interested in perfecting the art or learning to distinguish the crude from the classic. I will outline an engraving procedure and point out pitfalls to overcome. By no means do I consider myself an accomplished engraver - far from it.

My first attempt at decorating a gun was by etching. The results were fair but the lines were rough and there were places where acid undercut and blurred the design. The piece needed polished cuts that only an engraving tool could produce, so I felt I would never be satisfied until I learned to engrave.

There are articles on engraving but those I found were sketchy and badly wanting on "how to do" even the primary work of cutting away the steel. I consulted jewelers, but their methods are designed for softer metals, so when I tried working steel in the same manner the results were discouraging. It was only after trial and error that I learned to sharpen tools and cut lines - but it was far from engraving. Engravers seemed to be a tight-lipped lot until I met Bruce Meek, one of the fine American engravers. He was most helpful and took me over countless hurdles in a single visit. There is no reason why engraving should be kept secret. Competition cannot help but increase the quality of work. "Our small town's barber was the world's best - until another moved to town."

There are a number of gunsmith supply houses which handle the engraving tools, but one should not invest too much in the beginning as he may find that he is not cut out for such work. With the exception of a swivel vise, the remaining tools amount to very little. If one decides to go into it more seriously he should get an engraver's block which will hold almost any shaped gun part. However, I know one man who uses a pitch bowl exclusively to hold his work. (Almost any jeweler can give one the necessary information on where to obtain pitch and how it is employed.)

The tools needed for basic work are few: two onglette die sinkers' chisels; a couple of different-sized lining gravers, and a chasing hammer will suffice. The lining gravers are illustrated actual size in any of the catalogues so one can choose from them. Handles for the chasing hammer vary and are a matter of taste. An India stone as well as a medium-hard Arkansas stone are a necessity to me when it comes to sharpening tools. The India stone cuts fast and the Arkansas puts the final polish which is so necessary for cutting good, clean lines. Many stones are too soft and soon become gouged so are worthless for putting a good tip on the graver.

One of the most valuable assets to an engraver is his ability to sharpen tools. Learn to love it, because you'll spend many hours re-pointing the cutting edges. There is no such thing as "pretty sharp" when it comes to the engraving tool. I make it a habit of having several similar tools sharp and when they are all dull take time out for a sharpening bee.

There are several methods employed in putting in the background. A beading tool, which is nothing more than a tiny nailset-like punch used by jewelers, is preferred by many for stippling. Some engravers use a vibro-tool for background matting. I prefer to use a curved lining tool with which I remove steel from the background. But, it is much more difficult to do, so it should not be tried by the beginner.

The satisfaction that comes with even a meager amount of success is well worth the seemingly futile hours one spends in learning just the simple process of making a clean straight line. It would be nice to say that within a few hours one can learn to cut an even, polished coil of steel with a graver - but such is not the case. Steel defies tools and tests a man's ability to fashion designs. It takes time to develop the feel and discover the proper methods of sharpening and polishing the graver, not to mention the seemingly endless hours that go into learning how to cut metal evenly and at the proper depth. Despite what is offered on the market, good lines are not deeply gouged.

The beginner should choose a piece of flat, soft steel for practice as most gun parts are tempered and more difficult to engrave. As one progresses, he can advance to curved surfaces and the tougher metals. Case-hardened parts are next-to-impossible to engrave so should be avoided. Later on when the engraving of case-hardened surfaces is necessary, the parts should be annealed or the cased crust removed by polishing. However, unless one is a metallurgist he should not consider removing temper by annealing.

Under no circumstances should a piece be engraved without first being polished bright. This means all the original finish, whether it be blue or plating, should be stripped. The job of polishing is of utmost importance, for sloppy work with a wheel distorts edges and gives screw holes a "squint" look which spells "headache" to the engraver. It is not necessary to get a mirror finish on a piece you intend to "scratch up", as effects or depth and shadows are attained by the more skilled engravers by slight alterations in the finish of the metal. The late Cole Agee never would work on a gun which had a mirror finish because the tip of a graver does not bite readily into highly polished steel.

The chisels should be sharpened at roughly a 45 degree angle. One will, in time, discover the best angle suited for the type of metal on which he is working. The softer the metal, the flatter the angle. The most important detail in sharpening a graver is to make certain the tip is perfectly polished. The slightest flaw will cause the tool to wander aimlessly. When the tip goes you will feel it. That is the time to re-sharpen. An extra lick or two with the chasing hammer will inevitably force unclean words posthaste. This is especially true of borders where the tool wanders off into oblivion.

One of the well known American engravers, Cole Agee, had a special chisel which he used almost exclusively. It looks impossible to control, as it is a chisel-like tool, beveled on both edges. But once mastered, it gives the effect of relief work even though no background is removed because the cuts are left polished due to the bevel. When angled acutely, it makes a knife-like cut which is very effective in scroll work. There are two cutting tips on each chisel which gives a double life, so to speak, to one tool, and it is especially good for border design as it chips and scallops well.

To start your practice, use a simple scroll in the beginning. Too many become discouraged because they have chosen too intricate a design at first. One of man's finest assets is a knowledge of his limitations, especially in engraving. No one demands more pity than he who "has no knowledge of the lack of his ability." Start at the beginning: this is common, old-fashioned, horse sense.

The angle of the graver in relation to the surface being cut is arbitrary as it depends upon the angle at which the tool is polished and the downward pressure exerted by the hand as it is driven forward by the chasing hammer. Practice alone will dictate your individual touch. The common error for beginners is to elevate the back of the graver or chisel too high which causes the cutting tip to bury itself into the steel. The chasing hammer has a slender handle which gives the necessary whip which is needed to drive the graver properly.

Curved lines are executed best if the back of the graver is raised slightly. Shading effects are gotten by canting the graver. There are many types of gravers which the advanced craftsmen use, each with a specific purpose. The novice can effectively study the cuts each is capable of doing by testing the cutting edges on oil clay, paraffin, or some such material.

Designs can be transferred in the following manner. Place a piece of thin celluloid over the design you have worked out on tracing paper. Copy the design from the back side or else it will be reversed when transferred to the metal. Sharpen a scribe to a polished needle-point and scratch the design into the celluloid. Put a very thin layer of Damar Varnish on the gun part with your finger and allow it to set for a few moments until almost dry. Rub a bright, dry, color pigment into the scribed surface, lay it on the varnished metal and rub it with a polished instrument. Remove the celluloid and the design will be outlined on the metal. It should then be re-scribed into the metal with the stylus as the pigment alone will rub off as you engrave.

As you progress, use honest criticism concerning your work. Don't let the pats on the shoulder fog up your judgment. After you've been at it for a number of weeks, go back to your earlier work and make a comparison. If the first encounters look good to you you've had it. For as I mentioned before, no one begins at the top which means you are incapable of improvement and have all the qualities necessary only to cobble up firearms. However, if your early work verges on the horrible - you are on the right road. With a stubborn determination to better your technique and complete disregard for the time involved, I am certain you will make the grade as an engraver. There are no deep dark secrets - no magic words nor potions to hasten success. "Hard work, with the will to better what has gone before are what will eventually make you an artist in steel." This was the advice given to me by the Master engraver, Arnold Griebel. You can learn to be pleased with your results but never satisfied.

As time goes on, you will learn to appraise other engravers. The general impression is that the best craftsmen are in Europe. Such is not the case, for we have had and do have, some of the world's finest engravers in this country. To mention a few: Arnold Griebel, E. C. Prudhomme, Alvin White, Joseph Fugger, Max Bruehl and Bruce Meek are some whose work will stand against the finest Europe has to offer.

One must be familiar with his subject before he can realistically portray it. I study animal anatomy, for part of my museum work deals with the preparation of birds and mammals for exhibit. This training has made me quite critical of the animals which adorn (to use the word loosely) many of our engraved guns. Perpetuation of error is common in birds and mammals of European craftsmen. Two of the most common errors seen pictured time and again in photographs of old world engraving drive me up a cliff. One is the side view of a running deer in which the hind leg is buried deep in the rib cage. (If animals had to knee themselves in the belly in order to run, the forests would echo with grunts!) The other common anatomical "impossibility" is the sway-back duck. The middle of the back has the most unrealistically gracious curve as the bird tries to escape from a would-be assailant.

Such mistakes are not on the cheap arms. In fact, I know of one article describing European engravers whose meticulous regard for detail has prompted them to study and copy their animals from mounted specimens, and shows engravers using mounted specimens as models. This is a fine practice, except their specimens are atrocious examples of good taxidermy which seems as rare as fine engraving. They fail to realize that here, as in engraving, the mechanical task is not enough. You must know your subject. You can't get a reproduction of your foot by pouring sand in a sock! The good taxidermist is an artist who can recapture the characteristics peculiar to his subject and in so doing, breathe life into the animal. I mention this to bring home this matter of anatomy. It would be nice if one could spend the time studying animals in the field but this is out of the question for most. Do the next best thing. Choose your subjects from photographs or from the works of good wildlife artists. For the most part this excludes our calendar artists whose flair for color far excel any anatomical knowledge of their subject. Animals are difficult. Don't hasten into them blindly.

Refrain from sensationalism for its purpose is usually to cover up inabilities through distraction. Beware of "A red-tongued eagle holding a furled flag with one foot and grasping an arrow from its breast with the other."

A few pointers to look for and attempt to maintain in scroll work. Smooth flowing lines; curves follow through; cuts smooth, not choppy; clean and constant depth throughout design unless shading in some manner has been intended. Too large a scroll pattern usually indicates lack of design ability as well as lack of engraving technique. However, some Early American scroll patterns meet the requirements of good design and if artfully employed on the steel come up to the standards of good engraving. This type of engraving is naturally best on the firearms of that era and not on modern pieces.

There are some basic types of scroll which are more or less related to one another. Most commonly recognized is the German type engraving most generally seen in America. Although there are other types of European engraving, I stress this one because most comparisons of excellence are made in relation to this school. Kornbrath was the master with his typical leaf, vine and flower scroll. Modern German engraving has evolved from this into less detailed but still the same basic, well rounded, smooth and perfect pattern scroll. It is highly stylized and extremely ornamental, flowing effortlessly into each gun part.

Early American engraving was an attempt to imitate this, but it failed. It is a large and bulky scroll with little detail. It's proper in its place but leaves much to be desired.

English and Scottish scroll, not frequently seen in this country, is a minute and extremely detailed type which requires a magnifying glass to be fully appreciated.

Cole Agee's style is a distinct type which has been much imitated, but not too successfully. It is broad and curvaceous, somewhere in size between the Early American and German. The scroll is large, heavy, and almost identical throughout a complete layout on a gun. Incidentally, if he had engraved all the guns people attribute to him, he would have had to have obtained the biblical age of Methuselah.

Amounts of coverage should also be considered. Time involved in doing a complete gun is tremendous and often a three-quarters layout is more appealing and not so sensational. Coverage in engraving is not the primary nor basic norm on which to judge workmanship. A few clean, well cut designs are much more tasteful than a gun gouged from stem to stern with huge, coarsely chiseled curlicues. Scroll should be smooth and balanced. The layout is of prime importance and when one compares the work of artists with that of the production boys, you can easily see that the latter is propelled by the almighty "dollar."

Inlay work with gold, platinum and silver is the artist's final touch on a good piece of steel engraving. This adds variety and color to a finely finished gun and because of the much softer metals involved the engraver can work more meticulously. In my personal opinion, I prefer sculptured steel to most inlays. This is by far the more exacting. No second chances - when the steel has been cut away it's gone for good. Too often an inlay, because of its contrasting color, tends to distract from the scroll which may be far superior in design and workmanship.

The majority of my animal inlays are modeled and cast in gold. This is not the usual method employed but I find I can achieve better results in this manner.

First of all, the animal outline is scribed on the steel and an onglette graver is used to cut the outline. The inside area is removed with a chisel after which the outline of the animal is undercut with a small onglette graver. A small chisel is then tapped into the undercut which deepens it and throws up a wall of steel.

Acrylic plastic (Duzall) is then mixed (dental wax can be used) and pressed into the cut out section and flattened even with the rest of the receiver. Just before it has completely set it is removed. This gives an accurate cast of the cut-away portion.

Either wax or more acrylic is modeled over the base cast to anatomical proportions. Such details as feather and hair are not included in the model but added after the gold cast has been completely inlayed in the steel and burnished. For most gold castings, I use 22 Karat gold, as there are times when you may want to move or stretch it a little. Since the process of casting gold and silver is a field in itself, I suggest you learn it first hand from a dentist or goldsmith.

Once cast, the piece is placed in the steel and tapped gently into place. The edge of steel which was thrown up is pressed down over the gold and then stoned and burnished. Now the fine anatomy is applied to the inlay and the work finished.

In closing, the most important thing to remember is to go into engraving with a will to succeed. An hour or two a day over a period of months will more than repay itself in the satisfaction you will get from expressing yourself in steel. When you look at the men on top in the field, just remember that the word "Plugger" was a big companion to ability.

- *John R. Rohner, Curator of Exhibits, University of Colorado Museum, Boulder, Colorado*

MAKING A HACKSAW SAW

Was hacksawing through a piece of 1x1 inch stock the other day and the blade was a little dull and started to bind. Dopped on some cutting oil just to see what it would do. Bob, you got to try this one!! The blade cut much easier, but most important, the end of the metal is smoother when you use the stuff on the blade. I tried it on several other metals with a good blade, and you can tell just as soon as the cutting oil gets down on the teeth. Feels like you greased it, and the chips come out smooth with the cutting time reduced by about a fourth!

- *Ralph Walker, Selma, Alabama*

FANCY WOOD PAPERWEIGHTS

When I am building up a fancy stock for a customer, I take some of the larger scraps and cut them into cubes or other interesting shapes to make into paperweights to present to the customer along with his finished gun. It is no problem to finish them along with the gunstock, and it does make a really nice desk memento for the proud owner of one of your fancy stocks.

Should mention too, that I also make these up as gifts and presents for friends out of scraps of fancy wood that are lying around the shop. Cause a lot of favorable comment, and I am sure they do a lot for good public relations!

- *Bob Black, Huntsville, Alabama*

PIDDLIN' AMOUNTS OF ACRAGLAS

When I am repairing something that only requires very small

amounts of Acraglas, I measure the materials by drops off the end of a match stick. The method always works successfully for me, and never have had one not set up.

- *Donald Truman, Elmore, Ohio*

THE GALS AROUND US

Then there's the one about the girl who always slept nude and awoke one morning to find herself completely dressed. "My God," she screamed, "I've been draped!" AND:- There was this little girl of nine who was frequently reprimanded by her mother for untidiness. Suddenly she began to clean her room and place her toys and books where they belonged. The startled mother sought an explanation. "What has come over you, Mildred?" "I'm frightened, Mother. I read in last night's paper that two girls were arrested for keeping a disorderly house."

- *Fred Moulton (earlier from Clemson College Chronicle)* - The American Rifleman

CLEANERS & OILERS

Couple of suggestions from Larry Sterett: "Those Q-Tips make wonderful cleaners of small recesses when used with solvent...Also, those plastic hypos the docs are using now. Retrieve the next one he throws away, grind off the point, fill with light oil. Really puts oil in those hard to reach spots."

- *Larry S. Sterett, Biggsville, Illinois*

OIL CAN

Use empty Ronsonol lighter fluid cans, the type with the flip top, for oil around the shop. Just take a screwdriver and pry off the cap and fill it up. They work fine to put in a tool box. You can't lose the cork.

- *Garry Newell, Lewiston, Idaho*

SQUIRT CANS

The best thing for keeping gun oil, powder solvent, Do-Drill, etc., in around the shop is those lighter fluid cans with the red swing spout. Spout can be flipped off, the can filled and the lid put back on.

- *Russ Kalz, St. Louis, Missouri*

UNUSUAL BORE CLEANER

Discovered the other day that I was out of Hoppe's and for some reason which I cannot explain, I stuck some Tap Magic on the cleaning patch, followed it with some on a Bronze brush and back to the patches. Results were so outstanding that I went ahead and tried it on some others that were already clean. A really clean barrel even came cleaner!! So clean, in fact, that inspection in most cases produces a hypnotic effect as your focus point proceeds down the barrel.

- *Raymond Strong, Memphis, Tennessee*

CLEANING UP A "JUNKER" WITH TASGON

Last spring a kid brought in a shotgun that had laid under the seat of a farm pick-up for at least a couple of years. As you might guess, it was covered with rust, chaff, mud and manure. He wanted me to take the rust off and put it in working order, and didn't want to spend much on it.

Had almost decided not to take on the job, when the smell of the almighty dollar beckoned. Finally managed to get out the screws and beat the gun apart - but then was stymied until I spotted a can of Tasgon on the bench. So, I slopped it all over the parts and set them out in the sun to cook for a while. When I brought it back into the shop, I buffed the rust off with a soft wire wheel, and I'll be durned if the gun did not come out looking like new. Maybe this trick is an old one to the trade, but thought if not, would surely like someone to tell me about it if I didn't know. Works better than any of the other kerosene or fancy concoctions I've heard of, bar none!

- *Henry Mar, Brookings, South Dakota*

GETTING TOOL MARKS OUT OF CYLINDER GROOVES

I take a heavy pin punch with a good sharp edge - or you can take a piece of drill rod of the proper diameter and harden it after grind-

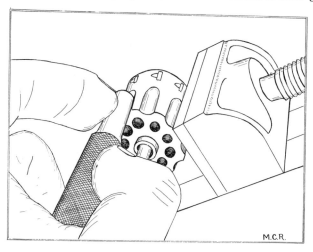

ing the end square - and use it like a scraper. Push it endwise at about 5 or 10 degrees angle and it works real slick. Did up a drawing so you could "get the picture".

- M. C. Ray, *Cleveland, Ohio*

CHECKERING STEEL WITH THE MMC CHECKERING TOOL

One of my friends was being subjected to my bragging about how strong the new gears are in my electric checkering tool. So! he suggested that we should try to checker some steel. I had an old defective carbide cutter which we tried on an old bolt handle. It isn't easy to stop on a line due to the high load on the tool and the tendency to grab, but after some practice, I think it could be mastered by anyone proficient with the machine. I think it could be used to checker front and backstraps of target handguns and serrate shotgun ribs. The toughest part of the job is to make straight guide lines on a flat surface. I do not know how long the cutter will last - but sure will know when it gives out!!

- Bob Sconce, *maker of the MMC Checkering Tools, Deming, New Mexico*

MOTORIZED CASE TRIMMER

H. M. Pratt wanted to motorize his case trimmer. "The old Burroughs," says he, "had a reduction unit driven by a motor and when a key was operated the motor would turn the unit. I turned an adapter and threaded one end of it to fit the cutter after unscrewing the crank. Now, by stepping on a pedal, the reamer turns at just the right speed and the whole thing didn't cost me anything, only a little time. The unit was given me by the company."

- H. M. Pratt, *Middlebury, Vermont*

THREE PHASE POWER

Quite often the shop owner wants to install 3-phase power in his shop only to discover that it costs a small fortune to get the power company to run the wires in. And in some non-industrial areas, the cost is so high the power companies just won't even consider doing it. R. A. Keirle & Associates wrote us that you can purchase an International Electric Phase converter which changes 220 volt 1-phase to 220 3-phase. Though the cost of the converter is a bit on the high side, it could be a real lifesaver for the man who is doing a lot of work and wants the extra power and convenience of 3-phase.

If you are interested in such a converter, write and ask for literature from: International Electric Company, 5710 Santa Fe Avenue, Los Angeles, California, 90058.

- R. A. Keirle and Associates

"ACRAGLAS BEDDING" YOUR SHOP EQUIPMENT

Try bedding lathes and other heavy equipment in Acraglas...
Man, is it solid.

- *Taylor's Gun Shop, Wolf Creek, Montana*

BUFFER WRENCH

I have to change wheels all the time while buffing and have to
hunt the #$%¢&* wrench each time. So, since the work I have been
doing lately is polishing and bluing S&W revolvers, I filed the nut
on the buffer shaft off on two sides so can just take the butt of the
frame - the open space in the grip frame, you know - and haste is made
loosening that nut with the pistol as a wrench. Crazy enough, huh?

- *Joe Head, Magnum, Oklahoma*

CALL OF THE OUTDOORS

Don Brown has a society all going for that outdoor biff - it is for
the preservation and restoration of outside toilets. They call it the
Birch John Society...!

- *Don Brown, Asheville, North Carolina*

CARBON TETRACHLORIDE

In a Newsletter we mentioned, in one place, the use of carbon-tet
as a cleaner. Boys, that was a plumb mistake and I hope everyone of
you read this. It is a good cleaner but do NOT use it. I suspect we
got in two dozen letters from people telling us why it should not be
used by anyone for cleaning.

"If used with bare hands the carbon-tet will be absorbed thru the
skin. It can honey-comb kidneys and there isn't a damned thing that
can be done. This might be worth passing on to some poor devil who
doesn't know about it..."

- *John's Gun Room, Toulon, Illinois*

"...using carbon-tet as a cooler or evaporator to dissipate heat
when drilling. I was working in Maintenance, then to manager and
back to maintenance after developing ulcers at a certain plant, and in
the main plant they used carbon-tet. We got medical reports from the
various plants at times and one day we got one stating they had a
fatality there. The reason was carbon-tet. We changed to Solvent
M-50. You can get it from John B. Moore Corp., Nutley, N.J., and on
the label it says 1,1,1, Tricholoroethane, inhibitor. Have tried it as
a cleaner - Wow!! Must be used in a well ventilated place but is not
fatal like carbon-tet."

- *Kline's Gun Shop, Ravenna, Ohio*

"...several of the St. Louis fire fighters use my shop as a sort of headquarters and general loafing spot (Okay, so I don't make any money but look at all the free fire protection I get)...These firemen say Carbon Tetrachloride is one of the most deadly poisons known...is a highly volatile liquid, and breathing the vapors for any length of time in most cases proves fatal..."

- *Russ Kalz, St. Louis, Missouri*

"...I am very concerned about the use of carbon-tet for either cleaning or drilling. Carbon-tet is extremely toxic stuff and rots your liver like corn whiskey but without the fun. And breathing the fumes from a hot drill job is a splendid way to absorb a toxic dose."

- *Dr. George West, Davis, California*

Well - hope we got that point across - and thanks a jillion to all the rest of you who wrote about it, too. Our advice is NEVER use Carbon-tet. It is just way too dangerous. Can enter the body through the skin, get into the blood stream and deposit in the liver and later cause all kinds of serious damage. Energine non-flammable Spot Remover (1,1,1 trichloroethane) does as good a job and is much safer to use for jobs around the shop.

- *Bob B.*

MORE ON CARBON TET

And here's one about Carbon-Tet that has me stumped: "The other day I was welding and my torch back-fired on me. I continued welding but soon noticed that my steel wool was on fire. Not much of a fire, just the flame crawling over the exposed ends of the wool. I laid it on the floor and stomped out the flame but the fire smoldered on, so, not wanting to wet it with water, I took the fire extinguisher with Carbon-Tet and gave it a squirt. Caused a small explosion! I moved it out in the yard and put some more Carbon-Tet on it. A thick red smoke arose and a loud roar followed. The wool was soon consumed! If I had tried putting that fire out in the shop I'd have had a real fire going!"

- *Jack Blurton, Ramsey, Illinois*

ABOUT THAT STEEL WOOL

I cannot help offering a short chemistry lecture because I seldom get a chance like this to flaunt my chemical engineering degree in connection with my gun work. The explosion was due to a highly exothermic reaction between the iron and the carbon tetrachloride. (In this case burning steel wool on a gunsmith's bench.) In the presence of oxygen (air) and a little heat to start it, the reaction proceeds rapidly (explodes!). Here is the way it goes, the red cloud being $FeCl_3$: $4Fe + 3O_2 + 3CCl_4 = 4FeCl_3 + 3CO_2$ - in other words: Use a dry type extinguisher around your shop!!!

- *M. C. Wiest, Oak Ridge, Tennessee*

ANOTHER KIND OF POISON

..."Feel that a few more words should be said about Trichloro-ethane as a commercial solvent. Great care should be exercised in the use of these chlorinated hydrocarbons as degreasing agents before arc welding because the vapors in the presence of an electric arc generate Phosgene Gas which, as you undoubtedly know, was one of the WWI "Poison Gasses"...

- *Stephen D. Gramam, Boulder, Colorado*

SPEAKING OF HEALTH PROBLEMS AND VENTILATION

Got a letter from Col. Frank Chamberlin who lives in Bethesda, Maryland, where many of the homes have their own water supplies. The five year drought they've been going thru has lowered the water level to a point where water enough to flush toilets poses a serious health threat. The good Colonel has been working many hours, he says, on finishing up a new invention that permits excellent toilet facilities requiring no water. He thinks it should be a world winner. First you get a board about 4' long and 18" wide, cut three holes in it - and make a door with a half-moon or a star - build a little building around it and set up in one corner of your estate and, Presto! A real outdoor Biff...Some of our Deutsch friends here in Iowa call them Thunderen-boomer-zimmers...Remind me to tell you sometime of when my oldest sister tried to make homemade bread and it wouldn't rise so, to keep her young husband from knowing what she'd done she shoved it down one of the holes in the privey where the heat and bac-teria put it to work to a point where it came up to all three holes, white and spongey, and of what my brother-in-law said when he saw it - or when my father poured contraband black powder down one of the holes. Later Grandfather B. prepared himself for a comfortable after-noon's pipe smoke and dropped the still burning match down the other hole. After the smoke had cleared he stuck his head up out of the car-nage and remarked: "Something I et, no doubt."

- *Bob B.*

GASOLINE

I think that about the best reason there is for NOT using gasoline around the gunshop as a cleaner came in the other day from John Turn-bull. He'd clipped it from the Peoria newspapers and the first para-graph went like this: "Pekin - A gasoline and gun powder explosion in the garage gunshop of Paul Gebhart in a new residential area of north-east Pekin at 12:15 p.m. Saturday killed Gebhart, injured two neighbor women and damaged nine houses...The concussion of the blast was felt by residents in their homes within a half-mile radius.

"Gebhart, with blood oozing from the pores of his entire body, was able to tell attendants on his way to the hospital, 'The gas blew up in the shop,' referring to gasoline he was using to clean guns."

The Illinois state demolition experts of the state police estimated that there was not more than 250 pounds of gunpowder in the garage. Personally, I wonder if the powder did any of the real damage (if it were smokeless, that is) for further in the article it was stated that "there was a tall column of white smoke above the house." Doesn't that sound like powder BURNING and not EXPLODING?

Anyhow - keep that gasoline out of your shop...

- *Bob B.*

THE NEW GUNSMITH

Sporting goods store owner to prospective gunsmith employee: "You're asking a large salary for a gunsmith with no experience."

Prospective gunsmith, "Well, the work is much harder when you don't know anything about it."

- *Bob B.*

SPECIALIZATION

And I blush, but cannot remember who sent this: These two gals were discussing their sons and one said, "My son is a naval surgeon." The other chewed this over for a spell and observed, finally: "My, but aren't they getting specialized these days!"

- *Bob B.*

PERSONALIZING FISHING RODS

Discovered this one entirely by accident one day while stirring around in my good wife's sewing box. Spied a spool of very fine monofilament sewing thread that is made to be used on fancy patterned or plaid cloth. Being a bookbinder also, I had the equipment for stamping the name on very thin vinylite in 24 karat gold (you probably could get this done by a local book binder - BB). Then wrap this around the rod near the butt, holding it in place with plastic electricians tape while wrapping it to the rod with the transparent thread. Cut the vinylite about 1/16" shorter at each end than the wrap and put on a good standard guide finishing wrap with the thread. Looks great - is a fine way to give a rod a little extra personal touch, and the customers go for it in a big way.

- *Joe Van Horn, Canton, Ohio*

PROFESSIONAL ROD BUILDING METHODS

With a small amount of practice on a pencil or dowel rod, it is possible for anyone, even if he has five thumbs on each hand, to turn out a right passable rod-winding job. A bit more practice (to get over the shakes and gain confidence) and the finished rod will be quite professional.

By studying the following illustrations and the pictures of windings, anyone from 8 to 80 can produce a rod to be proud of.

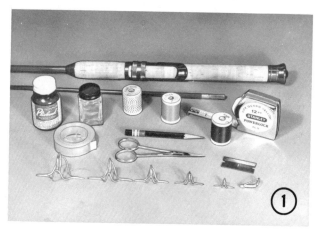

Above are the items you will need. They are: Handled blank complete with winding check, reel seat, butt cap; Ferrule cement (Pliobond 30) for tip top; Water clear varnish for the windings; Thread; Ruler for laying out guide distances from tip top; Cellophane tape, Pencil, Razor blade, Scissors; Guide set. Not shown, a few pieces of pipe stem cleaner.

Before proceeding, there are a host of so-called "simplified" instructions for rod winding, and by following them, one can get a good, average, over-the-counter, job. However, it is our feeling that since you are buying the very best in rod blanks, you will also want to turn out the very best in completed rods. One thing is certain: you are entitled to know HOW to do the job professionally. And, after reading the following, you can still use the simplified, one-thread-color wrap and do it better. The choice, and the information on how to do it one way or the other is here for you.

Attaching Tip

Assemble your rod, being very careful to have the light prick marks on the joining ferrules exactly lined up. These two marks indicate the TOP side of the rod. Lay the rod on a table with prick marks UP and hold rod in position by placing a book along each side of rod handle so rod cannot turn.

Take Tip Top guide and slip onto uncemented rod tip as far as it will go. With sharp pencil draw a line around the rod at the edge of the tip top tube. This is your ferrule cement line.

Before removing the uncemented tip top from the rod tip, practice lining it up with the two prick marks on the center ferrule. The guide ring should be pointing UP and in perfect alignment with the marks. You can check the alignment by picking up the rod and sighting down its length as you would a rifle sight. Do this a few times so you will feel confident of your procedure when you apply the cement and make the final attachment.

Should the tip top seem a bit too tight, very lightly sand the tip of the rod until the tip top slips on with just a faint amount of resistance.

NOTE: If your rod has a fixed reel seat, be sure to align center of reel seat with the prick marks on the ferrule and the guide ring of the tip top.

Cementing

Remove tip top and re-block the rod on the table. Be sure the prick marks are UP. Apply a small amount of Pliobond 30 (ferrule cement) to tip of rod, being careful not to extend back beyond your pencil mark. With a toothpick, apply cement to inside of tip top tube, twisting the toothpick around so you are sure you have full coverage. Do not gob the cement - spread it. Allow to dry thoroughly - 15 to 20 minutes.

Heat tip top to about 180 degrees F. and slip onto rod, aligning with prick marks. After tip has cooled, peel off any cement which might show, using your thumbnail or a dull knife.

Professional suggestion: heating can be done on an electric stove with plate turned to lowest heat; with a cigarette lighter, candle, or a gas torch such as is found in most home shops. Do not over-heat as excess heat could damage the fine rod tip. If tip will not slip on the first time, reheat to a bit "hotter". Use pliers or wear gloves to handle hot tip. Tip can be removed in same manner.

Preparing Guides

The guides you will choose for your kit are the best Brownells could find and are ready for winding. However, it is always wise to be sure. So! rub the bottoms of the guide feet on a flat sharpening stone or a piece of flat emery paper to be sure all burrs are removed.

Also: place the feet of the guide on the edge of a ruler and sight between ruler edge and feet to be sure guides are giving good contact. If not, bend feet with your fingers until bottoms (especially tips) of the guides are giving close to full-length contact with ruler-edge.

Locating Guides

Refer to chart showing guide distances for your particular rod. Note distance from tip to farthest guide (One closest to handle). Starting from the ring guide of the tip top, measure off distance shown in the chart and make a pencil mark cross-wise of the rod at this distance from the tip. This mark indicates where the CENTER (ring portion) of the guide should be located on the rod.

You are now ready to attach the first guide.

Locate the proper guide with guide ring above your pencil mark and the guide in line with the tip top. Wind on with the desired thread.

Suggestions on how to proceed:

Rod builders use a variety of methods to hold the guide to the rod while aligning it with the guide ring in the tip top...these run all the way from electrician's tape to rubber bands and clothes-pins. Personally, I have found that a short piece of pipe cleaner wound around the guide and rod and twisted tight is the most satisfactory for this one step.

With the guide held in position on the rod use the "gun sighting method" to align it with the tip top. (Remember that on fixed reel seat rods, the center of the reel seat, rear guide and tip top should all three be in alignment). The pipe cleaner winding will permit your moving the guide from side to side - and hold it to where you move it.

When the guide is in position, cut off a short piece of cellophane tape and firmly secure the other guide foot to the rod. Check to be sure guide is still in line.

Make a short, lengthwise pencil mark on the rod at the point of each guide foot. Remove pipe cleaner. Check to be sure points of guide feet are on the pencil lines you have just made.

Make a pencil mark around the rod about 1/8" or 3/16" from the end of each foot. This is where you will want to start your rod winding.

Balance of Guides

After winding on first guide (see following instructions) check the chart and mark off location of the next guide up the rod from the butt. Attach in the same manner.

As each guide is attached, you will find it easier to keep all the guides in perfect alignment. Pick up the rod, hold it out from you and sight down not only the center of the guides towards the tip top but also down the tops of the guides. Your eye will quickly detect any misalignment.

If you should discover that any already wrapped guide is out of line you can, by holding the rod and guide firmly in the fingers of each hand, slip the guide a tiny bit around the rod and into line. The faintest movement will line up what seems to be a badly out-of-line guide. Final varnishing will tighten up all the windings.

Thread Holder and Tension

Whether you use the Thompson Rod Winder shown in the photos below or the book method of thread holding as shown in the sketch, adjust your tension so it is firm but not so tight as to break the thread.

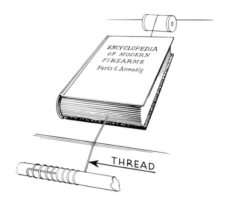

You might need an extra book or two to give sufficient tension. If you use the books, drop your thread in a small glass or jar lid. Do not let the thread wind off the end of the spool as this will cause it to twist. Spool should be free to roll in its container.

Cut off a 6" piece of thread, double it and place where you can get to it easily. See Photo No. 8.

Starting the Wind

This is the operation on a rod that people look at and say, "I wonder how in the world they do that!..." Here is how:

Some wrappers like to have the thread come under the rod (see

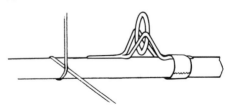

drawings); others like to have it come over the top where they can see what it is doing. See Photos. Following the latter process:

1. Pull the thread out from the holder towards you and lay it down over the top of the rod at the penciled thread guide line mentioned above. Make a single wrap around the rod - under, up the back and over the top and out towards you. The turn of the thread should be between the thread from the holder and the guide.

2. Hold the loose end of the thread in one hand with a minimum of tension. Grasp the rod between index finger and thumb of the other hand and twist towards you. As the thread starts to wind on the rod, move the rod so that the thread will "jump" or wind over that first wind you made. Make one or two careful revolutions this way (without holding the loose end of the thread) and Presto! you have the wind started.

Note: when practicing this, you might want to hold the thread in place on the rod with the thumb of the hand that was holding the loose end of the thread.

3. After making the few turns mentioned above, clip off some of the extra thread and draw the wind tight on the rod.

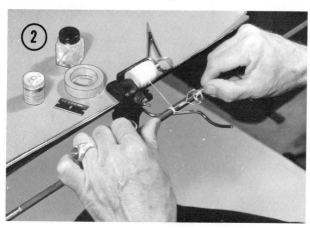

As per Photo No. 2 above I like to do this first wind holding the rod in the air, rather than on a rest.

After putting on enough turns that you can pull the thread tight without it slipping on the rod, use your thumb-nail to squeeze the winds together and get them straight around the rod and close to the penciled line.

4. Now start the actual wind, rotating the rod towards you. As you turn the rod, keep the thread at a slight angle to the rod so that it comes in tight against the previous wind.

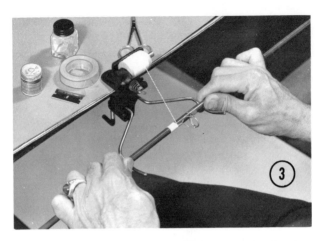

5. After making about eight winds, cut the loose end of the thread off with either the razor blade or scissors. See drawing No. 4.

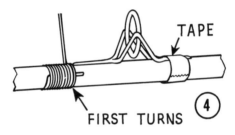

TAPE

FIRST TURNS ④

6. As you wind watch for gaps between the threads. Should one

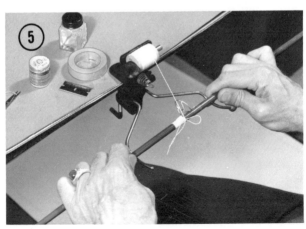

show, press the end of the wind with your thumb-nail. Hold tension on the thread at all times. Should you have to stop, hold the windings

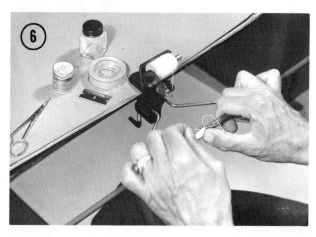

with the tip of your thumb to keep from loosening, as in Photo No. 6.

7. Continue winding up to the guide foot. Before going on to guide, be sure tip of guide foot is in line with pencil mark. Now, continue winding until you are 6 or 8 turns from completion. Holding the thread to the rod with your thumb, pick up the doubled piece of thread and start winding over it. See Photo No. 5.

8. Wind until the thread comes to the branching of the wires of the "U" frame of the guide, about 3 or 4 turns farther than shown in the drawing No. 7.

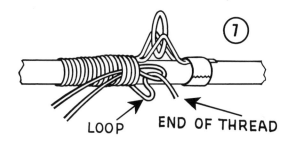

LOOP   END OF THREAD

9. Study drawings No. 6 and 7. They not only show you how to run the end of your thread thru the loop but also how to hold the windings with the tip of your thumb. (Photo No. 6).

The "loop" shown in Nos. 6 and 7 is very important. It not only greatly helps prevent thread breakage, it also helps prevent impos-

sible-to-remove thread twist kinks from forming as you pull the thread
end under the wind.

10. Pull doubled loop thru the windings, drawing free end of
winding thread under windings. Pull the thread snug - see Photo No. 8.

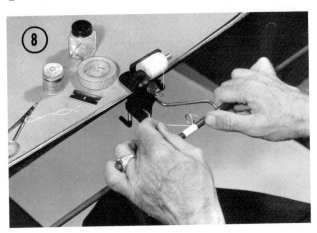

11. Lay your looped thread to one side. Grasp the end of the
winding thread and pull it gently towards the guide. This opens up a
slight gap where it comes out from under the windings. Relax the
thread and cut down into this gap at right angles to the rod. This
cuts the thread down below the surface of the winding. See Drawing
No. 9.

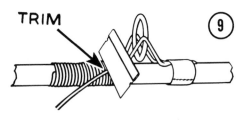

12. Close the gap with thumb-nail and work the balance of the
winding tight in the same manner. This leaves a very smooth finish
on the winding.

13. Re-sight (re-align) guide with tip top. It is easier to move
guide a bit now rather than trying to make adjustments after windings
are made on the other end.

14. Remove cellophane from other end of the guide and wrap it.
Always start winding from the rod and go up and over the guide,
rather than attempting to start winding on the guide and go down

over the guide foot tip.

15.   After you have the second guide wound on the tip section of the rod (do not count the guide on the butt section) you will find it easier to handle the rod if you separate the two sections and work with just the tip section.

Special Winding

Center Ferrule

See the illustration for "Space Dye Thread". This gives you an idea of how far the guide should be set from the ferrule and how the thread is wound onto the ferrule. In this instance, start on the ferrule and after making several winds, force the windings back to the built-in thread stop on the ferrule.

Black & White Space Dye thread with a few turns of Black
at each end to give more balance to the complete winding.

Some rod-winders start the ferrule guide winding 1/8" from the tip of the guide, wind on the guide and finish off. They then make a second winding going the other direction and up onto the ferrule, using the same color thread. This makes the smoothest possible job.

Butt Winding

In Photo No. 10 three elements have been used to give the rod additional accent: two contrasting colors of thread and inserts of bright metallic tape.

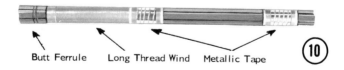

Butt Ferrule   Long Thread Wind   Metallic Tape   ⑩

Winding No. 1 was first applied, starting on the rod and working towards the butt ferrule. The narrow accent winding (see instructions below) was then applied.

At No. 2 a short piece of metallic tape was wrapped around the rod, flush with the windings just completed, with ends of the tape overlapping. Both thicknesses of the tape were cut thru with a razor blade and the surplus tape removed. The joining ends of the tape were then smoothed down with thumb-nail and the windings applied as shown in the photo.

Further decorative windings and tape were then applied at No. 3 in the photo, using the same technique.

Photo No. 11 shows contrasting accent windings without the metallic tape but with the inclusion of a hook keeper up against the winding check. In this photo the windings are on the F70 fly rod blank. The same technique will work, however, on all types of rods.

Tip Winding

See Photo No. 12. Start winding at the tip top and work back on the rod. When winding is well started, force back against tube of the tip top to give a smooth appearance to the winding, and finish off wind.

The only difficulty you might experience when winding the tip is holding the rod. You will find it a great help to lay a book or board on your table with the end sticking over the edge. Let the rod rest on this when wrapping the tip ends. It prevents the rod from bending and whipping while winding - and makes the whole business simpler.

Narrow Windings

Narrow "accent lines" - If the accent line is to be only 8 or 12 threads wide (depending upon weight of thread being used), start the thread as for a regular winding but at the same time have the "pull-through loop" (the piece of thread in Photo No. 8.) on the rod and make the winding over it, too.

When the accent winding is complete, cut end of thread from spool and pull thru winding. When snug, pull on end of thread with which you started winding. (Both threads are under the wind). When snug, cut both ends of thread and force the accent wind up against the basic wind.

This same procedure can be used when there are as few as three or four threads in the wind.

"Double Wrap"

Altho "double wrapping" or "double winding" is generally used only on re-enforced guides, many rod builders use it on all wraps for an extra look of "professionalism". See Photo No. 13.

Before starting the base wrapping, be sure to have pencil marks on the rod indicating where to start and stop the wrap. When base wrap is complete, find its center and make a faint mark indicating where center of the guide should be when the second wrapping is wound on.

Fly Rod Suggestion

In the photo below you will note that the Aetna "Foulproof" guide has been pulled out so that the rings of the guide are not touching. This gives a great deal more flex to the guide.

This is done by holding the feet of the guides with pliers and carefully pulling until you have the separation shown in the photo. When you do this, you will have to twist the guide a bit while pulling to keep the bottoms of the guide feet parallel.

After spreading the guide, check the feet on a flat surface. If not even and level, carefully twist with pliers until they are. A bit of experience and you can do this quite easily.

Final Varnishing

Examine all your wrappings to be sure there are no gaps between any of the threads. If there are, they can be tightened by working the threads towards the guide with your thumb-nail. If gaps are left open they will look like black lines in the finished job.

If you have used our thread you will not have to give the windings a coat of color preservative. So, give all the wrappings a coat of water-clear varnish with finger-tip or camel's hair brush. Extend the varnish onto the rod for about 1/8" beyond the ends of the windings.

Lay the rod flat on a couple of water glasses after varnishing is completed. Turn the rod a bit from time to time to be sure the varnish is not settling in one spot.

After the varnish has thoroughly dried, examine the windings to see if any nylon fibers are sticking up thru the varnish. If there are, lightly wipe the windings with finest steel wool.

Apply a second coat of varnish, but not quite so heavy as the first coat. Examine after it is thoroughly dry. If you wish the surface smoother, a third thin coat can be applied to give more of a glass-like appearance.

When the final coat of varnish is dried you have a fishing rod second to none!

   - *Bob Brownell*

OLD FASHIONED PEANUT BRITTLE

If you guys have wives like mine used to be when I was gunsmithing full time, you get your ears chewed down to nubbins every so often for cooking up weird and smelly messes on her pet kitchen stove... especially is this true if you happened to do your first blue job with our Oxynate No. 7 - spilled a bit and had it eat off all the enamel or make a hole in the new linoleum - sure can make a woman unhappy, can't it!

Well, here is a mess you can "whomp" up on the kitchen stove that will come up with a different reaction. Before going any further, I am the world's worst cook and practically killed my Dad and a friend off on a hunting trip once - the pancakes rose to about the thickness of this Newsletter - and tasted just as good. But come Christmas, and this I can do and not fail (fizzled with me the first time but since then have batted 1000%):

Smear some butter on your wife's cookie sheet about the same as you would were you smearing grease on a gun for storage..not so much as to make it gobby - but enough to cover real good. On this, sprinkle about 1/4th teaspoon of table salt. Now, in an aluminum stew pan dump 3/4 cup of white sugar, 1/4 cup of white Karo and 1/4 cup of drinking water. Stir a bit and then put on the stove and turn on the heat. Stick in a candy thermometer (or you can use your bluing thermometer if you get all the salts off it so's it won't pizzen you) and let the mess boil until the temperature reaches exactly 238 degrees F. (Do not stir once it starts to boil.) When it reaches 238 F. add 1/2 pound of shelled raw peanuts and let it keep on boiling for four or five minutes - or until you hear the first peanuts start to "pop" or things start to smell a wee bit like well roasted peanuts - a bit of smoke starts coming at the same time.

Now, whip it off the stove and add 1 teaspoon full of baking soda. This makes the gunk fizz - stir it thoroughly while it is doing this and as fast as you can, dump it out on the cookie sheet and spread it out thin with your spoon. Makes the best dingnabbed peanut brittle you ever sunk your teeth into and doesn't take, from start to finish, more than about 15 minutes - not a whale of a lot longer than a short TV commercial. (Got this from Bruce Meek's wife, Jeanette, - him whot is the gun engraver. She didn't tell it to me exactly in the words I used!)

- *Bob B.*

CARAMELS

Seeing as how this is getting on towards the candy chewin' season, here is a bit of a formula for whompin' up some of the best caramel candy you ever stuck your false teeth in. Follow closely, use the proper instruments and you can't miss - I make it by the tubfull and can't even fry an egg properly!

Material List: 2 cups of white sugar; 1 cup of 1/2 & 1/2 cream; 1 cup evaporated milk; 1-3/4 cups Karo (white); 1 cup butter (or oleo); 1 cup chopped nuts (hunter's choice); a few grains of salt.

Procedure: Have your wife line the above all up for you along with a candy (or cleaned up bluing) thermometer, one 8" x 16" or two 8" x 8" pans, a mixing spoon, a cooking kettle, a stool to sit on and smoking supplies handy.

Then: - Mix all the material together in the kettle EXCEPT the cup of evaporated milk and the nuts. Turn up the fire to "medium" and bring to a boil - stirring the mess so it cannot burn or stick to the bottom of the pan. Get out your watch, turn the fire down a bit, and let it boil (and keep stirring) for 30 minutes. Then pour in the evaporated milk and do it slowly, mixing it in as you do. Put in the thermometer and let boil SLOWLY (dial on the stove closer to "Low" than it is to "Med.") until the temperature on the thermometer reaches exactly 246 F. ...that takes a good half-hour to three-quarters more. Right fast like, pour in the nuts, stir a bit and then pour into the well buttered pans which your wife has been preparing for you while you cooked. The next evening cut into small squares, wrap in waxed paper and grow fat! Notes: dip your knife in water after each cut, cuts easier. Don't worry about the melted butter that comes to the top the first night - it works back in. If you can blue guns you can make this gunk. Kids love it. You get best candy, generally, if you don't let boil too hard - about the same kind of easy boil that you have in your bluing tank when it is operating properly - not the hard foamy kind of blasting boil.

- Bob B.

CHRISTMAS PUDDING

When you approach Ye Olde Yule Tide, give the following formula to your ever-suffering wife and instruct her to whomp up some for you and eat it for Christmas Dinner Deezert. It goes back to about Year One in my wife's family and, if after eating it you don't lean back, pat your belly and say, "Man! if that Brownell knows guns like he knows puddin' he knows it all..." It is a two part operation. You mix up one mess in one pan and another mess in another pan and when they are done you pour one over the other, while still warmish to hot, and EAT. Yeowee.

Pudding ingredients: (Serves 8): - 1/2 cup butter; 1 cup cold water; 1 cup sorghum; 2 cups flour; 1 teaspoon soda; 1/2 cup raisins (optional). Procedure: Let the butter soften at room temperature (72-75 F.) and when soft, stir in the water and sorghum. Sift the flour & soda together and add this to the first mixture. Add the raisins. Put all this conglomeration into a well greased pudding mold and steam for 2 hours. NOTE: tricks - put a piece of waxed paper in the bottom of the mold and grease the lid of the mold to prevent sticking. Also, fill the mold only HALF full. You can use a 2# coffee can, or 2 1# cans or something like 4 baking powder cans as molds if you wish.

Pudding sauce to pour over it - and, Brother! this makes the whole business strictly from heaven: - Ingredients for the Pudding Sauce: 1-1/2 cups sugar; 3/4 cup butter; 2-1/4 cups of hot water, 3 tablespoons corn starch; 1-1/2 teaspoons vanilla. Procedure: - Cream the butter and sugar together. It is important here that you do a right good job of creaming - No Lumps, Kid. Add enough water to corn starch to make a paste. No Lumps! Add this to hot water. Pour over creamed mixture and cook a few minutes. Add vanilla. Now, if you find the stuff isn't exactly smooth, beat until smooth with an egg beater. Serve hot - to be poured by eater over his individual portion... Guaranteed to add pounds to the hips and deep gleams of love in a gunnut's hungry eyes!!

- Bob B.

GLOGG

From Scandinavia, via Al Abramow, comes this recipe for a solution used by those people that goes by the name of Glogg. You take four cups of water, 4 cups of sugar, 24 cardamom seeds, 24 cloves, 24 almonds, 12 prunes, 4 cinnamon sticks, 4 handfuls of raisins and one dried peel of an orange. This you mix together and let simmer for 1/2 hour and then put it into a closed container, at room temperature, for a period of two months. There is one little sticker, however, and that is if you are going to complete the concoction you should do it out in the gun shop. Before putting the simmered yuce into the closed container you add one gallon of port wine and two quarts of whiskey. As you who know me well are aware, I am a non-drinker and agree with the guy who said: "You can pour my share back into the horse..." BUT having run candy and other assorted recipes for the likes of me, it is about time we had something for the friends who think I have odder ways than theirs...as Al says: "for us who have more noble tastes..."

- *Al Abramow, Rochester, New York*

SAUERKRAUT

I've a Deutsch brother-in-law who makes the best kraut ever offered to the human male. Once a year I visit their house and my request for special guest feed is some of George's kraut with spareribs and then they give me an extra pint and I eat it on the train back to Chicago and from Chicago home. It ain't the sour kind that puckers the hell out of you - nor the real flat kind - but the kind you can eat every day by the handful (if your companions can stand the side effects without gas-masks, that is!).

For this you need a 20 gallon crock or jar, 100 pounds of shredded cabbage, 2 pounds of salt, time and patience. Of course, you can scale the quantities down to whatever you have on hand, but the procedure is the same...and you can find a "kraut shredder" in most hardware stores, or if not, then get a big salad chopper and get to chopping. So:

In the bottom of your jar put in 3" of loosely shredded cabbage and over this spread a handful of "Common" salt - put in 3" more cabbage and a handful of salt and work thoroughly. Use up the cabbage or until you get to about 3" of the top of the jar or crock.

Cover the top of this mess with whole loose cabbage leaves and on top of the leaves lay a plate, upside-down. It is best if you can get a plate about the size of the inside of the jar - or as close to the I/D as possible. Right soon the surface will be covered with fluid. Dip off this excess fluid until just the plate is covered.

Each week remove the plate and whole leaves and wash off the slime or scum which might form. At the end of the second week, do as the first week but also - and this is the secret of GOOD Kraut - mix the whole mess up very thoroughly from top to bottom. If you don't, you'll have some rotten cabbage on top and some green cabbage on the bottom of the batch. Repeat this weekly.

After three or four weeks - or when the stuff tastes like good kraut to you - pack in jars with Ball lids and cold pack for 20 minutes. Another trick: after cooling, remove the little metal holding ring that holds the lid down and put wax paper over the lid and jar and then screw the metal holding ring back on. This keeps the rings from rusting.

Gad - my mouth is watering so after reading the above, I think I'll have to call George & Mary and have them send out a couple of jars...You see, I've just talked him into releasing the above to me this spring. 'Tis exclusive!

- *Bob B.*

STEW - FOR THE INNER MAN

Get your wife to try this and if you are 70 you'll be able to handle two 20's and if you are 20, you'll feel you can support the whole world!

Stew 2-1/4 pounds of heel or rump beef and suet until tender. Then, cut into small pieces and add water if necessary to have 3 quarts of broth.

Dice and add: 6 Medium Potatoes - 5 Medium Onions (white preferably, any color satisfactory) - 4 carrots - 3 turnips and 3 stalks of celery. Cut 1/2 small head of cabbage and add. To this mess also add: 1-1/2 quarts of tomatoes - 1 small can or 1-cup of peas - 1/2 tsp. Oregano - 1/2 tsp. garlic salt (or 1/2 clove of garlic if preferred) and 1/4 tsp. barbecue spice...salt and pepper to taste.

Start to boil, then turn down to simmer and cook at least 4-1/2 hours. Six hours is better...

- *Mrs. Melvin Fleming, New Sharon, Iowa (Wayne Fleming's aunt)*

BEETLE HOUND NAMED GLIMMER

Larry Blennon, my helper, opened his mouth the wrong time the other day, ended up with a Beetle Hound named Glimmer. Had about as much use for a dog as a sow has with a sidesaddle. Tied the damn thing to my camp trailer back of the store, and it nearly chewed the fenders off before I noticed. Gets away every 2-3 days and takes 1/2 a day catching him. He won't eat dog food, won't eat raw meat and doesn't like my cooking either. Larry got him a pretty good hunk of meat the other day, which Glimmer promptly buried (probably to ripen). Larry dug it up and put it on the stove in a kettle (my best one) and let it simmer so's Glimmer would eat it. I was at home a bit later and found the pot simmering - smelled pretty good, too. I figured he had got ambitious and was cookin' up a mulligan. So put some smoke-meat extract in it, some garlic, a few bay leaves and parsley (just to keep it from being flat tasting). Would have eaten a bowl if I had time, too. After closing the store, I was getting ready to serve us a couple of bowls when Larry spread the word. That damned dog ate the whole works and Larry and I had baloney..."

- *Raymer Durnell, Cabool, Missouri*

RABBIT ESPAGNOLE

We had rabbit espagnole for Thanksgiving dinner. Had enough snowshoe hares hanging to be able to use just hind legs. Never have gotten enthusiastic about varying harying hare loins. (Cottontails will do.) Make up your 'espagnole' sauce of onions, tomatoes, celery, peppers, both sweet and a bit of hot, a tiny amount of smoked meat such as bacon or ham, or even smoked loin, and bed the rabbit legs down in the sauce in a pressure cooker. Use very little water because the sauce makes its own liquid. Have a little bit of corn flour or quick cooking cereal like Cream of Wheat handy, mixed in cold water to introduce to the pot as soon as it is done. Half an hour will cook the dish at 15 pounds pressure. Put in the "gravy" thickening as soon as the cooker pressure goes down and put the cover back on for a few minutes before taking the dish to the table. Baked potatoes and Vienna or French-type bread goes good with this. Dessert should be cloying, such as Ground Glass. Ground Glass? Grind up peanut brittle and mix with whipped cream that peaks. Tell your company it is ground glass and light into it before they wise up and take it away from you, the pigs!

- *Aathar D. Anderson, Richford, Vermont*

FLAPJACKS MIT MEAT

Mix up your favorite formula for pancakes, spread out a thin one on the griddle and then spread a thin layer of potted ham over this and over the top of that mess spread another spoonful of pancake goop. Fry in the usual manner. First three or four bites you ain't so darned sure whether you want to eat it or not - but as you go on it gets better and by the fourth cake you are looking for more room under your belt to hold one more. But, if you are in the mountains and camping up high, don't do like Lois did a while back (she is my boss). Mixed up a mess of regular cakes, putting in the normal amount of baking powder. Man! They rose until they were as thick as normal baking powder biskets - weren't much to them. Seems the altitude has something to do with the way the baking powder reacted...indeed did blow them up high.

- *Bob B.*

BELLY-BURNER HOT SAUCE (or Gut Singer)

Say, you are always running in recipes, so here is one for hot sauce that I picked up from a Mexican hunting-camp cook. You can mix it in your bluing tanks if you wish: *1 cup of small, fresh peppers (1-1/2 cups of jalapinos work okay if the fresh ones are not available); 4 cans tomato sauce (small); *1 large can tomatoes; 1 tablespoon salt; *1 tablespoon pickle spices; 1 Qt. vinegar; *5 onions; *1 garlic. (*means grind in good grinder. I run them thru the blender with very good success.) MIX it all and simmer slowly for 45 minutes. Makes about 3 quarts. This is wonderful on meats, cottage cheese, and anything else that you like flavored up. At its best on hamburgers.

- *Bruce M. Jennings, Jr., Corpus Christi, Texas*

PIPE-TOBACCO

You 'uns who suck on a pipe all day like I do and then roll your tongue around your teeth come bed-time to get all the blisters broken so's they can heal during the night, try this for a mix and I guarantee it will either kill or cure you...Given me this spring by R. F. Miner, sales rep for Weller shooting and fishing supplies of Sioux City, Iowa... Take one can of Granger Rough Cut and with it mix 1-oz. of Perique and 1-1/2 ozs. of Latikia...you gotta cut up the Perique into wee hunks...Mix it up good (I use an old cookie jar) and then repackage and put 1/4th of a winesap apple in each jar for about four or five days. Let cure for around two weeks prior to smoking. Have been smoking it six months now and like it better every pipe-full. Makes a wet heel but who cares if you can smoke it all day and like it as well at 10:00 p.m. as at 7:30 a.m.?? This information is fer free. (My wife says it smells like I was smoking toenails - but anyone who smokes a pipe knows it's got to smell that way or ain't fitten to light-up, I allus say.)

- *Bob B.*

WHERE MEN ARE MEN

A westerner went into a local saloon with his three year old son and ordered 2 straight whiskeys. "Hey, Pa," the kid asked, "Ain't Ma drinkin'?"

- *Kenny Bredean, Anaheim, California*

CHAPTER 11

BUSINESS SAVVY

It's not my place to shoot dry shots
  Your trigger you must pull -
It's not my place to praise your loads
  When the case you have too full.
It's not my place to judge your gun
  It's care I can't foretell -
But let the damn thing miss the "X"
  And see who catches HELL!

SPORTING GOODS

Of course, one must be careful about spending money in too big a chunks. People might start wondering about them like the little old lady the boys at Poverty Ridge Gun Shop, write about. Seems she was making some terrific donations to the church. After a while the Parson and the Deacon got to talking about it. They decided they should have a talk with her, knowing she was on Social Security and maybe burdening herself by such heavy donations. So the Reverend says to her: "Mrs. So-and-So, aren't you causing yourself a hardship by donating so much?" She replied, "No, my son sends me $1000 a month. In fact, I can give more..." This took the Reverend by surprise. He had known the boy and a thousand a month is a lot of bux. "What kind of a job or business does he have now?" he asked. Said she: "I believe he is a veterinarian. Just last week I got a letter from him saying he had a whole string of cat houses now..." so watch it, boys!!

- Poverty Ridge Gun Shop, Rea, Missouri

NEIGHBORS

I sort of go along with a note Lee Estes put in a recent letter to us. "A newcomer to a valley inquired of the native, "What kind of people do you have here, Oldtimer?" Said the oldtimer: "What kind did you have where you came from, Newtimer?" Said the newcomer: "A bunch of damned S.O.B.'s." Oldtimer: "That's just the kind you'll find here!"

A few days later another newcomer quizzed the same oldtimer about the kind of people in the valley. The oldtimer again asked what kind of neighbors he had at home. Second newcomer answered: "The best in the world - kind, helpful, etc..." Said the oldtimer: "That's the kind you will find here!"

- Lee Estes, Portland, Oregon

PRICE CUTTERS

M & T Sales sends the pleasant following bit of philosophy to which I fully subscribe: "MY SON, never speak unkindly of price cutters! Never knock them, because God made them the same as HE made crabs, hornets, lizards, roaches, ants, centipedes, fleas, lice, wasps, snakes, skunks, and other unpleasant things which crawl out from under rotting logs and slimy unspeakable places. In HIS inscrutable wisdom HE made them. Why HE made them only HE knows. Some day HE may enlighten us...but up to now...I'll be damned if I understand."

- M & T Sales, Boulder City, Nevada

EXCEPTION TO PRICE CUTTERS

H. R. Havstad took exception to our comments on price cutters in the Newsletter. Says he, "...I feel that some harm is done by them, but also feel that a good deal of the crying is done by people who are not capable of competing in a free market. Let's go back a bit in history and see what price cutters have done for our good. I believe that Henry Ford made it possible for John Q. Public to own a horseless carriage, and it seems to me that Weaver made other manufacturers find out real fast that it wasn't necessary for a plain 4X scope sight to sell for in the neighborhood of $110.00. I believe that certain aspects of price cutting have done much to bring more goods to more people, thereby providing more jobs and lifting the overall economy of our country.

"When strict laws regulating prices, production, and profits are enacted, we will have taken a great stride in the direction of countries where few of us would choose to live today. My philosophy is like buying oats. If you want good, clean, fresh oats, you must pay a fair price. However, if you are willing to settle for oats that have already been thru the horse, these come considerably cheaper.

"It has been my experience that a person able and WILLING to produce good work is never begging for work. I realize that tight competition from small margin operators on standard retail items can hurt, but I can happily tolerate it as a necessary evil for the preservation of our American Way of Life."

- *H. R. Havstad, Paramount, California*

COST OF PRICE CUTTING

Charlie Heckman sent on this bit of information which we found quite interesting and which might give you a new slant on pricing: "We have gotten together some figures that you may pass on to the dealers, some of whom might have thought that possibly cutting the price to some degree is the answer to greater dollar profits in the coming years. These figures will show exactly what cutting prices will do to them. Assuming that the normal burden or overhead would be roughly one-third of the profit, let us just see how much additional business would be required with certain discount figures.

"If the initial retail price is reduced 10%, it would require 50% more business volume to be equal to the same volume of business if the regular retail price is maintained. If the original retail price is reduced 15%, 300% more business must be done to be equal to the same dollar profit as the merchandise sold at the retail price. If the dealer gives a 20% discount off the retail price on the products he sells HE IS THEN GOING INTO THE RED on every single sale, and the greater volume he does the worse off he will be...so you see, shaving the retail price is not the answer to greater profit."

Dick Shaw, sales manager for Weaver, told us a year ago of some guy on the west coast who took over the sporting goods department in one of those super shopping centers, did a couple million in business and was exactly $100,000.00 in debt (over and beyond all assets) at the end of a year. Bankrupt but good!

- *Charlie Heckman, El Monte, California*

SAVING MONEY

Where he gets them, I can't guess, but Dave Wyer offers this one as his latest: "Buying cheap goods to save money is like stopping a clock to save time..." Then he adds: "Nobody ever went broke when making a PROFIT."

- *Dave Wyer, Muleshoe, Texas*

SPEAKING OF THE OLD TWO-HOLERS

A buddy of mine had one of these road house juke joints up in Wisconsin. This place was in the form of an old barn and was all rigged up with rugged furniture and so on. Outside, he had two outhouses with a couple of holes each - one labeled "He" and the other "She".

Well, this buddy was a big joker, so he had a microphone/speaker hookup in the ladies with the speaker mounted out of sight below the seat. When the lady (victim) excused herself, enough time would be allowed to elapse for the lady to be seated and then a voice would come from beneath the seat:

"Would you mind moving over to the next hole, Lady. I'm painting down here."

- *Ralph Walker, Selma, Alabama*

$50,000 SUIT IN GUN MISHAP

From Slim Spears. After reading, you will understand why Slim wants us to "tell the fellows they can't be too careful." Slim is so very right. In our own shop we never permitted a customer back where we worked - under any condition. This, because a customer nearly shot one of our own boys in the middle of the back with a Single Action he'd smoothed the hammer spur on for "fanning"...Insurance is the wisest thing you can own - just in case!

"A $50,000 suit has been filed in Reno County District Court by a Hutchinson man who alleges he suffered a bullet wound due to a gunsmith's carelessness.

"The suit was filed by Fredrick E. Orth, 710 1/2 North Monroe, against Roy A. Jackson, 14 Sunnydell, South Hutchinson.

"Orth alleges he was in Jackson's workshop on March 27, 1964, when the accident occurred.

"Jackson had clamped a rifle to a bench and was checking its operation by putting rounds into the chamber, the suit alleges.

"The rifle discharged and the bullet struck Orth in the left forearm, shattering bone, artery and nerve, the suit alleges."
- *Slim Spears, Hutchinson, Kansas*

OBSERVATIONS

Was drinking a cup of coffee with the local Farm Extension Director the other day and he came up with an observation that I think is a dilly and certainly applies to most of us most of the time. Said He: "You know, people are always mistaking the rearrangement of their prejudices for serious reasoning." How true, how true. The guy's name is Roger Standish and if he thought that up himself his name should go down in history for something or other.
- *Bob B.*

SHOTGUN SALES PATTERN

"Dear Bob: As we indicated to you when we gave you this dope for last year, the old 'rule of thumb' used to be 50%, or 30% and 20% for the 12 gauge, 16 and 20 respectively. Following we will list for you both a repeat of last year's percentages and those for this year so you can do a little comparing:

"12 Gauge - 1961 54.8%, 1962 55%. 16 Gauge - 1961 22.4%, 1962 22%. 20 Gauge - 1961 22.8%, 1962 23%."
- *Sheldon M. Smith, President of Ithaca Gun Company*

THE SIGN OF AN ARTIST

Spring must for sure be in the air, boys - even Stan, the Gun Man (Sperl), Waukesha, Wisconsin comes up with a Poem: "There once was a fellow named Swifty...Who decided to reload to be thrifty... But he's in heaven you see...For in loading some .243...he used Bullseye in place of 4350." Me, I am all for this poetry business, tra la tra la. Just show me a gun builder who isn't a poet and an artist at heart and I'll show you a gun maker whose stocks would make better gate props, whose fleur-de-lis in his checkering look like ruptured acorns and the general lines of his stocks could easily be mistaken for pregnant garter snakes!! Ya gotta have beauty in your heart or it won't show in your work! Maybe you'll growl and snarl to hide it - but it's there. Horrors!!
- *Bob B.*

DIRTY COMPETITION, SKUNKS, & YELLOW DOGS

A bit of real home-spun philosophy that struck pay-dirt - every one of us should print it on a card and hang it on the wall for all to see -- and to guide us when we start to do something in the way of retaliation, which we shouldn't. Happened thus: -

Walter Howe, past Editor of *The Rifleman* , and I were doing some visiting about some other matters and somehow we got to discussing that occasional, one in a thousand customers who makes you want to take up hash-slinging. You know, the guy who is so downright damned ornery that no matter what you say or do, he keeps right on acting like a she-wolf with one teat caught in a bear trap. I made the remark that right about then I would blow my stack and say something I might regret. "Well," said Walter, "My pappy always told me it was a mistake to get into a peeing contest with a skunk. No matter how hard you tried, you always lost." Man, how true - fighting price-cutters, dirty competition - you name it. A skunk will out stink you every time.

My pappy always had two comments in that direction -- "Better to have a yellow dog your friend than your enemy." And - "When you declare a vendetta dig two graves: one for yourself and one for the other guy." You know, when one stops and thinks about it, it's amazing how smart our old men were--!

- *Bob B.*

THE BRAND NEW AND IMPROVED

Sometimes we around here wonder if we might have holes in our heads. We refuse to take on every new item that shows up on the market and never do jump up and down and holler "Yoiks and Huzzah!" when someone announces they have made vast improvements on some standby piece of goods you guys like. Such things sorta give me cold robbies around my gizzard but never could put it into words. Once, a while back, Frank Bryan, our local fixit-upper and TV salesman/repairman was out putting a new tube in our then rather ancient set. "You know, Bob," he said, "I could talk trade with you but I haven't the guts. They have made so many vast improvements on TV sets since you bought yours that right now they're only about one-half as good as this one you've got." Them is my sentiments exactly, only Frank managed to get it into the right succinct words. Too many times us humans feel that if it is "new" and "different" it MUST be better. It just isn't that-a-way a-tall.

Darned if I know what brought on the above burst of philosophy! Was just sitting here thinking and that came out. Somebody I was reading once said - either Toynbee or William Foxwell Albright (and if you can understand everything Albright says you gotta better grasp of the English language than my unabridged dictionary!) - that anytime a civilization starts living on its past, it is doomed. Now, do you suppose that makes a doomed race if we insist on quality? If so, Okay, me for one is doomed!! Core, better get off this track before I get us in so deep neither of us understands what I am saying.

- *Bob B.*

READING BOOKS AND MAGAZINES

Been reminded recently about the subject of reading books in order to learn more about the trade as one goes along. When I went away to college my pappy talked to me about many things but mostly I remember his words: "Study it thoroughly and don't try to remember it word for word...Learn to remember that you read the answers and, if possible, where." At different times Walter Howe, past Editor of *The American Rifleman* and author of *Professional Gunsmithing*, and I have discussed this reading business. I think a paragraph in a letter from him the other day hits the nail squarely:

"I have found that there are more than a few gunsmiths and professional gun dealers who don't even read *The Rifleman* through and there is certainly information of one sort or another in there for gunsmiths. Not everything he needs to know, to be sure; however, even at that there are not as many gunsmiths as I believe there should be who read the books on gunsmithing. Many gunsmiths, both amateur and professional, continue to try to learn everything the hard way. They just simply haven't gotten around to learning that it is much better to spend a couple of hours reading something than it is to spend days or years in ignorance.

"Gunsmiths often give the excuse that they haven't got time to read -- and they probably haven't according to the way they work. Nonetheless, unless they take time out to read they will certainly have less time to read. That may sound rather awkward but it means just that. As you and I very well know, doctors, lawyers, engineers, and of course others of that plane go to school not only to acquire immediate knowledge needed for their professions but to learn how to look for information and to realize that they cannot possibly commit to memory more than a fraction of what they need to know. Nevertheless, they are taught and if they acquire this knowledge in depth, they profit."

Walter couldn't be righter if he tried!!

- *Bob B.*

A GUNSMITH'S STUDY WITHOUT BOOKS IS LIKE A ROOM WITHOUT A WINDOW

This might stir up a ripper of a Hurrah! but I seriously believe that a bunch of well read books, both past and current, are about as good an indication of what's going on inside a gunsmith's head as the number of tools and pieces of equipment scattered on the floor and walls of his shop. There isn't a one of us (or group of us!) in this game who can possibly know the many, many things so vital to successful gun work. Walk into a top flight lawyer's office or doctor's office and the first thing you see are shelves and shelves of mighty well thumbed books - and stacks of current books and magazines devoted to his profession. One of the secrets to knowing a lot of answers is to rely, thru good books, on the research carried on by many others - some of whom have devoted a lifetime to covering just one subject.

The *Gun Digest* is a good example. Edited by John Amber, its contents consist of the work of many of the leading writers in their particular field. Me, I have a complete file of *The Digest* (and Years of *The Rifleman*) right beside my right ear - and every one of them is darned well used. When a new issue comes out I read it thru and then put it on the shelf. Soon a question comes up and I get to knocking around in my head wondering "where in blue blazes did I see the answer to that one?" Generally can remember whether it was in the pile of *Rifleman's* or *Digests* - so dig them out and start thru - and there it is!
    - *Bob B.*

BOOKS, BACK ISSUES & BUSINESS

Author, Editor and Noted Sage - E. B. "Bev" Mann

More years ago than I care to admit, a man I very much admired made a remark I have never forgotten. I was complimenting him on his seemingly infallible knowledge of the subjects on which he wrote. I said, "You must have a marvelous memory!"

He said, "I've got a lousy memory! But I've got a fine library. A man who knows how to read can be an expert on almost any subject if he just knows what facts he needs, and where to find them."

I sometimes wonder if a lot of dealers in guns and shooting equipment aren't missing some bets (and some profits) by failing to give that remark some study. Nobody in the world knows all there is to know about guns and shooting -- the field is too broad, too complex, and (let's face it) too controversial. But unless you live in a community different from the ones I know, your customers expect you to know it all. They'll come to you for everything from assurance that the rusty sixgun they picked up from an unsuspecting old lady for four pesos is truly a Walker -- to "What velocity will I get from a 163-grain gold plated, boat-tailed stove bolt ahead of forty-leven grains of No. 606 powder in a Remchester Ring-necked Whizzer rebored to .237 caliber, using match-heads for primers?" And you, buster, better come up with the answer! Right? So what do you do?

I'll tell you what I do when readers write letters to the Editor asking questions like that -- and they do, brother; they surely do! What I do is -- I look it up in a book! Like the man said, I've got a good library...and long practice has made me fairly good at dodging questions not even the books can answer. (Of course, the guy with the four-dollar Walker needs special handling. You can always tell him it doesn't look quite like the Walker you picked up off a junk heap in Puxatucket back in the thirties, but -- maybe yours isn't a Walker, either.)

What I'm driving at is that, in my considered opinion, every man in the gun business, in whatever capacity, should own a book. If he's as dumb as I am, he should own a hundred! And he should also own consecutive files dating back to about the time of the Spanish American War of every gun publication in the business -- especially mine, but even including my competitors! (Big-hearted, that's what my friends call me! I can even see some good in those 'Brand X' journals!)

What's more, he should read them. This doesn't mean trying to commit them to memory. All you need to do is to become familiar enough with your books to know which book is likeliest to hold what answers. The magazines are less easy to cross-index in your memory, but they are often even better than the books if only because they are more current. Let some egghead bust loose with a new wildcat and you're sure to get a rash of questions about it. The answers won't be published in books until next year, if ever; but the magazines will have printed the story. Your problem is to remember which magazine, and what issue. A secretary or clerk with time on her hands (the one that's spending so much time in the washroom) can solve that problem by cross-indexing the issues on 3x5 cards. It's easy if it's done as the issues appear; and a card file like that can make you look like a genius when that customer pops his question.

You think looking like a genius is unimportant? Let me tell you a story:

Last winter, I was yakking with a gaggle of gun nuts, and something that was said reminded one hombre that he was fresh out of 130-

grain fodder for his .270. He said, "If tomorrow's a decent day, guess I'll drive up to Joe Whosit's and buy me a couple o'boxes."

I said, "Joe Whosit's? That's fifty miles, any way you slice it."

He said, "Sure. I always buy my stuff from Joe. You know somethin' - I never yet asked Joe a question he didn't answer! The guy knows more about guns than John Browning!"

I said, "Come to think of it, I need a few boxes of .22 rimfires. I'll go with you. Maybe the man can tell me which kind I ought to buy."

The guy gave me one of those looks -- you know the kind: "Is this guy a kook, or did I miss something?" But I went with him; and you know what I found? Right! Joe had a library, almost as good as mine. He didn't give me any low-down on .22 rimfires that would shoot nothing but Xs, but he confirmed a lifelong conviction. Namely, that genius is mostly a matter of knowing where the facts can be found! Joe knew. What good does it do him? Well, in this case, the profit on a couple of fair-to-middlin' pieces of business. Because, you see, my buddy and I bought, not only the bits and pieces we wanted, but a considerable passel of things we didn't know we wanted till Joe told us. That's the way with us gun moguls: easy come, easy go.

Joe had some other things, along with his genius. For a little old store on a back street in a not-very-big town, he had a fine inventory. Walk in and ask for almost any reasonable piece of gun equipment, and Joe's likely to have it. But he had a hidden weapon there, also. A tall filing cabinet in his back-room office is full-to-bustin' with catalogs. Old catalogs, new catalogs, Joe's got 'em. He's got something else too that some gun dealers seem sometimes to lack -- and that's a willingness to do business! Joe is more than willing; he's even downright eager. You want something Joe hasn't got? "I'll get it," says Joe, quick and emphatic. "You want it soon? I'll phone for it -- likely have it tomorrow."

He will, too. He'll phone, while you're right there in the store. And if you say, "What's strange about that?" I'll be sorry I'm giving you all this wisdom! You know what's strange about it. An awful lot of gun dealers (I hope not you, but plenty I've encountered) don't like special orders. If they haven't got it, why should you want it?

But you do want it...and tell me, if you will, what's wrong with a profit on a sale you can make with no more investment than a phone call or a letter? Not the only reason, but one of the reasons for your distributor's existence is -- to stock stuff you can't afford, or haven't room, to carry. Mr. Bell (I think it was Mr. Bell, though the Russians claim it) invented a gadget that makes your distributor a next-door partner in your business. Distributors are all filthy rich, wiser than Soloman, and big-hearted. He's got all the stuff you haven't money enough to stock, is so wise that he's stocked stuff you wouldn't have thought of if you'd had the money -- and he's in business solely to help you make a profit. Call him!

Seriously, why is it that some dealers sluff off the special-order buyer? I'm damned if I can understand; but I know it happens. The times it has happened to me, I haven't gone back to that dealer. There's an old saying, "The customer is always right," and that's silly. You and I both know that the customer can be a jerk. But if he's a jerk with money, money he wants to spend, and you don't get it...who's stupid?

There's a thing these days called Public Relations. Cynics say it's just another name for Salesmanship. They're right. Public relations is salesmanship a la mode -- you know: with ice cream on top. It's the best way in the world to sell pie!

Public relations is making the public think you're a wonderful guy, a smart guy, and a guy whose sole aim in life is to make Mr. (and Mrs.) Public happy. That kind of public relations can be the difference between being a prosperous gun merchant and wishing you were driving a bulldozer. With a bulldozer, you could at least plow some of your competitors under!

But before you go out and buy a bulldozer, consider buying a book. It's cheaper; you could buy a hundred and still have money left for magazine subscriptions. Catalogs you can get for free. Dust off that telephone. And last but most important -- dust off those old antiquated assets called manners! Manners is 90 per cent being kind, and being kind is 90 per cent showing an interest in other people's problems. His problem is what bullet with what load in what gun? Look it up in your books and magazines. His problem is he wants something you haven't got? Look it up in your catalogs, and get it. So he's stupid to want it? So you can laugh at him -- on your way to the bank. That's what Joe Whosit does...

And you know something? I've been back up to see Joe several times lately; sort of got into the habit of buying my stuff there. After all, 50 miles is not far; just a pleasant outing. The wife enjoys it... And, damn it, she's bought some stuff from Joe, too. I never should have let her see that neat little over-under -- that is, see the picture. Joe didn't have it...but he got it! That guy is a genius!

- *E. B. "Bev" Mann, Editor* GUNS *Magazine,* GUNS ANNUAL, SHOOTING INDUSTRY

GUNSHOP LOCATION

Just read your article about gunsmiths moving out of town and thought you'd like to know I took that move back in '45 -- We were set up on Main St. where nobody could park and no lady cared to carry Pa's gun into us for fixin'. So we set up here where we have half a block of parking area, and does it make a difference!! Our shop is very small, so our customers can sit in their cars in the parking lot and shoot the Bull and let us work.

- *Slim Spears, Hutchinson, Kansas*

WORDS OF WISDOM

Someone once asked an industrial tycoon if there was a key to success. "No," quoth he, "I know of no key to success. There is one sure key to failure, however, and that is: Try and please everyone."

- *Bob B.*

IF YOU ARE PLANNING ON BUILDING A NEW GUNSHOP

From a newspaper clipping:

"Harold Hoffman's Gun Shop Burns"

"The Harold Hoffman Gun Shop one mile west of town was completely destroyed by fire Tuesday afternoon. Nothing was saved from the building.

"Harold had only resumed his gun business about three months ago following another burnout. His new steel building replaced the frame building destroyed by lightning last winter.

"The amazing thing about Tuesday's fire, which also carries a warning to all who own factory-insulated steel buildings, is the fact that it was the insulation on the inside walls of the building that caught fire. Harold was drilling out a gun barrel and a hot shaving hit the insulation. Harold says he only had time to shut off the electric motor before the interior of the building was ablaze. He dashed out the door through a wall of flame and was lucky to escape with his life.

"Besides losing all of his own equipment and supplies, guns from a number of states, the Bucklin American Legion firing squad rifles, and guns of local sportsmen were lost, plus all of Harold's records. Firewatchers were treated to a second Fourth of July when the ammunition exploded as the building burned.

"It will be interesting to follow the insurance settlement of this fire. The question most asked is whether a building manufacturer can line his structure with an apparently highly flammable material. Unless Harold's building was an exception, a very dangerous situation exists in every similarly built building."

- Harold lives at Bucklin, Kansas, and has been trading with us for Lo! these many years. Fire, I think, is the universal nightmare of all of us in the gun business. To go thru two of them in such a short time is asking just too damned much -- especially when you've just built a new building that would "look" like it could never burn. Would be a most sound idea to test out insulation with your gas torch before installing it. The rest of us can learn a valuable lesson from Harold's bitter experience.

- *Bob B.*

BUSY SEASON SIGN

Busy season sign that might be hung above your bench: "Your decision to speak in no way influences my desire to listen."

Sales to Legitimate...We've a sign on our street door which reads: "Sales to legitimate dealers and gunsmiths only." This has given rise to a lot of comment and a lot of wags have wanted to know just what we are driving at with that "Legitimate" business. To all of this I've had just one answer: "Perfectly obvious! We just don't do business with bastards!"

- *Bob B.*

"ACCURIZE YOUR GUNS WITH ACRAGLAS"

Remember when selling Acraglas to use the above phrase - "Accurize your Guns with Acraglas". Never, NEVER, use the phrase "Plastic Bed your guns". When you convince your trade that you actually are Accurizing their guns when you bed them in Acraglas, you are making the gun better because you are smarter. And this is a most desirable way to have the customer think about you. If you talk about "plastic bedding" the customer is most likely to think you are actually covering up sloppy inletting or mistakes...!!

- *Bob B.*

NOTES ON ADVERTISING

The other day Phil Ekern, who runs the Our Own Hardware at Flandreau, South Dakota, sent along a copy of his ad in their local paper. At first glance you never saw such an affair - hunting and fishing and picture-taking yarns worked in with things he was advertising that week. But darned if I didn't read it all the way thru. Says Phil, "The surprise comes when you learn that the returns from this little effort is much greater than from any fine display work of art I've ever run. Nobody, but nobody, reads those display ads in spite of what the ad experts tell you. But from these ads I get fabulous readership and generally sell out soon on the items mentioned very casually. I've had people from all corners of the county come to see a catfish you southerners would throw rocks at, it's so small. Today a farmer called to invite me out to try for a movie on his farm - over 100 deer were bedded down in his creek bottom.

"It would be my suggestion that any dealer you have would profit greatly from a little story each week in the paper or advertiser. Like your newsletter it takes a little time, but so does a well thought out display ad. And if they can get the paper to cooperate, the deal sure pays. Mine is an old and feeble typewriter but the editor tries to correct the spelling and punctuation." (Note from Bob B. - a lot of our customers do have weekly columns in their papers - and all report the same kind of success as Phil. Darned near 100% of you who write me letters about this & that could write excellent reading stuff for your local paper, work in your goods for sale, and have everybody enjoy it!)

- *Phil Ekern, Flandreau, South Dakota*

WATCH THAT AD!

As you who read this Newsletter know, we never recommend anyone's work. The prime reason for this is the fact I can make some horrible "misteaks" in what I sometimes say and get everyone in trouble. Not so much errors in facts but in typing or spelling - like that old whizzer where the guy ran the ad in his local paper: - "FOR SALE, slightly used farm wench in good condition. Very handy. Phone 2456. Charlie Smith." The next day the newspaper printed a correction: "Due to an unfortunate error, Mr. Smith's advertisement last night was not clear. He has an excellent winch for sale. We trust this will put an end to jokesters who have called Mr. Smith and greatly bothered his housekeeper, Mrs. Jones, who lives with him." ...The following day, this ad appeared: "My winch is NOT for sale! I put a sledge hammer to it. Don't bother calling 2456. I had the phone taken out. I am not carrying on with Mrs. Jones. She merely loves with me. Charlie Smith."

- *Bob B.*

DURING YOUR IDLE MINUTES

During your idle minutes between now and then do some serious thinking about your advertising program...AND THEN ADVERTISE. Get a simple set of books, find out what's making you money and what isn't - and then promote the moneymakers...but never forget: Sell Yourself, YOUR NAME, to your trade and not the name of some outsider who probably doesn't care one whoop in hades if your shop keeps or not, so long as he gets his. If you do gunsmithing on a part-time basis, remember it is difficult when serving two masters not to love one and hate the other -- try to love the one (gun work) and at least tolerate your regular job and do your best for your boss...the guy's gotta live, you know.

- *Bob B.*

MORE BUSINESS

In our own shop we receive business from all over the U.S. and Puerto Rico, most of which is a direct result of advertising. I believe that if most gunsmiths would place a small classified ad in their local paper they would be amazed at the results. Not only lets people know where you are, but gets you a share of the cream business such as trades, sight, scope and accessory sales...and a GOOD business card is a MUST.

- *Northeast Gun Exchange, Indianapolis, Indiana*

DIRECT MAIL FOR YOUR SHOP

Last summer, Charles Davis sent us a copy of a letter he mailed out to the sportsmen in his trade area. It was a very nice bit of advertising and couldn't help but do him a lot of real good. Would like to quote parts of it for many of you could well do the same for yourselves this coming year:

It starts out "Dear Sportsmen" and goes as follows: "You wanted and you have admirably supported a gun shop in West Chester. Thanks to your patronage and ever increasing business, I am moving to a bigger and better location at the Food Fair shopping center on East Gay Street.

"You will have free, unlimited parking. Repair work will be speeded and more of the items you like to see and examine will be on display... As usual, the line will be 100% guns and related items such as reloading supplies, tools, gun racks, cabinets, gun books and magazines and police supplies...Service and workmanship will be the highest and best that we can make it..."

Charles then goes ahead and introduces his help, their abilities and such and ends up: "We are anxious to help and talk with the boy or girl who is buying their first single shot .22, and of course we will be glad to hear of the experiences of those old timers who have hunted in Canada and Africa or perhaps outshot the Nation's finest on the rifle and pistol ranges at Camp Perry...If you have gun problems, come out and see us. Come out anyway and inspect the new shop. Hope you like it and we sure will appreciate your continued patronage..." end of quote.

There are certain cardinal rules one must always follow in direct mail promotion - and I believe the above sticks to every one of them. First of all the rules are Sincerity and an Absolute Belief in what you are saying or selling. It has been my own experience that if you don't honestly believe it yourself you cannot make others believe it, no matter how you dress up your words - nor how many you write. That old sincerity always seems to shine thru and rub off on your readers. You might be wrong, but if YOU believe it, others will.

My father has said many times: "Son, if you want to hunt rabbits, go where there are rabbits. And if you want to shoot a sparrow don't be using a 12-gauge shotgun when a .22BB will do the job." These two bits of homespun philosophy are certainly true when promoting your own business in your own locality. The big ad in the large circulation local newspaper is the shotgun blast to knock-off a sparrow. The direct mail approach to a select group of known potential gun shooting customers is doing your hunting where the rabbits are.

Now, I do not know how the sale of hunting licenses is handled in all states, but I do know that in many of them whole blocks of licenses are issued in book form to various outlets throughout the county. When these books are filled, the copies and monies are either turned over to the state game commission or the local county treasurer. After that happens, it is too late. But, if a guy were to become a bit better acquainted with the license sellers, it is quite possible one would be permitted to copy the names down, street addresses and all, just before the books were turned in. Man, them names are 10-carat diamonds and worth all the work they are to get. They are more than the 'rabbits' you were shooting at -- they are the Big Game. A couple of sincere, honestly written notes to them twice a year will do more good than all the blasting there is.

- *Charles Davis, West Chester, Pennsylvania*

MORE ON GUNSMITH DIRECT MAIL PROMOTION

It is too bad, but few businessmen indeed realize the great potential of direct mail advertising. This is particularly true of us in the gun business. Too many of us are prone to have a simple faith that the Good Lord above will keep our workbench loaded and our bank account mushrooming - with a bit of word-of-mouth advertising. This just 'aint' true as hundreds of us in the game find out each year by simply going broke.

For less than the cost of a couple of ads in your local paper (read by a few and tossed away by all come nightfall) you can get a direct mail piece into the hands of every hunter who bought a license in your county last year.

A simple, direct, well-written letter on your own letterhead, printed by photo-offset, telling your story will bring you more business than you ever dreamed possible.

For example, right after the first of the year mail out a letter to your trade area telling the boys this is the time of the year to be getting their fine guns cleaned and examined by an expert...minor repairs made, etc. And mention the things you are qualified to do for them.

- *Bob B.*

LETTERHEAD

Bob Brownell's Gun Shop (With a name like that he MUST be a real gentleman and scholar and judge of purty gals) has the following notation on the upper righthand corner of his business letterhead: "Fixed Guns Repaired"--!!

- *Bob Brownell's Gun Shop, Olathe, Colorado*

LETTERHEADS

Writes Ray A. Davis: "Take a look at this stationery. It is NOT flossy. It is expensive as hell. But, folks look at the envelope, and by gosh, they read the contents, and this happens because the stationery is outstandingly different. Some of the very small outfits like my-self who have to resort to direct mail to a customer list might get better results from a good greeting in the form of outstanding, attention demanding stationery instead of having their letters hit the deep-six box.

"From a 2% return from a selected mailing list I have jumped to almost 7% as a result of the new look. My printer is paid and the stuff is now working out a profit for me. SOOOOOOOO." End of Quote.

How right Ray is, only people in Direct Mail can know. I agree with him 1000%. He does have a beauty of a letterhead and it will demand attention for it looks like business. Anyone who writes a letter should take his advice to heart. It is $$$$ in the old poke.

- *Ray Davis*

MORE ABOUT LETTERHEADS

We get lots of business letters every day with some very attractive letterheads. Too often these letterheads do not have your personal name anywhere. If you do not have YOUR name on yours, write a great big note to yourself reminding you to get YOUR NAME on your letterhead next time you have some printed - and hang that note where you cannot possibly miss seeing it so's you won't forget. An attractive name for your store or shop is a mighty fine and important thing. Of even more importance: who the hell runs the joint! Stop and think a moment: do your customers come to you because they have trust in you, as a person, as a dealer, as a gunsmith? They trade with you because YOU are YOU and for no other reason under the sun. Your customers don't tell their friends "Go over to Old Hickory Hill Gun Shop"-- they tell them "Go over to Joe Blow, Old Hickory Hill something or other he calls his place, and get your stuff. He'll take good care of you."

- *Bob B.*

MAKING CHANGE

We in the gun business are of a very cautious and conservative nature. To illuminate this point, there was this gunsmith who was standing at the bank window very carefully counting and re-counting the money the teller had given him for a cashed check. The teller had been watching the gunsmith with growing concern. Finally he could stand it no longer. "What in the world is the matter," he asked, "didn't I give you enough change?" The gunsmith shook his head and looked at the money in his hand. "Wellll," he says, "Just barely."

- *Bob B.*

FOOD FOR THOUGHT

It is estimated that by 1980 there will be 60,000,000 more people in the U.S. than there are now - the 35 hour week will be a fact and not talk. Local, state and the federal governments will have purchased and turned into recreation areas millions of acres of timber and lakes. The average family income up 40% over what it is now - people, millions of people, will have time AND money AND the desire to do things out of doors. The man who is on the stick, prepares himself and his business; thinking towards this growing market will be building for himself a golden future. The knowing public will want service AND quality and be willing to pay for it - IF it is quality.

This is where YOU, as a craftsman, have it way over the discount operator: Quality craftmanship has never yet been found for sale in a discount house or by a discount operator. Build your reputation on Quality and Service - cut either and you have cut the string on your door-latch.

- Bob B.

GUNSMITHS AND TARGET SHOOTERS

Every once in a while you hear someone say they have been in a gunshop and seen a sign which reads something like this: "TARGET SHOOTERS - TAKE YOUR BUSINESS ELSEWHERE". Having been a gunsmith myself for several years I know exactly how this feeling of resentment comes about on the part of the gunsmith. During the last few years, however, a new controlling factor has entered the picture - one we cannot ignore. Namely: a vast increase in the number of gun owners and a game and varmint population which will not support a tenth of the shooters. So it is a matter of simple arithmetic: targets of one sort or another or else!

I have done a lot of thinking about the darned thing and am now commencing to wonder if the basic fault of the difficulties between gunsmith and target shooter isn't the gunsmith's. His fault for not having a fixed policy, a fixed minimum price and then, come hell or high water, sticking to it. Why not a sign something like this?

TARGET SHOOTERS — WE SOLICIT YOUR BUSINESS
LABOR CHARGES:-Min. Charge:-$3.00 Per hour. Charge, including discussion of adjustments and adjustments, $3.00 per hour.
FOLLOW-UP CHARGES: - Once the gun has left our shop follow-up adjustments are considered as new work and the above charges will be made. No Exceptions.

I have worked with a lot of target shooters and have found them, on the whole, about the nicest bunch of guys you could possibly ask to come into your shop. I did, however, run into the charging problem early. I immediately set a policy like the above and after the grumbling, howling and boycotts simmered down, our relations were even better than before! I ceased resenting their coming in and once they became used to paying their way they actually felt better about it and spent more.

The above doesn't apply to most of you, I know. You already have admirable relations with your shooters and have done work for them which has made champions out of them. There are enough "discontent-seeds" scattered around, tho, to cause troubles in certain areas. Maybe I'm clean off base with the suggestion - maybe the price per hour is too low or too high - maybe something else is the answer. But the point is: 99.9% of the target shooters are nice guys, they can make you money now and it is possible they will be your chief source of income in years to come.

Had an excellent letter along this line from Tom Blakemore, Chicago, Illinois -- He UP't his business 25% by going into target shooting sales last year!!

- *Bob B.*

SALES GIMMICK

Donald W. Lawson and wife Pat (a right sharp looking girl, but about her I am not so sure as she is most vociferous about menfolks reading the Newsletter) have a Latigo sling on swivels in their store window - fastened to the window sill. When someone comes in they work it right there in the window. Causes comment and sells slings.

- *Donald and Pat Lawson, Ijamsville, Maryland*

THE "ONE-TIME-USE DISPOSABLE" WEAPONS

One of the toughest jobs in our trade is convincing some of our customers that there is just no such thing as a gunsmith who can repair "every firearm" regardless of vintage or condition. The confusion is compounded when Mountaineer Joe can still get most anything he needs for his old model 94 Winchester - but some relatively new arms can't be fixed.

Experienced gunsmiths can readily recognize the "unfixables," but the average customer and many sporting goods dealers do not. Basically it is just a case of too many new production cost cutting angles, resulting from stiff competition at home and some foreign imports which we can call strictly "mickey-mouse." Some of these manufacturers have even eliminated parts sheets and their addresses. In one instance we tracked down the importer's address, only to be told their single action frontier style revolver parts would interchange with Colt parts.

This makes a fine sales pitch, but you'll have other ideas after trying to repair them. I've contended for many years that IF the makers of super low-priced weaponry (and for that matter other cheap products) were compelled to take care of all the angry customers, and actually keep such guns operating, they would ALL be bankrupt within six months or less. In many instances engineering designs lack much in strength and dependability, and no repairman can, nor should, be expected to rebuild a $30 economy piece into something that will compare with a $60 to $90 gun. Within the trade, many of us have even referred to certain of these items as a "one-time-use disposable" weapon.

Dealers who lack knowledge of the internal construction of low-priced guns can help themselves, the American manufacturers of better class guns, and their own potential customers by advising them of the questionable quality that accompanies many of the super-low-priced ones. The fact that a gun is new does not mean it works perfectly, or for that matter, can ever be changed to work right!

From a business standpoint, no gunsmith can afford to tinker for hours attempting to correct malfunctions on those "mickey-mouse" creations. After a certain amount of experience with this type of work we realize it is not only impractical, but downright foolhardy. Why? Because we always have other work to do, which we know can be successfully and profitably accomplished.

Another tough situation arises from the fact that many bargain guns are in production only a short time, spare parts are limited and soon unavailable. Even though they seemed to work acceptably for a while, and a gunsmith can make a new part, the original design weakness cannot be improved upon because there is no room for beefing up the new part. It is almost certain to break again, and your uninformed customer comes to the conclusion you're not a good gunsmith. So, why not tell customers the truth in the first place?

You may sell fewer guns, but you are certain to have less problems. The profit from a $60 to $90 rifle is better than a $30 cheapy, and it makes up the difference, saves you a lot of time and keeps your customers happier.

Going back to Mountaineer Joe's old model 94 Winchester, you can tell customers that over 3,000,000 of them were made, and the reason it is still repairable, is that almost all the parts are still available. It was engineered and all-steel constructed almost beyond improvement.

- *William Schumaker, Reprinted by special permission from* THE SHOOTING INDUSTRY, *October, 1968*

SELLING MORE STOCK FINISH

You might be interested to know that we are selling G-B gunstock oil to the ladies to refinish antique walnut and other hard wood furniture. Works beautifully and takes three or four bottles for a dresser -

not a bad sale! (Here in Iowa we sell the 4-H girls much Tru-Oil for the same purpose! - BB)

    - *Phil Ekern, Flandreau, South Dakota*

MARK THOSE BOXES

I buy me up a whole bunch of those little address stickers you see advertised and have my shop name put across the top in capital letters and the address underneath. Then, I stick one on every box of ammo and on every other accessory I sell.

You can buy a thousand of the labels for a buck, and how could you ask for better - or cheaper - advertising!

    - *Ralph Walker, Selma, Alabama*

GUNSTOCK LAMPS

Found a way to salvage fouled-up stocks or old stocks and make a few bux on the deal.

I take the stock and cut if off at the magazine - or use the butt end of a shotgun stock - then put a really nice high finish on it, mount it on a nicely finished wood base and have me a desk or TV lamp that is a real dilly. I've sold a bunch of these in the past and they also make real good trophys at smallbore meets.

(Note from Bob B. - Personally, I think a lot of damaged or bad stocks with good figure in the butt could be used this way. A lot of gunnut/gunsmith wives would delight in buying one for their husbands. Said wimmin have one H of a time finding burthd'y presents for their lords and masters...and anybody whot liked guns would like one of these beauties!)

    - *Bob Black, Birmingham, Alabama*

WORKING WITH THE KIDS

We have an idea for advertising that has paid off for us which may be useful to other gunsmiths who do not have to depend on their shops for all their living. When we first started in 1947, we repaired the gun of any kid under 16 free of charge except for parts at cost. This included mounting scopes, sights, etc. We are still doing this and it has brought quite a few fathers, uncles, and friends, into our shop. The kids just can't keep their mouths shut especially when you tell them not to tell the other kids you did it for nothing. The first time we tried this, we had 7 broken guns that day ranging from B-B rifles to 12 ga. single shots. It tapered off after the first couple of days and now most of the kids come prepared to pay. We hope to collect on this program after their 16th birthdays, and in most cases, do. We do make a charge to these kids but no $$$ involved. It is:

KEEP THE WEAPON CLEAN. RESPECT IT. Then a very short

lecture on safety and respect for other peoples' property. This charge is always well received and we like to feel we actually have money in the bank. The actual cash may be in some farmer's pocket or the Bell Telephone Company through less property damage - but it is there just the same.

- *Bob Landon & Dick Taylor, Middletown, Pennsylvania*

APPRENTICESHIP PROGRAM

Writes Roy Dunlap, he's the man who wrote *Gunsmithing* which you should all read. "Regarding the boy wanting to be a gunsmith, apprentice, etc. I have written him the following dope: Apparently it is not well known that the United States has had a full apprenticeship program since 1937. The Fitzgerald Act, Public Law 308, covering everything up to and including gunsmithing, administered by state labor set-ups (in Arizona a four-year 8,000 hour deal) the salary being paid is slightly over $300 per month, this salary being paid partly by the employer, partly by the government, on a sliding scale -- when the boy starts, the employer pays only a few cents an hour; as he gains in skill and value to the employer, the latter's share of the paycheck goes up and the government's goes down until in the fourth year, the gunsmith is paying practically the full wage. Information should be available from the various directors of State Employment Services, no doubt reached just by writing state capitols. The apprentice should be careful and investigate possible employers carefully, of course. Some look for cheap help, teach little, may not have sufficient equipment or working room to do a decent job; big shops might teach production machine work, etc."

- *Roy Dunlap, Tuscon, Arizona*

FACE COOLER

When you are on the range or fishing and a mosquito bites you on the cheek, chomp your teeth down on his proboscis. Hold him thus and the breeze from his wings will cool you for hours. Warning - don't do this with the mature one tho, for their biters might go on past your teeth and probe your tongue!

- *Bob B.*

SCOPES & SHOTGUNS

In this day and age of rifled slug/shotguns shooting laws in many states, a lot of you are making a great mistake in not promoting the use of scopes on such guns. This would not be a gimmick nor would you be selling your customer something he doesn't need. A little demonstrating, a little knowledge to pass on, plus a wee bit of effort on your part, will not only sell YOU on the idea, but your shotgun trade as well. Here's my argument:-

FIRST:- Making a slug hit a given point on running or standing game takes EXACTLY as much aiming with a shotgun as with a rifle - maybe more. Shotgun shooters forget they do NOT have a 40" pattern with a slug!!

SECOND:- It requires less skill and less aiming, to put a bead on a hoped-for point of impact with a scope than with open sights.

THIRD:- With a 1X scope you are faster than with a peep sight -- with a little practice, that is. With open or peep sights you must FOCUS the rear sight, the front sight, and the game. If you don't, you miss. A scope does it ALL for you.

FOURTH:- When it is raining or dark you will see just as well with a scope (probably much better) than with open sights. Have you ever tried to find your front sight against a well concealed deer in dark cover -- then tried something similiar with a scope and found how well the game stood out?

Says Francis L. Grimes (Sr.), Almond, New York. - "We have used slug-guns for the past 20 years and they work out OK up to about 80 yards but sighting has always been a problem...Without sights some of the boys used to take the birds from turkey shoots with 5-shot, 10" groups at 65 yards...Then we started putting on peep sights about 12 years ago and the groups dropped to 7" and the going at the shoots got tougher...We are now just starting to get them going on scopes. I personally thought the installation of a scope on a shotgun was highly questionable until last fall. Had a 20-ga. Ithaca 37, stuck on a Buehler mount, a 4X scope...and at 65 yards poked 5 shots into 3-1/2". Convinced me plenty." End quote...

Personal suggestion: I wonder, for fast brush shooting, if the 1X wouldn't be best?

Why this talk on scopes for shotguns? To make you guys some more money. As is, the shotgun shooter who uses his squaw gun for deer isn't making you a penny, so to speak. With a bit of promotion you can sell him on the scope idea - as well as a sling. Not a lot of profit - but more than you are making now, huh?!! So why not attach a scope to one of your demonstration guns, have some of your customers try hitting a target at 75 yards with the scope and without the scope? Get a couple or three guys sold and you should sell most of the rest.

- *Bob B.*

SPEAKING OF INVENTORIES

Read an article the other day, can't remember where unless it was in *Dun's Review* magazine, to the effect that something like 65% of all business failures were caused by improper inventories -- and most of those sad situations were brought about when the companies being studied made a little extra money and bought too darned much of the wrong thing. If they had followed their usual custom of cautious buying they might not have gone busted. So darned easy to get to feeling "rich" and think, "Man, I am tired of being out of that item. This time I am going to buy enough to last awhile." Famous last words, huh? Me, I am a firm believer in "You can't do business from an empty shelf" but that can be carried too far...An amply filled shelf is so darned much better than one that is a bit too full.

The big successful mail order houses such as Sears and Wards make a thorough study of what they are going to need for a certain period. They then buy exactly half of that for immediate delivery, contract for one-fourth of the total and figure on taking a gamble on locating the other one-fourth if they need it. A pretty sound policy to follow after you've given it a bit of study...

- *Bob B.*

WATCH THAT INVENTORY TURN OVER...

A while ago I got into a big discussion about carrying profitable items - and what is inventory turn-over. As a matter of information, the sporting goods industry held the dubious honor of being third highest on the Dun & Bradstreet list of bankruptcies one month. A lot of this is due to a poor understanding of the importance of profit and a misunderstanding of what inventory turn-over actually is.

Too many times too many of us (I do it once in awhile without thinking) will take our total gross sales and divide that by our end of the year inventory and say we had turned our inventory so many times. Nothing could be further from the truth. In all probability there were many items in that inventory that did not turn even once during the year and other items that might have turned dozens of times. And again too often, many times those fast turning items are low or non-profit items - so the guy wakes up busted without ever knowing what was happening to him or why.

It never ceases to amaze me to walk into a sporting goods store and discover that the dealer is carrying in a prominent place on his shelves, items that carry a stupidly low discount. I can think of one line of items sometimes carried, that carries only a 15% discount less transportation - in other words, no profit at all. A pure loss. Yet, there are other items of the same type (and of better quality) which carry 33-1/3% to 40% profit.

A couple of years ago I told a customer of ours, to his face, that he had lost all his rocks for carrying the stuff, and named names. Boy, did it make him mad. A few months later (14 to be exact) he was back on the assembly line turning nuts and people were suing him for their accounts. To this day he doesn't know what happened.

Profit itself is not enough. You MUST be carrying an item that will turn several times a year or no matter how long the profit, you are losing money on it, for the money you have tied up in that item could well be invested in something that will turn faster and make you profit and not loss. Do this: go over your inventory and closely check every last item you have. If it is not making you a GOOD profit and is not TURNING several times a year in season, sell it for whatever-the-hell you can get out of it and put that money into something which will sell and make a profit. There just hain't no such thing as being in business for the fun of it, unless you had a millionaire uncle who just died and left you all - and even that won't last you forever.

Remember, we are in a position to not only see a lot of guys make great successes in the gun business - we also see a lot go on the rocks every year...

- *Bob B.*

NOBODY'S GOTTA TRADE WITH NOBODY

Twenty or more years ago Bill Pitka, our local Ford dealer, told me the following story. I've told it many times and even tried to take a real lesson from it. Many others could well do the same. ---"One morning during the first week on the first job I ever held," said Bill, "a fellow came into the garage and bought a part. I didn't know him and thought I knew the price so billed him for it without looking it up. I way overpriced it and he called me on it. I figured we were the only Ford garage in town, that he had to buy it from us, so I wouldn't back down. He threw the part on the counter and told me off in no uncertain terms and drove to another town for it. During the day my boss found out about it. He called me in the office and dug out that man's purchase record. 'Bill,' he said, 'here is your week's salary of $15. I want you to take it and go home and not come back until next week. Last year I made $75 off that man and if you hadn't come to work for even today I'd have been $60 ahead.'" End of lesson.

- *Bob B.*

OPEN ACCOUNTS AND BANKRUPTCY

Maybe some of you have wondered why we are so insistent that all accounts be paid up and wondered at our wisdom when we get a bit nasty about it. Here is a case in point: A very close friend of mine who is also a competitor had to close up his business recently. Fifteen thousand dollars would have put him back on his feet and in current position with his suppliers but he couldn't raise it. And here is the sad part: he has $30,000.00 on accounts receivable. Every time I think about him I feel sick. A devil of a fine fellow and in one of the country's best territories. To me that hain't about to happen...not that way, anyhow.

There are about 140 gun outfits per month that take bankruptcy, and to many of them one of two things happen: no control over overhead or too much on the books. It can happen to a guy so easy - and for just being a "good sport". Not only can it knock you for a loop to go broke, but it is a hardship on your family and the several families that depend upon you for their livings, too. So! Do not let too many people charge the stuff they get from you and, for Pete's sake, don't have any help around that isn't more than carrying their weight. It cost us a lot of money to get you on our mailing list, you know, and would hate like sin to get a note from Dun & Bradstreet saying you had to fold your tent and steal away - And us not hear from you no more - Nor you from us.

- Bob B.

JUST GETTING A FEW THINGS OFF MY CHEST

Well, it has been a long while since I last "gave you a line." Felt in such good trim last fall that I went wild up in Maine for almost a whole month with a Viger Indian for a companion a part of that time. We slept under the stars whenever the nightfall overtook us, weather permitted, and camp was inconvenient. Lived on game a lot- had a lot of amusement watching the various denizens of the wild; had some roistering laughs at the antics of some of the animals, like the doe that at fifty feet thought we were either a new specie of tree or a terrible dream and then got tangled up in some spruce whips when we didn't 'go away' and the look she gave us as she hoisted herself to her feet again to leave; the snowshoe rabbit that got tangled up in our gear one night and awakened us; the weasel that visited us the second night we used a same campsite and caught a shrew and a mouse nibbling at some camp scraps; and the beaver that slapped water all over my pal the day we kept tearing holes in a dam trying to get some good beaver pictures. Incidentally, I probably repeat myself, venison can get tiresome for a meat diet after a week of it without much else except canned army bread rations. I used up a full case of those armed forces bread rations, five hardtack crackers and two filled cookies in a can, this fall. It works fine and, surprisingly, one does not seem to tire of them. I can still sit down to a can of it and a bowl of stew or a nice medium steak. Sat right down and ordered in two more cases of it as soon as I returned home. Sure simplifies a lot of pack camp problems. In the same vein, a can of bread ration with a can of beans, chicken, sardines, kippers, tuna, viennas, meat product, bullion cubes, condensed soup, etc., makes a lunch that doesn't spoil, dry out, get stale, wet, or mashed for any occasion calling for a lunch that is easily transported; hunting, fishing, peak scaling, snow-shoeing, picture taking trips, or just being atavistic and taking for the open or back of beyond.

I suppose most every gunsmith must know about what alky will do for wood. Lots faster than water and heat, too. One of the best stock finishes I ever got I used up a part of a bottle of bonded 'Corn' that I couldn't get anybody to drink. Was it vile!!! Worst 'corn' I ever bot.

Denatured alky is one of the handiest liquids about a shop. It will raise grain, clean up filth, burn, thin shellac and some stains, dry up water in a hurry, and can even be used for a coolant in some instances.

Hell, I read the instructions once or twice that come with some preparation and then throw them away. I wonder, after reading about Oxpho, how many things I am doing with it that were never on the label. Got a beautiful blue-black finish on a case hardened receiver the other day with Oxpho and an Acetylene flame for just a little heat. Don't heat it so hot it will sizzle. My bottle has been around for a long time and is getting low, will have to reorder some day, come spring probably.

Speaking of smelling up your wife's pet kitchen; a 20# bottle of propane with a 6' hose and couple or three burner gas plate in the shop is a mighty handy piece of equipment. You can even warm your beans on it when you get thrown out of the house for some minor, to you, infraction; set an old spider or griddle on it for a little heat; and even take the whole outfit along on a picnic or an overnight camp for cooking and even a little heat.

You borrow the 20 pounder from your local propane supplier and pay him a couple of bucks for the contents. I might add that I have gotten rid of all gasoline camping equipment and use propane for cooking and lights. I have used a three burner stove and the 20# cylinders to prepare all the food for around 40 boy scouts on three different camporees, one a week's duration.

If your propane supplier is at all reasonable he will even get in some small cylinders holding 3.5, 8.9 or 12# that are right handy, 6"x16-1/2", 7-1/2"x22" and 27", instead of the 20 pounders and can be used around the shop for soldering, etc., at about 1/8th the cost of acetylene.

A torch handle and tip complete with a length of hose should not cost more than $12.50, or, if you buy the proper AGA hose for your plate in the first place, use that hose and save the major part of a saw-buck. The small tanks are called L-4, L-9 and L-12. Right along with this line, for the benefit of the boys using air-acetylene tanks, particularly the 'B' Prestolite, there is a small oxygen tank available to them for a more easily transported affair. They should contact their supplier for the small tank used for emergency cases of heart trouble.

You buy your tank the same as your 'B' tank and after that it is the same exchange as the 'B' or 'MC'. Some of your readers might be interested in this. It took me a long time to dig this out of my supplier.

Experience has taught me that each gun must have a 'trunk' type case built for it but that a 'trunk' for the whole outfit would not be practical. Some lose sight of the fact that 'trunks' are for shipping and such transportation and are not to replace the holster, scabbard, or other 'carrying' case. One carrying case may work for several guns and rifles but the carrying case was never made that will stand up under the abuse of shipping or other prolonged, severe transportation. Light 'trunks' of waterproof plywood have saved me hundreds of dollars thru the years from damage to guns and the ability to ship by economical transportation. With care, the trunk can be constructed so that it is impervious to moisture and so that the arm may be packed and stored for long periods of time, something that must be considered by any of the wanderers that hunt. I am finding an increasing market for such 'trunks'.

One other thing, it is not advisable to make a small 'trunk' for a pistol or other sidearm. I find that provision may be made in the long gun cases for the side arms, or that the side arms should all be 'Trunked' in a LONG case to avoid tampering, etc. I have never had a LONG case tampered with but have had three small cases tampered with and have lost one sidearm, as well as hearing of other similar instances. A bench saw, a box of screws, some waterproof glue, a piece of plywood and two hours time; I make it a practice to ship any custom job this way and so far have received no complaints on the charge. I use up cartons and cases that do not meet with my satisfaction for some reason or other for minor jobs being sent back. By the time I have put $3.00 in time and material into a case I know whether it will become a $10.00 job. Good shipping cartons cost enough so I am just as pleased to get rid of an unsatisfactory 'trunk' as use a carton. If you think the customer might complain about the price of the 'trunk' you can just include it in your labor cost and never mention it to him. Your own business acumen is your guide in the matter.

Ever consider how many times your shoulder gets wetted with tears during a year? When everything is rosy with a gun owner he stays away but the minute he misses a deer or grouse, or rabbit, he is in with a bucket of tears because, always, something is wrong with his gun - he is never to blame. He falls in the drink and sets the arm away to rust. 'The gun done it to him.'
- *Aathar D. Anderson, Richford, Vermont*

THE BIGGEST CATCH

"Dear Friend Bob," writes Harold Harten. "You ought to be down here. The fishing is so good that the fish almost come out on the bank and get the bait. Here a while back a couple of friends caught a deer on a hook and line. Well, really what happened -- it seems that this rancher friend had a pet deer that followed him down to the river every time he went fishing and when he got through fishing he would feed his extra minnows to the deer. This particular day the rancher and a friend got disgusted with the poor luck they were having and tossed their poles back on the bank. The minnow eating deer came up and took hook, line, sinker and minnow! And all got tangled up in the brush. The fellows heard a terrible ruckus and hurried up to see the poor deer all tangled up in the bushes. They finally got the poor boy untangled and the hook out. Some story, but it really did happen."

- Harold Harten, Lampasas, Texas

A FISHING REEL REPAIR SHOP IS A FITTING COMPANION FOR A GUN SHOP.

Why, you ask? Well, in many cases your reel customers are the same ones as your gun customers. Huntin' and fishin' go together like apple pie and cheese. And, if you have a well equipped gun shop - you already have all the hand-tools you will need to repair reels. Small screwdrivers, wrenches, pliers, files, drills, should be separated for exclusive use at the reel repair bench. Reel repairing will take up the slack during the off season for guns.

Don't let the lack of knowledge about the innards of a fishing reel worry you. Write each of the companies listed at the end of this article - preferably on your regular letterhead. Ask for "exploded" views, drawings, parts lists and prices with dealer discounts. I use a rubber stamp: "'SCHOOL BUS" REPAIR SHOP. All Types Fishing Reels Expertly Repaired.' This calls attention to the reel repair on my gun shop letterhead and the reverse side of my business card. And, by the way, the letterhead and business cards are a sound investment for any shop.

I get most of my work through a local sport shop. In fact, I even paid to run a small ad in the town paper:

FISHING REEL REPAIRS

Any Reel Repaired

TWO DOLLARS PLUS PARTS

Bob's Gun & Tackle Shop

Broken reels are left at Bob's shop. I pick them up, repair them and return with a bill for labor and parts. Bob collects the money from the customer and pays me. I don't have to meet the customer and Bob gets a chance to sell fishing gear. In a few instances the owner comes to me and we deal direct.

I won't forget the first spinning reel I cleaned and repaired. The two dollars labor fee averaged out to about two-bits an hour! Now I can turn one out in about thirty minutes.

I am still wrestling with the problem of stocking spare parts. I've hit on a rule-of-thumb. Let's say I have a reel that has a busted "gizmo". If this reel has a gizmo broken, chances are I'll get another in the same shape. The Company gives me a 50% discount (not unusual) so I buy two gizmos and put one in stock. Many reels have common parts in several models so I'm fairly sure of using the extra, and the first customer paid for the spare. Maybe later, when I know more about the mortality of certain parts, I will stock up a little heavier. I also have found that broken parts of several Japanese reels are interchangeable with parts from some American reels.

Most reels come to me for one or both of two reasons - abuse and/or lack of proper lubrication. Why a sportsman will save his pennies and dimes until he can buy a thirty dollar reel and then throw it in the trunk of his car, beat it against a rock, drag it through the sand and never use a dimes worth of grease, is beyond me. So I don't ask why - I just repair and collect.

One important point to keep in mind is that you will run into left-handed threads more often in reel work than with guns. Also, you may get tangled up with metric threads and metric nuts. Foreign car parts houses handle metric socket wrenches. And regardless of what work I do on a reel, I clean the outside and polish the chrome before I return it to the customer. Makes him real happy and a living advertisement.

Be sure to build up a "goody" box of old, wornout reels and parts. When a good friend comes in and says, "Of course I want it fixed today. If I wanted it tomorrow I'd have brought it tomorrow," you can rummage through the old reels and usually come up with a workable part.

I go in for more paper work than most, but I believe it pays off. I tag each incoming reel with the owner's name, what's wrong and what work is wanted on one side. After work is completed, I put the charges on the back of the tag. I also make out a 3 x 5 card on each reel, including owner's name, address and phone number. I put down date received, date returned, work done, parts replaced and charges. In the fall, after the fishing season has closed, I take the names and addresses from the cards and drop a line to each customer, suggesting he bring his reels into the shop so they can be checked out for the following season.

One other gimmick I picked up from the watch repair trade. Inside the case of each reel, I scribe my initials and the number of the month and year--PA 5/6. The customer doesn't know it's there but it identifies and dates my work on the reel.

• • • • • •

Names and addresses of some of the leading reel companies:

Aladdin Laboratories (Perrine), 620 South 8th Street, Minneapolis, Minnesota 55810

Denison - Johnson, Johnson Park, Mankato, Minnesota 56001

South Bend (Quick), South Otselic, New York 13155

Shakespeare Co., Kalamazoo, Michigan 48900

Garcia - Mitchell, Alfred Avenue, Teaneck, New Jersey 07666

Penn Fishing Tackle Co., 3028 West Hunting Park Avenue, Philadelphia, Pennsylvania 19132

Bronson Reels, 630 North Matteson, Bronson, Michigan 49028

Martin Reel Company, Mohawk, New York 13407

Wright & McGill Co. (Eagle Claw), 1400 Yosemite, Denver, Colorado 80220

Feurer Bros., Inc., 77 Lafayette Avenue, North White Plains, New York 10603

Berkley & Co., Spirit Lake, Iowa 51360

Hurricane International (Jap Import), 70 Tenth Street, San Francisco, California 94103

A. E. Dunn & Co. (Jap Import), 335 West "G" Street, San Diego, California 92101

- *Paul Adams, Babbitt, Nevada*

CHAPTER 12

HUNTING & RELOADING

CARE AND FEEDING OF THE CARTRIDGE CASE

Paraphrasing slightly, everybody does something with cartridge cases but few people talk about them. And yet the case is a component fully as vital to the overall performance of the finished handload as the primer, powder or bullet.

You can buy empty cartridge cases, brand new, in most of the reasonably popular calibers. They may be supplied either primed or unprimed at little difference in price. Unprimed cases can be sent by mail, which is handy if you have to order from a distant source. This is not the important consideration it used to be since most of the larger retailers can now ship via United Parcel Service - a private concern which will cheerfully carry powder, primers and similar unmailable items for about the same cost as parcel post. If you're picking up new cases in the store, by all means, the primed variety is to be preferred. Note, though, that even empty unfired brass is not necessarily one hundred percent ready-to-use, as received. Usually the inner surface of the neck is a bit rough and the overall case length is sometimes found to be a bit over-long - not often, it's true, but frequently enough to bear checking. Empty unfired cases for pistol calibers, such as the .38 Special, usually will have to be passed through the neck expanding die of your reloading set to slightly bell the mouth for correct seating of the bullet. If your expander die carries the decapping pin and if the cases are ready-primed, you'll have to remove the decapping pin from the end of the expander plug until you have processed the new cases (after which it is, of course, replaced). The practice of punching out live primers is a risky one and is best avoided.

The overall length of the cartridge is a critical dimension and it should be checked before cases are loaded for the first time and periodically thereafter. Case length is not necessarily controlled by the sizing die, as is case diameter. In fact, cases can emerge from the resizing die a few thousandths of an inch longer than before sizing. The reason is that the expanding plug, being dragged back out the neck of the sized case, can stretch the case beyond permissible limits. The remedy for

excessive stretching is to use some sort of dry lubricant inside the case neck. This is particularly true of the "bottle-necked" cases such as the .30/06, .243 Winchester, et cetera. Generally speaking, oil-base liquid lubricants, such as case resizing lubes, should not be applied to the inside of the neck; if they are used, it should be sparingly. Oils tend to deactivate both powder and primers, and oil inside the cartridge can cause weak rounds or complete misfires. Accordingly, the best method of lubricating the inside of the case neck is to place a small amount of a suitable dry lubricant (finely powdered white mica, graphite or molybdenum disulfide) in a small container such as a shotglass and dip the case, mouth-down, into it just before sizing. This will also materially reduce the effort needed for the resizing operation.

When it comes to determining the proper length for the cartridge case, consult one or more reloading manuals, as available. You may find some degree or discrepancy in the specified dimension and you should not be unduly confused. Manuals are assembled, printed and published by human beings and a human being is prone to err. To give a couple of examples: If you happen to have a copy of the current (43rd) edition of the *Lyman Reloading Handbook*, refer to pages 144 and 145. You'll find the case length of the .38 ACP given as .894" - which is approximately correct (it can be as much as .900"). . .but the overall length of the loaded round is given as .405". This is obviously incorrect since the total length of the loaded round can't very well be less than half the length of the case itself. The overall length of the .38 ACP - as verified from factory loads - should be approximately 1.280.

Over on the facing page, the case length of the .38 Special is given as .894" (it should be 1.153 to 1.155 instead) and the overall length of the loaded round is given as 1.55" - which is correct. You may wish to enter these corrections in your manual.

The .22 Hornet is another caliber for which you can find contradictory dimensions. The correct case length for this caliber is 1.403 inch as measured from the face of the head to the mouth in the normal manner. However, the current *Lyman Reloading Handbook* shows a dimension of 1.403 from the front surface of the rim to the mouth, plus the rim thickness of .065; a total of 1.468 inch - which is incorrect.

Almost any reference source may contain errors to some varying degree (definitely including this present discussion!), so the prudent reloader will regard all published material with a somewhat skeptical eye; he will compare data to that given in other sources if it seems dubious and, when all is said and done, he will let his own good judgment be his final guide.

The best method for measuring the overall length of cartridge cases is by means of a good, accurate vernier caliper - if you happen to know how to read one, and if you don't, it's worth the bother to learn. Note that I stress that it must be an accurate caliper, preferably graduated in thousandths of an inch. The cheap calipers offered for ninety-eight cents or so at your local supermarket are worthless for such purposes; I've seen some of these which indicate one thirty-seconds-inch when the jaws are completely closed. A good vernier caliper costs between $10 and $20. One of these is not hard to read, once you master

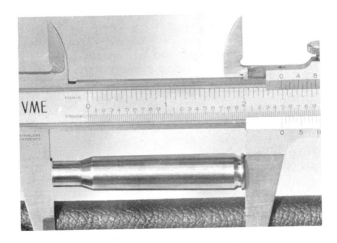

the knack, but it is somewhat difficult for most people to grasp the basic principle of its operation. There are various case length gauges available, some of which handle a single caliber, others usable for more than one. Lachmiller offers a gauge which can be converted to other calibers by simply interchanging an inexpensive piece of precision ground tubing. Wilson makes a combination gauge which measures both overall length and headspace of the fired cartridge; the version of this for the so-called "belted magnum calibers" such as the .308 Norma, .300 H&H, 7mm Rem. mag. et al, is offered with an adjustable collar to be precisely fitted to match the chamber dimensions of your individual rifle. The Wilson gauge measures for both minimum and maximum length. To some lesser degree, it is undesirable to have the cases too short since this permits a degree of wear and erosion in the chamber portion which is ordinarily protected by the neck of the case.

The big reason for guarding against excessive case length is that surplus brass in the neck is forced against the tapered fore-portion of the chamber and thus is tightly locked around the bullet, resisting its release for passage up the barrel at the moment of firing and vastly increasing the chamber pressure.

There are several methods and devices for trimming cases, many of which are excellent, and most of which are adequate. Personally, I use a Forster trimmer and find it fast, accurate and thoroughly satisfactory in every respect. I've had this machine for several years and long since have built up a complete set of pilots and collets for it along with reamers for most of the calibers I commonly reload. The reamers are particularly handy. You see, certain calibers have a tendency to thicken at the neck as the individual case is reloaded and fired a number of times. This has an effect similar to the one described for exces-

sive case length except that it is, if anything, more serious. There is ordinarily a few thousandths of an inch of "play" around the case neck when the round is in the chamber; this is normal, natural, and absolutely necessary. When the powder is ignited, the pressure of the burning gases expands the neck outward in all directions releasing the bullet so that it can start up the bore. If the neck is too thick, it fits tightly into the chamber, resisting release of the bullet and increasing chamber pressure to an undesirable, perhaps dangerous degree.

There is an easy test for cases which have developed excessive neck thickness. Simply insert a new bullet by hand into the neck of the fired case, **before** you resize it. If the case previously had been fired with a light squib load, the neck may not have been expanded. If the load was of normal power, the neck should be enough larger than bullet diameter to permit the base of the bullet to be inserted into the

neck with little or no effort. You may note, in the course of this particular test, that there is a pronounced constriction at the mouth of the case, but not deeper into the neck of it. This is usually an indication that the cases are too long and require trimming. NOTE, please, that it should not be possible to insert the base of the bullet into the neck of the case by hand **after** the resizing operation has been performed.

If the cases are too thick in the neck, they must be reamed - or discarded. It is dangerous to reload them for further use unless the condition is corrected. If you have a Forster trimmer, or similar device, you merely purchase a reamer of bullet diameter (.243 inch for calibers such as the 6mm Remington, for example). The case then is locked into the collet and the reamer is installed in place of the pilot normally used for trimming the length of the case. The trimming depth should be adjusted so that the case is trimmed to the proper length at the same time it is reamed.

IMPORTANT: Cases must be reamed **after** firing and **before** resizing; otherwise too much metal will be removed, making them unfit for further reloading! One additional tip: After the case has been trimmed and/or reamed, and after it has then been resized, the reamer can be introduced into the first one thirty-second inch or so of the neck to provide an exceptionally smooth chamfer of the neck, thus preventing scraping or gouging of the bullet during seating.

These are case reforming casualties. The .35 Remington (left) was having neck expanded; .338 Winchester mag (center) telescoped in renecking to .264; .30/06 case collapsed as it was reformed to .243 Winchester.

Going back to the opposite end of the case, we encounter other important considerations. First of all, check the headstamp and, if you are concerned with accuracy and uniformity (most reloaders are), sort the cases as to manufacturer and try to make up each lot of ammunition using cases of one given make and type. In a caliber such as .30-06, for example, there can be a considerable variation in the internal capacity between the various commercial brands and the output of the several lots of military brass. This varying capacity is reflected in slight changes in pressure, velocity and - possibly - point of impact. Another thing to watch for when reloading the older handgun calibers is the design of the case head itself. Older lots of such cases as .38 Special, .44 Special, .45 auto rim and .45 Long Colt, among others, often used the so-called "balloon head," which can be identified when looking down into the neck by the presence of a raised area around the flash-hole; most of the cases for these calibers, made within the past few years, have "web head" construction - that is, solid brass around the flash-hole instead of the projection found in the balloon design.

The web head case is stronger but it has less capacity than the balloon type and maximum loads developed for the balloon head case may give excessive pressures when loaded into web head cases. For example, in the .44 Special cartridge, Elmer Keith's traditional load of 18.5 grains of Hercules #2400 powder behind the Lyman #429421 cast bullet, which he designed, was developed for the older balloon head .44 Special case; when using the newer web head cases, he recommends cutting the powder charge to 17.0 grains of #2400.

In the matter of primer size, there is usually no need to sort cases within a given caliber. However, in a batch of .38 Special cases, you sometimes encounter a few cases which take the "Large Pistol" size of primer (.210-inch diameter); these usually are headstamped **.38 S&W Special.** Unless you have a lot of these it is best to set them aside as curiosities. It's a debatable point as to whether or not they'd be safe to reload to maximum levels since such loads were developed for the Small Pistol (.175 diameter) primer. You may even encounter a few early prototypes of the .357 magnum with primer pockets for the large size of primer and the same comments apply to these.

A somewhat more confusing situation exists with the .45 Long Colt, although it's not so apt to be a problem in this latter era. At one time there was a breed of .45 LC cases with a head diameter so large that they could not be inserted into the shellholders normally supplied for the .45 LC cartridge. If you managed to acquire a shell-holder that would fit the larger-rimmed cases, then the regular .45 LC cases would pull loose from the new holder and remain stuck in the sizing die - an experience calculated to cloud the sunniest disposition.

As noted, you are not apt to encounter any of these oddball cases in this latter day unless you fall heir to some really vintage brass. I had a protracted interlude of frustration with the .45 Long Colt in the days when I was the rankest neophyte reloader in the business and drove a poor, patient gunsmith to the thin verge of distraction with the troubles of getting a shellholder to fit this assortment of cases. The traumatic effect of this experience probably explains why the writer numbers himself among the world's leading non-fans of the .45 Long Colt.

Many calibers and headstamps of military brass have the primers stamp-crimped into place. This is done primarily to prevent the primers from backing out and hanging up full-automatic military armament. It is usually found only in those calibers used in full-auto guns, notably the .30-06 and .308 Winchester. Ammunition for the .45 ACP is rarely stamp-crimped although some of the World War II .45 fodder used the smaller Frankford Arsenal primer, having a primer pocket into which it is difficult if not impossible to seat a standard .210-inch Large Pistol primer; again, such cases are best discarded.

Brass may become brittle after many reloadings, leading to splits. The .44 Special case at left is down too far to be trimmed to .44 Russian, and the .22 Jets cannot be used again.

Stamp-crimped brass must have the crimp removed from around the primer pocket to provide a slightly chamfered edge for easy seating of the new primer. This can be done by one of two methods: Cutting (reaming) or displacement (swaging). In a pinch, the careful operator can do an adequate job of this with nothing more elaborate than a sharp penknife and a bit of skill. If a reamer is used, it should be utilized at slow speed and in perfect alignment; don't attempt the job freehand with the case being spun rapidly under power, as in a lathe or drill press. The preferable way to throat out the pocket is by swaging. The C-H company offers a small anvil set that can be fastened to the loading bench; this provides a heavy duty decapping pin (some form of which is usually needed for depriming a stamp-crimped military brass) and an integral pocket swaging position. Power is supplied by judicious taps of a mallet. The quickest, easiest and best method is with the use of a primer pocket swaging set for use in a regular loading press, and the best of these use a ram that goes down inside the neck of the case to apply force to the inside of the head, rather than depending upon holding the case by half of its head, as in a regular shellholder. The pocket swaging operation is apt to impose undue stress, distorting the rim, when the case is held in a shellholder unless the press is very precisely adjusted - and it often isn't.

Regarding the size or diameter of the flash hole, the desirable diameter is approximately .078 to .080 for most calibers. Certain makes of brass sometimes have somewhat smaller flash-holes, especially in small calibers such as .22 Hornet, and there may be interference if the decapping pin is a bit generous in diameter. Extravagant claims sometimes are made for the efficacy of various flash-hole gauges (by the people who make and sell them). I have never as yet encountered concrete proof that minor variations in flash-hole diameter make a significant difference in cartridge performance. You'll find some headstamps of military brass wherein the flash-hole is decidedly non-concentric with the primer pocket and, except in the most extreme examples, even this seems to make relatively little difference.

Corrosion and natural tarnish can be removed from brass cases by any of several methods. Various tumbling devices are available for polishing the cases, with suitable abrasives (such as hardwood sawdust, pulverized walnut shells, etc.) or chemical solvent cleaners. Most chemical case cleaners tend to act more vigorously on the copper than on the zinc (the two metals which compose brass). The result is that the cases emerge a somewhat startling shade of yellow. My own preferred technique is to make up a mandrel on which the case can be spun in a drill press or in a hand drill held in a vise. It is then a very quick and simple process to slap the cases onto the spinning mandrel, give them a fast dressing down with either fine steel wool, commercial

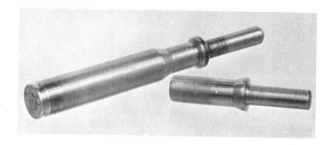

brass polish or jewelers' rouge on a bit of rag, and yank them off without having to start and stop the machine. It's a speedy operation, giving almost any desired degree of polish with minimum effort and mess. The brass case emerges a rich reddish gold color which lasts through the next several cycles of loading and firing.

Such mandrels are very easy to make if you have access to a drill press. Simply cut off a short (approximately two-inch) piece of rod slightly larger than the inside diameter of the case neck; chuck it into the drill press or a lathe and work it down with a flat file, with a slight taper and chamfer so that the case fits snugly enough onto the end of the mandrel to be gripped and spun. If the operation is performed after decapping, you can put a wee dab of fine steel wool on the end of a small piece of dowel and hold it into the primer pocket to clean the residue from that at the same time.

Faint crack appearing around the base of the round is an indication of possible head separations. Discard these cases.

Inspection should also include a check for foreign material inside the case, cracked or split necks and lateral lines just in front of the head which might indicate an upcoming head separation. If in doubt, reject it and make sure it stays rejected by flattening bad cases with a hammer or mashing them in a vise.

Remember: it takes good cases to make good reloads!!

- *Dean A. Grennell, Reprinted by special permission from* GUN WORLD, *June, 1966*

SHOTGUNNING
John Frazier, who's been gunsmithing for more years than both

you and I are old and has forgotten more about guns than the both of us will probably know, was in last week and said he'd seen something at a trap shoot the Sunday before that he'd never seen nor heard of before. One of the fellows shooting was big thru the chest and quite long armed and was shooting 12 ga. hi-brass stuff. Every time he shot he'd throw the gun way forward and then snap it back to his shoulder and fire. John was watching him shoot and on the last shot he fired that day he hollered "Pull" and went thru this exaggerated motion, laid his head over too quick, brought the gun butt back between his eyes, pulled the trigger and knocked himself out colder than a mackerel! One of these real slow motion affairs; kinda let his arms down and dropped the gun and slowly buckled at the knees. Couple of guys grabbed him before he hit the ground, but he was sure out for a spell. And talk about a couple of king-sized black-eyes!! Heck, that is worse than the time I bit myself in the left breast with my own false teeth in my shirt pocket.

- *John Frazier, Chariton, Iowa*

HOW TO IMPROVE YOUR SHOOTING

Like the outdoor writer who was doing up an article on "How to Improve Your Shooting" and he noticed in the records one guy who never could get out of the 80's and suddenly went to mostly all X's. . . So, he figured THERE was just the feller to interview and he did. "Well," says the improved shooter, "I used to hell around a lot and it did hurt my shooting, but then I got married" Then the shooter was silent a few moments sorta mulling things over. "But, My Gawd," he finally added, "there MUST be an easier way. . ."

- *Bob B.*

IN PURSUIT OF ACCURACY

With modern instruments it is possible to completely examine a rifle and tell whether it is properly made and within all normal tolerances - including hardness of steel and uniformity of bore diameter. But no one I've ever heard of - given an unlimited amount of time and money in the finest laboratories with any instrumentation desired can examine a rifle and tell whether it will shoot superbly or lousy. I've seen cheaply constructed rifles which would out-shoot beautiful custom jobs priced in the hundreds. The cheap rifle might be made with sloppy tolerances and the custom beauty with tolerances held to the minimum. (I am referring to individual rifles, rather than any make or model.)

I was working on rifle accuracy several years ago as a laboratory assignment and I expect that finding rifle grouping such a nebulous and mysterious quality, which seemed to defy scientific analysis, is

Author Pete Brown checking the accuracy of one of his pets.

the reason I became thoroughly fascinated by the subject.

I found that most of the factors influencing accuracy could be all measured and controlled to a large degree with the exception of one - barrel vibration. The bedding (or fit) of the barrel and action in the stock controls the barrel vibration. This business of bedding is an exceedingly delicate matter as any gunmaker knows.

Bedding of the barrel and action in the stock is the greatest single factor in accuracy. This is assuming that the barrel and action are made to specifications.

In 1947 I made up a device which was called the "Electric Bedder" and demonstrated that it was possible to install this device in the forend tip and adjust the tension on the barrel to attain the best possible accuracy. Once the setting for best accuracy was found, it was thereafter possible to return to that precise setting at any time. This could be done in spite of stock warpage which might take place. Arthur Cook had my pilot model of the Electric Bedder on his rifle when he won his Gold Medal at the Olympics in 1948.

Since that time a large percentage of the top smallbore shooters have equipped their rifles with Electric Bedders. Remington and Winchester in recent years have made bedders standard equipment on their smallbore target rifles.

Progress is being made in solving the accuracy problem, but the going is slow.

At the present time I have a new bedding device which is completely hidden in the barrel channel at the forend tip. It is very simple to adjust and seems to be proving highly successful for bedding high powered sporting rifles for best accuracy. I asked one manufacturer to send me one of his factory rifles which was an accuracy problem. He sent me a real stinker that grouped about six inches at 100 yards. This gave me some concern because any rifle that bad could be suffering from things other than bedding. I was lucky, however, and with the bedder installed I was able to shrink the groups to about one inch at 100 yards.

For bedding the receiver solidly in the wood, you can't beat "glass" bedding. It saves a lot of tedious time consumed in whittling and scraping around in the wood.

On Crowning

The crowning of the muzzle is highly important to accuracy. I believe that most shooters realize this, but I had a new awakening in regard to muzzle crowning during a test I was making last fall. I was cutting a .308 Winchester barrel off one inch at a time and shooting velocity and accuracy after each cut.

After removing each one inch piece a hurried crowning job would be done on the muzzle. It was done with abrasive on a steel ball held and rotated in a hand-held motor driven tool. The ball was wearing a little each time and finally got so small that it was reaching further into the bore on each occasion. Groups became worse and the centers of impact were shifting.

Examination of the muzzle under a glass revealed a poor crowning job with a trifle more metal taken out of one side. I found that an off-center crowning job could shift the center of impact as much as six inches at 100 yards. Hereafter when I find a rifle which is a poor performer I'm first going to make a careful examination of the "muzzle" edge of the bore. Here is where a Bore Sighter may have another application. If I find that a group is far from where it should be after aligning the sights with the bore, I'm going to become very suspicious of the crowning job.

As a result of my recent experience I'm a firm believer in not cutting the edge of the lands and grooves (at the muzzle) any more than enough to remove burrs. For protection of the muzzle, the end of the barrel can be recessed before the critical edge touchup is performed.

Short Barrels

One of my recent projects has been experimenting with short barrels. The tests involve starting with a long barrel, cutting it off bit by bit, and testing for accuracy and velocity at each step. It is then possible to plot some beautiful velocity vs barrel length curves. In big bore I have first tried this starting with a 31 inch barrel and cutting it off one inch at a time. Unfortunately, my accuracy tests didn't mean much because I got in trouble with muzzle crowning and to tell the truth, I didn't learn much about the optimum length for velocity uniformity either. From the curves there is a suggestion that 22" and 26" might be best for sporters. For the .308 Winchester high power target rifle, I'm inclined to think that the barrel should be 28 inches or possibly 30 inches. At this length the bullet seems to be still accelerating in the barrel.

In the .22 rimfire the results were most interesting and I believe they definitely point the way to better accuracy. In the smallbores a length of about 16 inches appeared to be best. This was with one powder, but I believe the 16 inch length will prove to be about right with most powders.

Bill Atkinson, of Atkinson and Marquart in Prescott, Arizona, based on the experimental results which I used in an article in the March, 1965 *Sports Afield Magazine*, cut his .22 smallbore match barrel off to 16 inches. At first he used a weight on a rod out front to give him the same weight and balance as the long barrel had in its previous state. The results were good, but the louder noise disturbed other competitors on the firing line. Next he fixed a tube extension on the end which gave him the same sighting radius as he had before. The noise is not loud, but it is different. It sounds a bit like shooting into a culvert. The accuracy of this 16 inch barrel is superb. I've cut a Remington model 40X off to 16 inches and I believe it is coming as close to an all "X" performer as I've ever experienced before. The 16 inch smallbore barrel with a bedder looks like it might be tops for accuracy, but there is still a lot of testing to be done to establish definite proof.

Holding for Accuracy

I recently made some tests in the field and on the range to see what effect different rests and holds had on center of impact and accuracy afield. My tests were conducted with a Model 70 chambered for the .300 Magnum Winchester and the Remington Model 600 chambered for the .308 Winchester.

I found that there was no significant difference in center impact when the stocks of the rifles were rested on a bare log, on a sandbag, or against the side of a tree. It may surprise some people to learn that the type of rest - hard or soft - made no significant difference in accuracy either. However, if the rifle is rested on the barrel it will raise the center of impact an inch or two at 100 yards. This is no way to rest a rifle.

I got the best accuracy afield by holding the rifle down at the forend. This can be done with the hand, or can best be done with a hasty sling. A hasty sling in combination with a steady rest is the best formula I can recommend for getting off a well aimed shot. Of course at short range the hunter will probably be called upon to shoot quickly and a rest is hardly necessary under the circumstances. It is at the longer ranges where we need all the shooting precision we can muster.

- *Pete Brown, Gun Editor of* SPORTS AFIELD, *Author, World-wide Hunter and Authority*

ACRAGLAS ON THE HUNT

I would just as soon leave my rifles home as my Acraglas. This is, without doubt, the most amazing stuff I have ever played around with. I have never had it let me down. For example, far back in the Selways in Idaho, I had the misfortune to drop my lower dentures on a rock and break them apart squarely in the center. I dug out the Acraglas, stuck them together and next morning they were good as ever - still are! I have made permanent repairs on axe handles, hornrimmed glasses, gunstocks, deer antlers, cracked distributor caps, knife handles, patched tents, stove-pipes, pack-saddles, china-ware, even smeared a batch of it on a scope mount that had the windage screw twisted off and, after 2 years, it is still holding zero. On porous material (this is a top quality tip) coat both sides and let set hard, scrape off surplus and apply to one side. Press together and set away for 24 hours.

- *Red (O. R.) Ballou, Riverside, California*

IT JUST WENT OFF...

Small boy explaining a broken window: "I was cleaning my slingshot and it went off."

PIG HUNTING

A friend, who had best be forever nameless, was going south for a "pig" hunt and was all steamed up about using a pistol. When he reported back, with no comment about the success of hunting pigs with pistols, I wrote and asked what happened. His only comment was: "Ever try climbing a cactus?"

- *Bob B.*

HORSE HOLSTER

Fellow went into Bob's Gun Shop, walked around a bit and picked up a saddle boot that Bob carries for his hoss-ridin' customers. "I've been looking for one of these for a long time," says the guy. "What do you call it? A shoulder holster for horses, isn't it?. . ."

- *Bob's Gun Shop, Hot Springs, Arkansas*

TARGET PACK

Speaking of genius, Larry Ahlman came up with a most ingenious invention the other day that is worthy of a lot of thought and quite a bit more development. Once worked out it could completely revolutionize the entire target printing game.

Simply stated - and pictures not being available yet for viewing - it is this: Take fifty targets and stack them neatly. Across the top attach a thumbscrew binding rod which will hold all fifty targets firmly but not interfere with target visibility. Hang this from the wall with picture frame wire. Do all your today's shooting at the target on the front. Then, like with bank calendars, when you come to the shop the next day tear off the sheet you shot at yesterday and, as Larry put it, "Presto! you have a fresh, clean target hanging with no thumb tacks wasted."

Wayne Fleming, here in the office, also pointed out that this could help save on ammo for postal matches. Take one shot at 10 targets and mail them in. . .if your first shot was an X all 10 will be X's and them kind of targets are hard coming by! As I pointed out - needs a bit more development.

- Larry Ahlman, Morristown, Minnesota

DIRECTIONAL COMPASS

I met a hunter in the Wisconsin woods this fall who was dragging out a huge buck by the tail! Having a devil of a time hauling it that way too. So I asked him, "Why don't you drag him by the horns?" He replied, "Would if I was going in that direction. . ."

- Ken Hoyt, Grafton, Wisconsin

DEER HUNTING

"They're going to call those who volunteered to be shot to the moon 'lunatics'. . .One deer hunter says to 'tother, 'Let's miss a couple more and go home.'"

- Raymer Durnell's column in Cabool, Missouri, ENTERPRISE

MINK

"What would a bull be doing out behind the barn with his eyes closed?" inquires Bert Popowski. Answer: "Bulldozing." Bert further said, "The other day I was out 'reading the newspapers' as an old buddy of mine used to call following tracks in fresh snow. Found some mink sign and decided I needed a little wit-sharpening by attempting to catch a couple of those coyote-nosed killers. Friend of mine had unknowingly become an accessory by giving me a little bottle of mink lure. I dunno what was in it, but one whiff of that and my hair snapped in the slipstream so violently that the barber won't see me for the next month.

"To compound the mischief I slipped and fell against a granite rock. You guessed it - right on top of my mink perfume, which was in a pocket of my deer-hunting coat! Whereinell can I buy a gallon of that deodorant "GONE" you mentioned? Meanwhile, I think I'll just hang that coat in the woods and ring it with traps. It's so powerful that I can hear it in black dark for 100 paces, running yet, into the wind."

- *Bert Popowski, Custer, Wyoming*

LADY SHOOTER

An extremely stout woman attired in a rather roomy pair of slacks passed by the judges table at a shooting match in the East recently. She was moving at a surprisingly fast pace, and the rear seemed to excite the risibilities of an old muzzle-loader shooter standing nearby. Catching the eye of another shooter, he observed with a chuckle: "Bud, I never thought I'd live to see a sight like that - looks like two little boys a'fightin' under a blanket."

- *Fred Moulton,* The American Rifleman

HUNTING ADS

If anybody ever tells you the guys in this business are dead on their you-know-whats, they have another think coming. Lot of you send in samples of your advertising and it always is good with lots of punch. Just this morning Philip A. Ekern, Flandreau, South Dakota, sent in a half page ad from his local paper. All but about four inches is devoted on how to shoot "Antilocapra Americana" - pronghorn antelope to you and me! And some of the ad is right clever:

"These animals are fast, fast, fast!" says the ad. "They drift about 20 mph. and if excited or pressed, 55 to 60 mph. is not unusual or difficult for short distances. . .Use a gun you have faith in. It is more important to hit them right with your favorite deer or varmint rifle, than to miss them with a borrowed moosemeat mangling magnum. Good common sense goes a long ways in shooting Antelope, too. The air out West is clear and you can see for miles. But you won't be apt to get a killing shot at over 200 yards. You don't have to pull the trigger very hard to shoot that far." End of quote. . .The selling part of the ad is only 7" wide and 7 lines deep wherein is listed the merchandise he is pushing this week; and I'll bet everyone who reads the ad - and all hunters will - will also read the sales pitch! (I like that business about moosemeat mangling magnums. I hunted, just once, with a guy using a 375 H&H - he hit a little doe mule deer weighing 70 pounds at the most. Only part of her that wasn't blown all to foam and splatter was the hole where the bullet entered.)

- *Bob B.*

HUNTING SEASONS

The hunting seasons aren't so very far off - open already in some areas. This makes one think of hunter safety and that brings up what Fred Moulton of *The Rifleman* said about the hunter who climbed into a tree so nobody would take him for a deer. It worked, too - the guy was shot for a bear.

- *Fred Moulton*, The American Rifleman

VARMINT PISTOL

The gun magazines indicate a widespread interest in handgun varminting of late. For several years I have had a gun which doubles as a field-and-woods varminter and a fine center-fire target arm too. Some would scorn the cartridge as an antique, but properly loaded it's very efficient in all respects. It's a K-32 Masterpiece chambered out to .32-20. For killing, I load the Ideal 100-grain hollow-point #31133 ahead of 6.0 gr. of Unique. Ideal for predator calling and also has the trajectory for longer shots. And not the least important is that the K-32 can be rechambered for about $6 and reloaded for 1/3 to to 1/5 the cost of .22 Rimfire Mags. The .32 is intrinsically as accurate as any bullet made, and particularly so for those susceptible to the blast and kick of the heavier calibers. For target shooting, the Ideal #313445 (Keith type) sized to .311", with a light charge, is top-drawer. Of course, you know all this, too, but sometimes we forget such things amidst the glamour of newer cartridges. I think you'd be doing the pistol-varminting boys a favor to bring this to their attention.

- *Dewey Allen, Karnack, Texas*

IF YOU DIDN'T GET A SHOT AT A DEER

In his column in the local paper at Cabool, Missouri, Raymer Durnell reports the following: "If you didn't get a shot at a deer last fall don't feel too bad, maybe you just didn't look close enough. Michigan fenced in a square mile of woods, put 39 deer and 6 experienced hunters in it. In clear weather with good tracking snow, the hunters hunted 4 days before one ever saw a deer!" (Maybe those hunters were like the Maine guide who told his hunter when they got lost: "I'm the best guide in Maine, only I think we are in Canada now.")

- *Raymer Durnell, Cabool, Missouri*

EXPANDING BULLETS

J. Bulwan sent in a very interesting photo of an Enfield that had a barrel looking somewhat like a half peeled banana! Seems a local fellow wanted some expanding bullets for deer hunting. He took some G I ammo and cut off part of the bullet with a hacksaw. . .the second shot did it. The picture of the gun was taken too far away from the gun and would have been too small to show when printed, but good food for thought. First bullet seems to have stayed in the barrel and the second time around the whole front end let loose.

- *J. W. Bulwan, Alliance, Nebraska*

SHOTSHELL PRESSES

A while ago a good friend of mine bought a shotshell reloader and started loading shells. Everything went fine for a while, then after loading some hulls he set out for the trap range. He was using a J.C. Higgins auto and after about three rounds the forearm dropped off, the stock cracked in half and the bolt was jammed in the receiver. "Well," he said to his brother, "them's real whoop'n-sockers, ain't they?" "Yea," said the brother, "let me try one.". . .Kerbang and so much for a nice L.C. Smith. Come to find out he had the charge bar in bass-ackwards - 1-1/4 ounces of powder and 30 grains of shot. (From BB: Most loaders are now fixed so's this cannot happen! Wonder it didn't blow them to Kingdom Kum!)

- *Thomas's Gun Shop, Hortonville, Wisconsin*

SAFETY CLOTHING

If you haven't read it already, everyone agrees the new flourescent color called "hunter orange" is the very best protective color to wear when hunting. We don't sell hunting clothing, of course, but you probably do.

- *Bob B.*

MUZZLE LOADER PATCHES

Feeding Soft Coal Burners (and Phew, do they smell good when you clean one of them with a wet patch in the summer time. A purely delectable aroooma!) "Seenyor Bob - For muzzle loaders I find that patch material soaked in your Sperm Oil and wrung dry is great for patching round balls. . .I have been using hominy grits on top of black powder. Shoots cleaner. Gonna switch to grass seed next spring and seed the lawn at the same time."

- *Paul Adams, Guatanamo Bay, Cuba*

FIRST HUNTING TRIP

Hey, for the love of Pete, if you are a gentleman or a woman, read no more. I gotta tell a story. Dwight Nichols, All-American football player from ISU at Ames, gave a talk at our local Lions the other night and told it. It has to do with following instructions to the letter (just like with our bluing instructions!) Anyhow with no more commercials: -

This little mountain Tad always was after his Paw to go bear hunting and FINALLY, when he got to be sixteen his Paw called him to him and said, "Son, you are now sixteen and neigh onto a man. It is time you went bear huntin' with your Paw. But you got to foller instructions and do exactly as your Paw tells you. One little mistake, do somethin' I tol' you not to just oncet and you cain't go again." So the boy promised with tears of joy on his youthful face and off to the mountains they went. His Paw stopped them at a stump and told his son:

"Son," he said, "this is your stand. You sit right thar on thet stump and don't you move fer nothin' exceptin' to shoot a bear. Don't you bat an eye-lash even if a tiger should charge you. You don't foller my instructions and you never git to hunt bear agin'." Naturally, the boy promised most vigorously and off up the mountain to his stand went the old man. After several hours of complete silence the old man heard a couple of shots and naturally thought that Tad had got himself a bear. Right proud he was, too, but when he got to where the boy was, there were two dead squirrels.

The old man gave the kid a terrific lacing down. Never again could he go bear hunting. Never in his natural born life would real mountain men associate with him. On and on. Finally the kid got to speak. "But Paw," he said, "You just ain't treatin' me fair. When a porkey-pine went by and slashed my leg full of quills with his tail, I never batted an eye. When a skunk smelt me, backed off and skunked me, I never moved. When a bobcat sharpened his claws on my back I never even took a deep breath. But when those two squirrels came along and one clumb up inside my right pant laig and the other my left pant laig and I heer one say 'tother, 'Let's eat one and store one'. . ."

- *Dwight Nichols, Ames, Iowa*

THE BEAR HUNT

These hunters were sitting in their timber cabin the night before the season opened bragging of their prowess as hunters, the trophies they'd bagged, the long shots they'd made and the hardships they'd suffered - all but one hunter over in the corner who hadn't said a word. Finally he said, "You guys are a bunch of sissies. If you had any guts at all you could get your bear barehanded - no gun!"

Hunters being what they are, the remark brought the house down and ridicule was pretty sharp. After about so much of this the fellow says, "Okay, make it worth my while and I'll do it." The purse was made up and put into the hands of a responsible person and the next morning, bright and early, the fellow left, taking no gun. About an hour later the hunters heard mighty shouts coming from the timber, "Open the door - open the door!" Here came the guy running flat-out with a huge bear snapping at his heels.

Using their heads, like the close friends they were, the boys in the cabin opened the door. Two got on one side of the door and two got behind it to slam it shut between the speeding, about-to-be-devoured hunter and the bear. Just as he got to the door the fellow swerved to one side and the bear went in. Seeing the flash of movement, the guys inside slammed the door, thinking they'd saved their friend.

"Now," shouts the guy outside the cabin, "you skin that one and I'll bring you another."

- *Bob B.*

DOG HUNTING

Rich guy plunks down $500 for pedigreed pointer and another $500 to get the mutt trained first class. Wins many field trials and works like a champ in the field. Neighbor talks him into loaning him to take quail hunting. Comes back and relates the following. "At the beginning the darned fool wouldn't hunt - just stood stiff as a board with his tail out straight and his front paw lifted. But, after a few swift kicks in the arse he kept moving around. Guess I broke him of that bad habit." Then there was the one snake that said to the other, "Aw, cut it out. I knew you when you didn't have a pit to hiss in."

- *Bob B.*

WEDDING BELLS

Office Gal: "Do you think a seismic explosion can cause enough vibration to bring on rain?" Busy Gunschmidt: "Naw, but I know of a shotgun bringing on a shower."

- *Bob B.*

KEEPIN' THAT OL' JUG COLD

Many of the Land Management Supervisors (we call them "Farmers" around here, but you know how everybody has to have a fancy title!) take one of those gallon size plastic bleach jugs, wash it out real well and then put it in the freezer full of water until it is frozen. On a hot day, you would be surprised at how long the ice will last, using what has thawed for drinking. Works well when you cannot carry an insulated jug or don't have one. Will not break either, and if you do damage it, just get another one. Keep one or two frozen at all times so as not to run out when you decide at the last minute to head for the range.

- *John Turnbull, Toulon, Illinois*

PORTABLE SHOOTING TABLE

Am enclosing the plans for a portable, folding bench rest we came

468

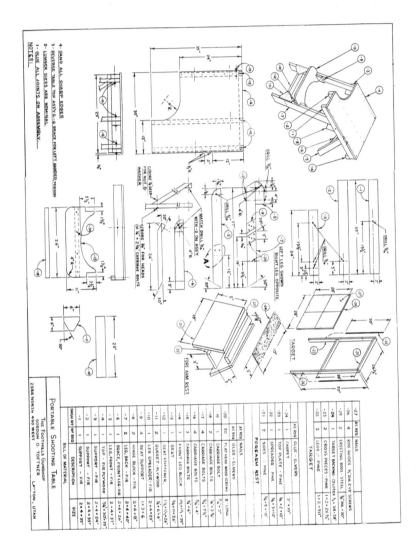

up with here after swiping an idea here and one there. These are a real asset to anyone out in this country, where we shoot anywhere out on the desert. Have shot coyotes at a half mile from one. Have also missed a hell of a lot more than I hit.

    - Gordon Toftner, Layton, Utah, Reprinted by Special Permission

THE CASE OF THE CAREFUL RELOADER

    The gink who's about to start loading his own ammunition is fearful, thinks the job requires an engineering degree and the patience of a saint. The gink who's been loading for years, admits to being something of an expert, tells his novice friend that loading is a cinch and then smothers him in the confusion of technical advice. Neither one is right - handloading isn't hard, doesn't call for a sheepskin from Cal Tech, but the successful reloader truly is he who works carefully, with attention to the least detail.

    The real fun of handloading lies in the selection of bullets for a given rifle and shooting job, the development of just those combinations of powder weight and type that will, out of your own pet rifle, either put bullets into a coin-sized cluster or execute a moose like a bolt of lightning as you prefer. These are the benefits, and believe you me, there is to a shooter little satisfaction greater than the joy of seeing his private concoction punch a raggedy hole in a target or unhinge a buck antelope four hundred yards out and running. These are real satisfactions as thrilling as a first kiss. But they're come by with more care and considerably less audacity!

    A prime requisite to top performance of handloads is case care. Sloppily handled brass makes for sloppy results - yet the time involved in keeping your lot and we say "lot" advisedly because for any one rifle you should always keep segregated one batch of the same make and lot number, some 60 to 100 cases being plenty unless you're bound for Africa - of cases clean and properly manicured is very small. It will pay off in results all out of proportion to the few minutes you spend.

Take the matter of inspection. The loading companies spend fortunes on visual, mechanical, and ballistic inspections of their cartridge - some 119 inspections in the instance of one brand of shotshell, for example; so presumably after the first firing your batch of brass is perfect. Would 'twere so, but 'taint. You may have split a neck - toss that one away since variation in neck tension means a blooper shot. Your batch of brass may, just may, contain one case that has a flash hole that's out of round or is markedly over or under size. Since the powder charge that is OK with a normal-sized flash hole will burn over-fast, with excess pressure may conceivably rush to the point of detonation if it's ignited with an extra-hot flame through an overlarge hole; these oddballs go out too. Since the precise diameter of flash holes varies slightly from one caliber and maker to the next, we won't bother you with dimension - just equip your loading bench with a set of small drills that includes sizes from 3/64 to 3/32.

You'll find one that approximates the hole diameter normal to that caliber and make, will serve as a "normal" gauge.

You note a slight but definite hump just above the cartridge cannelure or belt, with the brass smooth below it but chamber-roughened above? That's the normal expansion ridge apparent after firing in most types of rifle action. Normal, that is, unless as you play with loads you observe that the hot or marginal powder charge has pushed this expansion mark back markedly closer to the cartridge head, back down into the "fat" of the case perhaps only 1/16th of an inch above the cannelure. Then it isn't normal; you've pushed pressures too far and are asking for trouble.

Or about 3/8th of an inch above the cannelure you notice something that isn't a minor bulge but a line that looks suspiciously like the beginning of a tear? That's just what it is, an embryonic case head separation, caused more than likely by your having set the die down too far when you last full-length-sized those cases, so shortening the shoulder and creating an excess headspace situation. Or possibly you used full-sized cases just one time too many, over-worked the brass.

Up around the shoulder of the case there are a lot of little dintings, sort of scalloping around the slope? Dangerous? Nope - they'll disappear next time you load and fire the round. If inspection after sizing indicates such minor dints where they didn't exist before, you've got too much case-lube slobbered up into your die. Just wipe it out and get along with as little lubricant as you can.

Hold the case up against the light. Does the mouth look square or is it lop-sided-as it is very likely to be in any caliber after two or three firings? Sort of slanch-wise? Since common sense indicates this isn't right it can't have anything but a bad effect on bullet behavior during those fast and furious micro-seconds when the primer is flashing, the powder is starting to burn, the case mouth is expanding to let the bullet loose, and the bullet is starting on its way up the barrel, so let's fix it. How? Trim it off. We'll come back to that later.

While you're conducting this inspection take a look into the case mouths to see whether or not the chamfered brass looks equally thick all the way around? Bit bulgy on one side? Let's check these again after they've also had the trimming they probably need - and as to the trimming or possible reaming methods, once again we'll come back later.

At about this point we come to perhaps the most important inspection of all, safety-wise, that for overall case length. A cartridge case which is short in the neck section for its individual chamber isn't going to do any radical harm, but if it has grown overlong, it can raise merry hell. If the neck has lengthened to the point that when you bolt the cartridge into the chamber the mouth section is squeezed in the throat, squeezed tight around the bullet with no place for it to go when the brass is expanded with as much as 50,000 or more pounds of pressure, the end result is to push your powder's burning rate higher, jazzing the pressures to new and most irregular heights. Accuracy goes to pot because velocities and times-up-the-barrel vary; and if the pressure peaks are high enough you may end up with a busted gun and a rueful, if not wounded expression.

And brass cases do grow, never forget it. Especially with slope-shouldered cases in calibers less than .30 - which group includes cartridges with from 17 to 21 degrees of shoulder slant, to wit the .220 Swift, .257, .243 and .270 - the effect of repeated high-pressure firings is to push the brass forward into the neck section, either lengthening or thickening it, in many instances both. The types with more zoot-suit in the shoulder, like the .222 family, the 26-degree .244, all the steep-shouldered wildcats and the "improved" versions with or without a belt, seem to change their collar sizes less frequently, probably because the brass doesn't flow around the corners. But any case can and will grow; all should be checked.

Now - and Bob Brownell will crack down on me for saying this because after all he's in business to sell goods - you don't NEED to buy a case-length gauge. The human eye is markedly perceptive; a once-fired case you've kept as a sample will show up distinctly shorter in comparison to one that has "grown" to anything like the dangerpoint.

Of course, it's a darned sight simpler to dump your kid's piggy bank and get one of the inexpensive C-type length gauges, one make of which is good for a dozen calibers, through which to run two dozen rounds a minute for length. If you're a real precisionist - and you are, aren't you? - you'll up the ante to buy some of the barrel-type gauges, made with great exactitude so that you can check maximum and minimum on both headspace and case length at one and the same time.

So the cases do, in a few instances, seem overlong or oddly thickened about the neck? Tsk!

The cheapest system of length-trimming would be to file 'em off by hand and eye, but this will end up like trimming your mustache. A leetle mite on this side and a leetle mite there - and you'll soon cut off the whole business! All the loading die manufacturers offer trimming dies, specially hardened on the top end so you can file off any protruding brass without marring the glass-tough surface. Not very expensive. Not very fast either.

A better answer is one of the trimming tools that looks like a midget lathe, hand-operated. That's what it is, actually, and you can set every one of the several types to trim case after case every one to precisely the same length, running 'em through faster than the Japanese can make Christmas tree ornaments.

Now, when you have trimmed the cases their mouths will show bright brass and it will be immediately obvious whether there exists any serious fattening of the neck metal in a lop-sided fashion. And herein lies the great advantage of the midget-lathe type of trimming tool. Almost all such models have provision for neck thickness control, either by reaming the inside metal on centers, or by turning any excess evenly off the outside. Me, I like the latter approach because it seems more likely to come out all even in the end, but the inside reamers have a good argument too.

Neck-thinning is a cinch to be necessary when you've made a short-cased wildcat out of longer brass, a .219 Wasp out of the Zipper, for example, or sweated out the job of making .243 brass from that mess of G.I. cases you bought so cheap. It's often - and this is a real secret - the answer to improved accuracy in that .22 magnum in which you're using early-production brass, just between us. But neck control, in respect to both length and fatness, is as important to the successful handloader, especially the accuracy bug, as it is to the Size 18 dame who wants to get into a Size 14 by Dior!

Brother Brownell suggested that somewhere along in here I should insert commentary about the cleaning of primer pockets, necessity therefore and methods applying thereto. Well, here goes his blood pressure again because frankly, I think that primer-pocket scrubbing is as over-rated an activity as every-shooting-day bore cleaning, with today's primers. If it's vital at all it should be vital in a rifle and brass for bench rest competition, no? Sorry - the old .222 bencher that was good enough to keep me in the top twenty for years, in the top five nationally much of the time, had assigned to it a lot of 60 cases. They never had their necks polished (though they were trimmed religiously) or their primer pockets given anything more than a glance and perhaps a slight decarbonizing with small screwdriver during the life of that rifle, probably some sixty or seventy reloadings!

But if carbon does accumulate to any thickness, or in lumps, it obviously hinders proper seating of the primer. If nothing else it creates variances in seating depth which in turn create variances in firing pin blow on the priming pellet and so affect ignition. But we don't have to get all haired up about it. A small stiff-bristled brush of proper diameter does just dandy if you don't have that little screwdriver, and ingenious souls are forever turning out pocket cleaners and reamers, even for the lazy who must do everything by machine.

Another bugaboo for the beginner, and the source of much learned argument among the experts, is this business of setting up bullet-seating dies to get the proper seating depth. This one is considerably more sound than fury, more murkiness than real mystery, seems to me, and in earlier years there was a lot of hugger-mugger written about it in terms of so many thousandths, or so many calibers, of seating depth. Frightful, and totally foolish.

The one thing you want to make sure of is that all your bullets are seated to the same depth. Beyond that it's a matter of simple compromise. Set the die so that it pushes the bullet into the neck far enough to give you an overall length that will feed smoothly through the rifle magazine, and so that the bullet will almost but not quite touch the lands when you chamber the round. That's all. Permitting a "jump" of some 3/32nds is the most usual accuracy practice, seeming to give somehow more even pressures and so better accuracy than the custom of seating bullets so they are actually engraved by the lands. But let us not confusticate matters by trying to measure in thousandths how far the bullet must go down into the hole of the case mouth - far enough to hold it yet comply with the two obvious requirements above is just far enough.

Many starters in the loading game, and some old enough in it to know better, get all in a swivet with long-shanked bullets when they seem to be shoving the slug way down into the case in order to achieve the magazine-and-throat compromise mentioned in the previous paragraph. "Why," they cry in horror, "the butt of the bullet is way down below the shoulder, almost a sixteenth of an inch!! What if it started cockeyed?" The answer to that is that it won't start cockeyed, the effect on pressures in any combination otherwise sensible seems to be nil, and the worst that can be said of this situation is that it (a) limits the amount of case-room available for the slower-burning powders and (b) it doesn't look pretty. Handsome is as handsome does, chums!

And one final word - on crimping this time. The pistoleer brewing up a batch of either full-power or wadcutter loads has to crimp. If a bullet is jarred forward by revolver recoil, he may well jam up the cylinder and so lose the rapid-fire match. The rifle loads that are meant to be used in lever-actions or early pumps with tubular magazines, or in Bill Ruger's tube-fed little .44 magnum carbide, these have to be crimped securely too. But seldom if ever do proper loads for a box-magazine rifle, even hunting loads for a junior-cannon caliber, require any crimping to position the bullets against recoil jar. If with your chosen bullet, and with your lot of brass, you find that your trusty-rusty old .30-06 shoves the bullets of magazine loads down onto the powder, send away for a new expander plug to go into your sizing die. Order it smaller by about a thousandth than the present plug, and chances are your troubles will vanish. Too light neck tension is often a sympton of uneven neck tension, and that's a valid cause for poor-shooting ammunition.

Once upon a time it was said that we handload to save money, and mebbe we did. The pistol-shooters and the shotgunners, neither of whom are prone to much experimenting, undoubtedly still do load to save money. But today's rifle reloader doesn't - he hand-loads because it's FUN. He gets better results on the range with his concoctions and he certainly derives far greater satisfaction from banging his annual deer with a home-grown load. And furthermore, think how he can escape from hassles with the little woman by retreating to his loading bench - "Gotta gauge a few cases, dear!" Or can he?

- *Warren Page, Gun Editor of* FIELD & STREAM, *Author, World-wide Hunter and Authority*

BE KIND AND GOOD NATURED

Got a real cute little poster from Bill Schumaker, writer of renown and well known gunsmith on the west coast. Caption "Be Kind and Good Natured. You'll Always Get Your Reward" and showing a real sad sack with a big wood screw running thru his belly and out his back. Got a big laugh out of it until I thought of the darned unhappy thing that happened to one of our better known gunsmith/shooters here in the mid-west. I'll call him John rather than give his real name for reasons which you will see shortly.

He - John - was getting ready for the Regional Matches prior to going to Perry this year and had been practice shooting every available minute. By his own admission, he is high strung and should never have pushed himself quite so hard, especially when his job was quite demanding. Anyhow, the pressure got him and he suddenly realized that he had this great big screw sticking right in the middle of his gut. He told me this wasn't right, he was sure, so he went to a head-shrinker in Des Moines. After the usual couch business they got down to the bit about the screw and how it hurt and how it is keeping him from doing any prone shooting.

"Think nothing of it, John," says the headshrinker. "This sort of thing happens with people who are pushing too hard and the cure is quite simple. One of these days when you are out shooting on the range and just ready to touch off a shot, you'll see a big screwdriver in your scope. When this happens, lay down your gun, go get the screwdriver and remove the screw. Simple as that - and you'll be cured."

Well, John was in our place about a couple of weeks ago and I went down to visit with him. I knew nothing about all this, of course, and when I asked him what the ever-lovin' that big sling was running from shoulder to shoulder and down across his hips, he told me about the above. "Well," I asks, feeling sure he was now cured, "did it work?"

"Too well," says John. "But now I'm in worse shape than ever. I was out there on the range and just like the Doc says, the pain got horrible and I did see this big screwdriver. Even tho there were a couple of women on the range, I laid down my gun, stripped down my pants, grabbed that screwdriver and took out the screw."

"So?" says I. "Yeah," says John. "That really did it! When I took the screw out my arse fell off!"

- *Bob B.*

CASE CLEANING

Think I've found a more noble and glorious use for Brownell's rust remover. As a cleaner for corroded cartridge brass, use one part rust remover to two parts soft water. Chuck in gucky cases and leave in solution about 10 minutes with a little shaking. Drain, wash and dry. A light rub with #00 steel wool and there they are, Beautiful, BEAUTIFUL!

- *Chuck Edwards, Hartford, New York*

CLEANING BRASS CASES

Use 1 to 1/2 oz. of Potassium Bitartrate to 1 quart of water. Dump in the dirty brass and bring to a boil for around 10 minutes. Drain and save the solution for future use. Flush the brass with hot water and wipe each case with a soft towel or flannel cloth. (The Potassium Bitartrate is just ordinary Cream of Tartar used in baking and can be bought in any grocery store!)

- *Al Yarc, Wenona, Illinois*

CASE DEBURRING

A little tip you might pass on to the boys. A "Church Key", the kind you open beer cans with, can be used to deburr cartridge case mouths in an emergency!

- *Henry B. Tillinghast, Jr., Colorado Springs, Colorado*

BULLET PERFORMANCE

When any scientific problem presents as many variables and unknowns as the selection of a proper sporting bullet, one can hardly arrive at a definite solution. Under the circumstances, many theories are apt to be evolved.

Theories are wonderful things. They can be expounded without proof, and can be bandied about for years - supported by nothing but the barest of evidence. You can rest assured that there are about as many theories on bullet selection as there are experts - and you'll find an expert behind pretty near every other gun.

I don't mean to deride the theorists. If it wasn't for the inspired individual constantly striving to prove he has a legitimate brainchild, we probably wouldn't even have progressed to the stone age. Nevertheless, confounded with uncertainties, the new shooter is generally confused - especially if he has conferred with more than one expert. How would YOU tell a hunter which .30 caliber bullet he should use for deer hunting?

In the first place, what would he consider the most important single requirement in a bullet? According to my theory, accuracy is most important. I believe that within reasonable limits of bullet weight and design about 90 per cent of taking game effectively is in making well placed shots.

However, I think it is certainly possible to recommend those reasonable limits of bullet weight and design for taking certain kinds of game. That should remove much of the confusion. The manufacturers design their bullets with definite limitations in mind.

Generally speaking, the lighter bullets for any particular cartridge are made to mushroom or disrupt easily and are intended for light skinned small game. The heaviest bullets are intended for the largest game considered appropriate for the particular cartridge.

Let's take a well known example - the .30-06. .30-06 bullets weighing from 100 grains to 130 grains are usually intended for varmint shooting and are so constructed. In the .30-06, a 130 grain bullet is a light one, but in the .270 Winchester this same weight bullet is considered medium and is used for deer or sometimes larger game. The 150 grain bullet in .30-06 is medium light weight and is best adapted to game such as deer. In the .270 Winchester for example, this would be the heaviest bullet and will be used for deer, elk, moose, etc. The 180 grain bullet in .30-06 is medium heavy and is appropriate for game such as elk and moose. The 200 or 220 grain .30 caliber bullets are for the large heavy game such as brown bear, or some of the heavy African game.

You can apply the same general formula to other cartridges like the 6 millimeters (.243 Winchester and .244 Remington). The light bullets are for varmints and the heavier 100 grain bullets for game such as deer. This takes the 6 mm cartridges up to the limit of their use as generally recommended. If you don't agree with limitation, then let's say that the heaviest of the .243 Winchester and .244 Remington bullets should be used for anything the size of deer or larger. That should forestall any argument here.

Within the bounds of reason, as explored above, we can therefore pick bullets of suitable weight. We don't HAVE to stay within these bounds. For example, we may use 130 grain .30 caliber bullets for deer, or we would use 180 grain .30 caliber bullets on large African game. I would not discourage such selections in the case of experienced game shots who have the ability, patience and sportsmanship to place their shots precisely in a vital spot.

This is where accuracy comes into the picture. If I must make the choice between the 180 grain or 220 grain bullet for brown bear, for example, I will take the weight and make of bullet which proves to give the most consistent accuracy in my particular rifle. As a matter of fact, I shot a big brown bear with a .30-06 on the Alaskan Peninsula in the spring of 1960 with a 180 grain bullet because it did happen to give me superior accuracy.

It is not possible to tell a shooter which bullet will give him the best accuracy in his rifle. This may sound unreasonable and like hedging, but it is absolutely true. There is only one way to determine which bullets will give you superior accuracy and that is to test them on the range in your rifle. It is interesting to note that hollow point bullets, for some reason unknown to me, frequently give very fine accuracy. Several years ago I ran onto this when testing some Long Rifle ammunition. The hollow point bullets giving only mediocre accuracy at 100 yards beat the match ammunition at 200 yards.

Bullets must mushroom properly over a wide range of velocity. We sometimes bank too heavily on ballistics at the muzzle and count on this for down range performance. Many a shooter will declare that a .22 rimfire is woefully inadequate for chuck shooting at any range, yet he will not hesitate to take a 400 yard or longer shot with a high powered centerfire. At 100 yards the .22 Long Rifle is far more effective than a high powered centerfire at 400 yards. For one thing, a vital shot can be delivered with greater precision at the shorter range. A most important consideration to be sure.

DIAGRAMS OF BULLET PERFORMANCE

The shaded area in the illustration below and in those on the following pages diagramatically represent a cross-section through a deer. The section passes through the heart and lungs. The bullet enters from the left into an area which is not necessarily the most vital, but typical for a bullet fired at big game standing side-view or quartering away.

The dark area shows how the bullet performs. It reveals the area of greatest damage by the bullet in the game. We might say it represents the manner or rate at which the bullet gives up its energy. This energy given up is a measure of potential killing power. So, how and where the bullet gives up its energy is a most important factor.

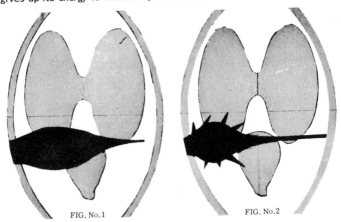

FIG. No.1   FIG. No.2

FIGURE #1 — Represents good performance from a big game bullet. The bullet has mushroomed and held together as it comes to a stop in the animal, thus giving up its entire energy in doing work in a vital area.

FIGURE #2 — Shows what might be the same bullet as represented in Figure #1, but driven at a higher muzzle velocity or fired at shorter range. In this instance, the nose of the bullet has disrupted, but the base holds together and drives deep into the animal. After losing most of their energy, bullets frequently stop against the hide on the far side of an animal. This is good bullet performance.

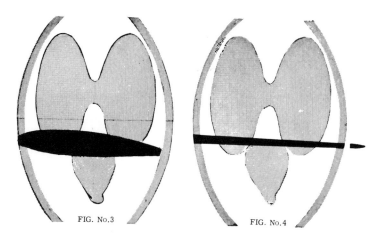

FIG. No.3

FIG. No.4

FIGURE #3 — Represents the same bullet as shown above, but at a much lower velocity - possibly long range. Performance is good, but the bullet did not have quite the explosive effect, not as much overall energy, and won't produce as much shock as shown in Figs #1 & 2. This could also represent the performance of a large low velocity bullet. With the big bullet the large frontal area presented by the bullet as it plows through is in itself shock producing.

FIGURE #4 — Represents a bullet which might be a full patch (jacketed non-mushrooming nose) such as military bullets or some match bullets. This could also be an expanding-type bullet which is too tough for game like deer and does not mushroom. Or, it could be a game bullet which is striking at such long range that there is not sufficient energy remaining to expand the bullet. In any event, a bullet which goes all the way through carries energy with it which is lost as far as producing shock to the animal is concerned. The energy expanded within the animal is the difference between the energy on entering and that energy remaining as it leaves.

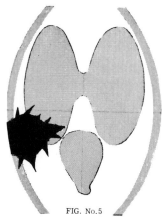

FIG. No.5

FIGURE #5 — Represents a bullet that is used completely, disrupts and produces an explosive effect too near the surface. The energy is expended in the animal, but would produce much more shock if it went deeper and disrupted near more vital organs. This could be the same bullet shown in Figs #1 & 2, but driven at much higher velocity. It could also be a varmint-type bullet which would be fine for woodchucks, but not suitable for big game.

The old .30-30 is far more effective at 100 yards than the .330 H & H magnum is at 500 yards. The remaining energy of the .30-30 will be slightly higher, and again, at the shorter range, it is possible to be much surer of a telling shot.

We can hardly discuss bullet performance without touching on the subject of twist. This subject is a gun nut's delight because it can almost always be depended upon to precipitate an argument. I once made some tests wherein I loaded some bullets down in velocity to simulate performance at longer range. This was for a test of bullet performance in clay. I received some highly explosive letters from readers who were going to leave me in shreds because I didn't know that loading down to simulate long range performance for short range testing did not produce the same twist as would be present at actual long range firing. This I must admit is perfectly true, and I really should have made mention of this fact in my article. You see, at long range the bullet has slowed down considerably, but the rotational velocity imparted by the twist of the rifling has slowed down very little. There is very little resistance to the rotational velocity.

A bullet fired at 3000 feet per second muzzle velocity from a barrel having a twist of 1 turn in 12 inches (1 foot) will be rotating at a speed of: Velocity/twist (measured in feet) = 3000/1 or 3000 revolutions per second. At a range of 300 yards, the remaining translational or forward velocity of the bullet will have dropped to about 2200 feet per second. The rotation of the bullet will not have dropped off in anything like the same proportion. Let's say, for sake of argument, that it is now rotating at 2900 revolutions per second.

If I handload down to 2200 feet per second to simulate 300 yard performance, I give the bullet a rotation of only 2200 revolutions per second. Now the question is: does the difference between 2900 revolutions per second make any significant difference in bullet performance at the target? No, I really don't think it does, and I'll tell you why.

Using the formulas in Cranz's *Textbook of Ballistics, Vol. II (Part 2)*, the bullet energy represented in the spin of such a bullet is about .8 per cent of the forward energy of the bullet. Therefore, if the forward muzzle energy of the bullet is 2500 foot pounds, the energy of rotation or spin is only 2500 X .008, or 20 foot pounds. The difference between 2900 r.p.m. and 2200 r.p.m. therefore accounts for only about 5 foot pounds of energy. This difference in energy is hardly a factor worth considering.

The bullet is given a spin to stabilize it. This spin is an important factor in stabilizing the bullet during flight. It is therefore a factor in accuracy. Once the bullet hits the target, spin, as indicated by the low energy involved, has little effect on how the bullet performs. There is one way in which spin can have a marked influence on killing power.

If the spin for a particular bullet is low enough so the bullet is on the verge of instability the bullet may have a tendency to tumble as it enters the target. It therefore has a buzz saw action as it tumbles end over end. This will no doubt lessen its penetration and increase the shock effect. I doubt that this influence would be any greater shock than that induced by a properly expanding bullet.

We can now conclude that a game bullet which carries its energy deep into the vital areas, but mushrooms, expands, disrupts, or what have you to thus dissipate all its energy within the animal, is a good bullet. In fact, there is no way you can get any more out of a bullet. The energy figure, providing the bullet is designed to mushroom properly, is without doubt our best measure of killing power potential in a bullet. The rest is dependent on the shooter's skill with his weapon.

- *Pete Brown, Gun Editor of* SPORTS AFIELD, *Author, Worldwide Hunter and Authority*

ROUGH CASE TRIMMING

For you guys trying to save money on brass, take a piece of 2" x 4" Formica (Note, extra hard walnut will do) drilled and chambered for 308 Win. & 7 mm or whatever and planed to approximate thickness. Reform your '06 cases full length and insert in the holding block you just made. Neck sticks out about 'so long' and cuts off real easy on a jig saw. Simple way to save much case trimming. (Note: Job should be finished up on a regular case trimmer, however.)

- *Jim Rosen, Great Falls, Montana*

ANNEALING CASE NECKS

Drill a hole just slightly larger than the outside diameter of the case neck in an iron bar. Heat the bar red hot. Insert the case neck in the hole and when the color starts up the shoulder, pick out with your fingers and dump in plain water. John, who has been a top gunsmith for more years than many of us are old, says this is the fastest and easiest way of annealing brass he has ever tried - and no burned fingers.

- *John Frazier, Chariton, Iowa*

CASE LUBE

Charlie Swearingen, erstwhile gunsmith at Marshalltown, Iowa, comes in quite often to buy, gab and make comments of one kind or another. The other day he wanted to know what the hell all the helter and skelter was about grease for daubing on cases when forming and sizing. He just goes to the drug store and gets a tube of lanolin. It lasts practically forever, costs next to nothing and so far he's found nothing to surpass it. If things get real rough he puts in just a shade of colloidal graphite. . .

Charlie also says he lubes by squirting a few drops of Anderol gun oil on a cloth and then taps the tips of his fingers on the cloth, rubs his hands together and then rubs the cases with his hands - almost in the normal course of loading. Gives excellent results - and Charlie loads thousands.

- *Charlie Swearingen, Marshalltown, Iowa*

SIZING

Glen Malin thinks that a 39¢ brown bottle of castor oil works as good or better than lanolin for sizing and is cheaper. Gosh, it should work, come to think of it. Makes lots of things that are tight work easier.

- *Glen E. Malin, Santa Fe, New Mexico*

BALL POWDER

A way to answer this customer's problem: The customer called and wanted to know if Mitch had any of this new "ball powder" and upon being advised that he did, had this to say: "Well, I've been using this other kind with the sharp corners and I thought that this new ball powder ought to be easier on the barrel."

- *Pickens Gun Shop, Grand Junction, Colorado*

BULLET RECOVERY

"Polyurethane foam - that stuff you find in packing and some display cartons - is excellent stuff for bullet recovery without deforming the bullet. Keep gun at least 4 feet from the foam as it burns easy!" (Note from us - start out with several feet of it and somewhere so that if you don't have enough you won't be shooting a hole in somebody's out-house! Your box won't have to be very large - just long! Stick in a piece of paper every foot so you can easily tell where the bullet has stopped.)

- *Public Relations Bureau, Olin Mathieson Chemical Corporation*

RELOADING

Gunshop Customer: "Are the loads in this gun pure?" Gunsmith: "As pure as the girls in your dreams, Mister." Gunshop customer: "Guess maybe I'd better get my reloading done somewhere else."

- *Bob B.*

PLASTIC BULLETS

When they say the bullets (those plastic ones) can be used up to 15 times they sure do mean it. I have a Colt .44 and a 45-70 in the shop that I let the customers shoot, and it seems that I don't get much done any more. Let me also tell you that these darned things really pack a punch. I can say this from experience because a customer shot me in the thigh at close range. Should see my laig. Looks like I'd been kicked by a bay mule. . .

- *Custom Gun Shop, Bath, Michigan*

PLASTIC FUNNELS

Many plastic powder funnels get so charged with static you cannot pour powder thru them. Your local photo shop can supply you with an aerosol anti-static called 'Photo-Sweep'. Spray this inside and out and No. 5066 will run through like dry sand!

- *A. W. Hinchman, M.D., Medical & Surgical Hospital, Brady, Texas*

A STATIC-STICKY POWDER FUNNEL

Next time you are reloading and the static electricity makes the powder stick to the plastic funnel, just wash it in "Joy". Do not rinse or wash the funnel, just let it dry. This is not a permanent thing, so you will have to repeat every so often. But sure does cut the static and the powder doesn't stick at all.

- *P. W. Hanna, Shelton, Washington, read in an article by Bob Steindler in the* HANDLOADER

BROKEN CASE REMOVAL

When a cartridge case breaks off in a full-length resizing die, take the decapping-expander plug and rod out of the large end. Take a piece of drill rod that will just enter the case neck in the die and put it through the small end about halfway into the body of the case. Put a couple of wraps of string around the drill rod and lower it back until the string seals any space between the case neck and the rod. The rod should still extend a ways into the body of the case but not all the way. Turn the die and rod combination mouth up and fill the case with hot lead or bullet metal or Cerrosafe. Let it cool, turn the die on its side in a padded vise, take one good hammer, give the rod one or two sharp raps and out goes rod, lead and case all in one unit with no damage to the die body.

- *John T. Larsen, Ellensburg, Washington*

REMOVING STUCK CASE IN SIZING DIE

Had a sizing die come in with a very tight broken case stuck in it. So I plugged the neck of the case with a short chunk of dowel rod, filled the case full of Acraglas and let it set up in the corner. Next day, just punched the case and Acraglas out with absolutely no trouble.

- *Thomas Hughes, Ennis, Montana*

CAST BULLET BOXES

Those styrofoam cartridge holders as in the Remington ammo boxes for pistols make wonderful containers for cast bullets. Utilize one to hold the bullets and one for a lid, and Presto!. . .a dust free bullet box which is easily labeled.

- *R. C. Hatter, Falcon, Kentucky*

LOADING PLASTIC SHOTSHELL CASES

Just a friendly note for your protection when loading shotshells. There are many bushings in use which throw powder loads designed for standard fiber wads only. If you are planning to reload for plastic shotshell cases or are going to use the new plastic wads, be durned sure you read carefully the loading information in the reloading manual you are using or in the shotshell press reloading instructions covering plastic shotshell components. If you go ahead and throw a standard load of powder into plastic, you are overloading it. The powder load for plastics must be less than those for equivalent paper cases, so check to be sure before you start exactly how much powder you can safely use with plastic components.

- *W. C. Luedtke, Alexandria, Virginia*

CHRONOGRAPH SCREENS - ?

One of my customers has his own Avtron chronograph, and uses mechanical pencil leads for the first screen. He claims they are cheaper and not bothered by a miss since they are stronger and the muzzle blast won't bother them!

- *Dave Cumberland, El Cerrito, California*

INDEX